WAYNE HILLER

WAYNE HILLER

An Introduction to
QUANTUM STATISTICS

WILLIAM BAND

Professor of Physics
The State College of Washington
Pullman, Washington

D. VAN NOSTRAND COMPANY, INC.

PRINCETON, NEW JERSEY

TORONTO   LONDON

NEW YORK

D. VAN NOSTRAND COMPANY, INC.

120 Alexander St., Princeton, New Jersey
250 Fourth Avenue, New York 3, New York
25 Hollinger Rd., Toronto 16, Canada
Macmillan & Co., Ltd., St. Martin's St., London, W.C. 2, England

*All correspondence should be addressed to the
principal office of the company at Princeton, N. J.*

To
CLAIRE

PREFACE

The physicist's interest in statistical mechanics has been stimulated in recent years by its promise of fruitful application in two very remote fields of discovery—cryogenics and nuclear physics. On the one hand, the anomalous properties of matter in bulk at temperatures near absolute zero, and in particular the superfluidity of liquid helium and the superconductivity of many metals, are at the present time a continuing challenge to theoretical physics, and their explanation is a proper objective of quantum statistics. On the other hand, a fantastic array of new facts is being currently discovered about the structure of the nuclei through artificial production of radioactive isotopes by nuclear fission, and, while no very satisfactory theory of nuclear structure as yet exists, it is generally believed that the larger nuclei are aggregates of parts which must obey quantum statistics. There is also the rather more speculative, but equally fascinating, question of deciding what kind of statistics apply to aggregates of the newly discovered elementary particles like the neutron, the various kinds of meson, the V-particles, and so on. Although the last-mentioned particles will probably never be observed in aggregates in large numbers, the question of the statistical behavior of assemblies of neutrons is no longer academic.

The present text reflects the author's personal interest by its emphasis on low temperature problems, rather than on nuclear physics. However, it is hoped that the nuclear physicist will be able to see clearly from the text where quantum statistics makes contact with his particular field. Historically the principal successes of statistical mechanics have been in the field of physical chemistry, namely, the prediction of the thermodynamic properties of bulk matter from the known (or presupposed) properties of the atoms of which it is composed; this is still the major emphasis of most other works on statistical mechanics. No discussion of statistical mechanics can, of course, neglect this historical achievement, and the present text includes at least a brief review of these applications, together with references to sources in the literature where more detailed information is readily available.

The new emphasis of the present text has prompted a somewhat different

v

method of presentation from the usual. As long as one is interested primarily in the prediction of familiar thermodynamic properties, it is right and proper to employ well-known thermodynamic short-cuts to arrive at conclusions drawn from the basic axioms of statistical mechanics. Indeed, the term "statistical thermodynamics" has come into general use in this connection: The statistics are used only to derive the laws of thermodynamics and to give them more particular content, but thereafter the formalism of thermodynamics is used throughout. When, however, we turn to the anomalous behavior of matter at extremes of temperature, the laws of thermodynamics of course remain true, but the average physicist, at least, loses confidence in his own ability to apply them rigorously. Some of the short-cuts suggested by thermodynamics are indeed misleading if applied by "rule of thumb" to the novel situations arising at very low temperatures, and, by the time the student has cleared up the apparent paradoxes for himself, the advantage of speed and brevity has been lost. For this reason, the present text, while making early contact with the laws of thermodynamics, makes little use of thermodynamic formalism in the deduction of results. Each practical problem is studied instead as a problem in statistics, rather than as one of thermodynamics. The basic methods of statistics are applied repeatedly in whatever form the particular problem demands, and appeal is seldom made to general thermodynamic laws to shorten the derivation.

The text is intended as a first course in statistical mechanics for post-graduate students in physics and physical chemistry. Its prime objective is not so much to give a compendium of successful applications of statistical mechanics to experimental data, although one cannot pursue the subject very far without repeatedly referring to experimental data. The emphasis of the text is more than usually theoretical, because its aim is to train the young postgraduate in the actual handling of statistical mechanics as a tool for himself, rather than to describe to him what more mathematically expert theoretical physicists have been able to do. Every step should be intelligible. The set problems at the end of each chapter are reasonably easy and have not been used as a device for including subject matter that should have been in the main text material. The references to current literature following the exercises do not pretend to be complete; the items have been selected in part because of ready accessibility in the average college library and also for their suitability as subjects for reading reports by the more serious students.

To get the most out of this course the student should have had the usual mathematics requirements for a physics degree and have had, or be taking, a course in quantum mechanics. The outline of quantum mechanics in Chapter I may seem a little "steep" for some first-year postgraduates, but this should not deter anyone from proceeding with the body of the course. It was felt more desirable to include background material wherever its logical position called for it, rather than to build up a set of appendixes at the end. The first seven chapters of the text are concerned with well-established theory, of which many classical applications have been made. By discussing only some of the most recent applications in current literature, the text should help the student to realize, even in this more classical part of the subject, that such theory is very much alive. In the later chapters, the student will be more immediately aware of reaching the frontiers of present knowledge, because unsolved problems are pointed up in every chapter— several of these being highly controversial at the present time. It is hoped that this presentation of the subject as an open, rather than a closed, discipline will stimulate the student to go beyond a passive attitude toward his study, and to develop the kind of creative imagination that is essential to a true mastery of theoretical physics.

It is a pleasure to thank Professor John W. Stout, of the Institute for the Study of Metals at the University of Chicago, and Professor Harold W. Dodgen, of the Department of Chemistry and Director of the Nuclear Reactor Project at the State College of Washington, for reading the manuscript and making valuable suggestions. Thanks are also due to many of the author's former students who have freely commented on his presentation of the subject matter over the last five years, and in particular to Mr. Raymond A. Nelson and Dr. R. P. Singh for proofreading the whole manuscript and checking the references and the formulas.

WILLIAM BAND

Pullman, Washington
August, 1955

CONTENTS

		PAGE
PREFACE		V

CHAPTER

I REVIEW OF QUANTUM MECHANICS 1
1.1 The philosophy of quantum mechanics 1
1.2 The formalism of quantum mechanics 3
1.3 The quantum states of several simple systems . . . 6
1.4 Quantum states of assemblies of identical systems . . 7
1.5 Spin and symmetry 11
1.6 The matrix formulation of quantum mechanics . . . 13
Exercises and Problems 15
References for Further Study 16

II THE FORMALISM OF STATISTICAL MECHANICS 17
2.1 The basic postulates 17
2.2 The number of complexions in any distribution-in-energy . 20
2.3 The most probable distribution-in-energy 24
2.4 The Darwin-Fowler method 27
Exercises and Problems 31
References for Further Study 31

III STATISTICAL INTERPRETATION OF THERMODYNAMICS . . . 32
3.1 The thermodynamic state of an assembly 32
3.2 Identification of the temperature 34
3.3 Equation of state of the ideal gas 36
3.4 Statistical definition of entropy 36
3.5 Identification of the chemical potential 37
3.6 Validity of the classical approximation 38
3.7 The second and third laws of thermodynamics . . . 38
Exercises and Problems 41
References for Further Study 41

CHAPTER   PAGE
   IV   THE PARTITION FUNCTION IN CLASSICAL STATISTICS   .   .   .   42
        4.1   The partition function   42
        4.2   Partition function for the ideal monatomic gas   .   .   .   45
        4.3   Most probable distribution-in-momentum: kinetic theory .   48
        4.4   The partition function for internal degrees of freedom   .   50
        4.5   Partition function for diatomic molecules   52
        4.6   Interpretation of rotation spectra   57
        4.7   Effects of magnetic and electric fields   58
        4.8   Einstein's theory of crystalline solid   62
        4.9   Assemblies with prescribed momentum   63
              Exercises and Problems   66
              References for Further Study   66

    V   EQUILIBRIUM BETWEEN PHASES   67
        5.1   Two gaseous phases: mobile monolayer   67
        5.2   Adsorption isotherm for mobile monolayer   .   .   .   69
        5.3   Langmuir's isotherm   70
        5.4   Critical phenomena in monolayers on solids   .   .   .   73
        5.5   Multilayer adsorption—the BET isotherm   .   .   .   75
        5.6   Sublimation from an Einstein crystal   81
              Exercises and Problems   83
              References for Further Study   84

   VI   CHEMICAL AND DISSOCIATIVE EQUILIBRIUM   85
        6.1   Dissociative equilibrium in a diatomic gas   .   .   .   85
        6.2   Simple gas mixtures and the law of partial pressures .   .   87
        6.3   Chemical equilibria in gaseous mixtures   89
        6.4   Dissociative cluster theory of saturated vapor   .   .   92
        6.5   Dissociative cluster theory of the virial coefficients   .   100
        6.6   Chemical equilibrium in nonideal gases   103
              Exercises and Problems   105
              References for Further Study   106

  VII   ASSEMBLIES OF DEPENDENT SYSTEMS   107
        7.1   The assembly partition function   107
        7.2   Debye's theory of the crystalline solid   112
        7.3   The Born–von Karman theory of crystalline solid   .   .   116
        7.4   Theory of imperfect gases   119
        7.5   Mayer's theory of the higher virial coefficients   .   .   126
        7.6   Approximate theory of the liquid phase   131

CHAPTER PAGE

7.7 Phase equilibria 137
Exercises and Problems 139
References for Further Study 140

VIII INDEPENDENT SYSTEMS WITH QUANTUM DEGENERACY . . . 142
8.1 Black-body radiation: photon gas 142
8.2 The phonon gas 145
8.3 Ideal Bose-Einstein gas of material particles . . 148
8.4 Ideal Fermi-Dirac gas—electrons 156
8.5 Quantum degenerate monolayers 165
8.6 A Bose-Einstein free volume liquid model 173
8.7 Bose-Einstein gas with prescribed total momentum and the two-fluid model for liquid helium 177
8.8 Entropy and the Heisenberg uncertainty principle . . 181
Exercises and Problems 183
References for Further Study 184

IX PHASE EQUILIBRIA AMONG QUANTUM DEGENERATE SYSTEMS . 185
9.1 Adsorption isotherm for mobile monolayer: Bose-Einstein gas 185
9.2 Adsorption isotherm for mobile monolayer: Fermi-Dirac gas 188
9.3 Adsorption isotherms for isotope mixtures 192
9.4 Localized monolayers and Bose-Einstein parent gas . . 195
9.5 Sublimation of a Bose-Einstein gas from an Einstein crystal 197
9.6 Saturated vapor and Bose-Einstein model liquid . . 200
9.7 Multilayer adsorption of a Bose-Einstein gas . . 202
Exercises and Problems 206
References for Further Study 206

X DISSOCIATIVE EQUILIBRIUM AMONG QUANTUM DEGENERATE SYSTEMS 207
10.1 Clustering phenomena in Bose-Einstein gas . . . 207
10.2 Clustering phenomena in Fermi-Dirac gas . . . 212
10.3 Saturated vapor pressure of isotopic mixtures . . 214
10.4 Nuclear reactions 220
Exercises and Problems 223
References for Further Study 224

XI QUANTUM DEGENERATE ASSEMBLIES OF DEPENDENT SYSTEMS . 225
11.1 The Slater-sum 225
11.2 Quantum degenerate imperfect gas: theory of Kahn and Uhlenbeck 233

CHAPTER   PAGE

    11.3 The second virial coefficient in quantum degenerate gases . 237
    11.4 The von Neumann matrix method   243
          Exercises and Problems   246
          References for Further Study 246

XII THE GRAND PARTITION FUNCTION AND ITS APPLICATIONS . 247
    12.1 Formalism of the grand partition function .   .   . 247
    12.2 Quantum mechanical virial coefficients .   .   .   251
    12.3 Theory of the liquid phase   254
    12.4 Co-operative effects 259
    12.5 The von Neumann matrix for the grand ensemble . . 262
          Exercises and Problems   267
          References for Further Study 268

XIII GENERAL THEORY OF THE LIQUID PHASE 269
    13.1 The condensation process 269
    13.2 Mayer's generalization of the grand partition function the-
          orem   272
    13.3 Formal equation of state of condensed assemblies . . 276
    13.4 Quantum degeneracy in the liquid phase   .   .   . 279
          Exercises and Problems   281
          References for Further Study 282

XIV SOME SOLID STATE PROBLEMS   283
    14.1 Ferromagnetism 283
    14.2 Order-disorder in binary alloys 286
    14.3 Ideal lattice imperfections in substitutional alloys . 291
    14.4 Phase separation of substitutional alloys   .   . 295
    14.5 The energy of the free electrons in metals .   .   . 299
    14.6 Thermal and electrical conductivity   .   .   . 303
    14.7 Theory of superconductivity 305
          Exercises and Problems   310
          References for Further Study 311

XV FLUCTUATIONS AND NONEQUILIBRIUM PHENOMENA .   . 312
    15.1 The concept of fluctuations in equilibrium   .   . 312
    15.2 Fluctuations in phase population and density   .   313
    15.3 Fluctuations in energy and pressure   .   .   . 314
    15.4 Fluctuations near the critical point.   .   .   . 317
    15.5 Fluctuations in quantum degenerate gases   .   . 318
    15.6 Fluctuations in microstates   321
    15.7 The fluctuation-dissipation theorem   .   .   . 322
    15.8 Irreversible steady-flow processes   .   .   . 327

CHAPTER   PAGE
15.9 Nonequilibrium phenomena in liquid helium   .   .   . 329
        Exercises and Problems   332
        References for Further Study 333

APPENDIX 335

INDEX   337

Chapter I

REVIEW OF QUANTUM MECHANICS

1.1 The philosophy of quantum mechanics. Classical physics describes the properties of matter in terms of the behavior of atomic particles. The state of a single particle is specified by its generalized co-ordinates and momenta, $2f$ in number, where f is the number of degrees of freedom of the particle. The laws of mechanics and equations of motion tell how the state of any particle depends on time. In classical statistical mechanics, we deal with large numbers of particles and develop the laws that describe the behavior of statistical averages in such assemblies of particles. This leads directly to an explanation of the laws of thermodynamics and permits us to predict the thermodynamic behavior of any physical substance or assembly from the mechanical properties of the atomic particles of which it is composed.

In quantum mechanics, the particle concept breaks down and is at least partially abandoned, and, instead of "particle," we often use the noncommittal term "system." The quantum mechanical state of a system is completely specified by a wave function that depends only on the generalized co-ordinates, or alternatively only on the generalized momenta, but not on both; there are only f variables for the wave function, instead of the $2f$ in classical mechanics. The laws of quantum mechanics tell how the state of a system depends on time. In quantum statistics, we develop the laws of average behavior of assemblies of large numbers of systems, and again this enables us to predict the thermodynamic behavior of any quantum mechanical assembly in terms of the quantum mechanical properties of the systems of which the assembly is composed. It is important that the distinction between classical and quantum statistics be properly understood, and to this end we include here a brief discussion of the basic ideas of quantum mechanics.

These ideas are most conveniently discussed in terms of the wave-particle paradox. Under some circumstances electromagnetic waves behave like a stream of particles called photons; the photon can hit an atom and exchange energy and momentum with it exactly like any other particle, and therefore may be regarded itself as a real substantial entity having position and momentum. Under different circumstances, the same electromagnetic radiation is pure wave motion, and its energy is completely spread over large regions of space. Similarly, the

1

fundamental particles of matter, like electrons, protons, etc., ordinarily considered to be real substantial entities having position and momentum, behave instead under other conditions like waves spread throughout wide regions of space; their wavelengths are easily measurable and their particle character is completely lost.

There are two ways in which we may try to resolve this paradox. The first way is to suppose that the particle of matter—or the photon of electromagnetic energy—is really a particle having definite position and momentum all the time as classically believed, but that possibilities of measuring these classical variables are essentially limited by the waves associated with the particle; in other words, both the particle and the wave are real—the wave guides the particle in an active fashion. The second way is to suppose that the particle does not really exist at all and that it is nothing but a group of waves which, under suitable circumstances, can simulate the behavior of a particle. This second point of view would be very satisfactory except for the fact that one would prefer the waves to be real in the sense that some tangible medium is doing the oscillating, whereas the matter-waves of quantum mechanics seem to be entirely abstract mathematical inventions with no supporting medium at all. The first point of view is even less tenable, because it proves to be easy to imagine circumstances where it leads to self-contradictions. These points are fully discussed in many works on quantum mechanics, and here we shall limit ourselves to a very brief review of the philosophy that appears best to resolve the paradox. This philosophy was proposed over twenty years ago by Alfred North Whitehead and developed by Bertrand Russell; it demands a complete rejection of classical materialism.

Starting out from the theory of relativity, Whitehead expounded the view that the basic elements of experience are events that have finite extension in space and in time. The external world of reality is a succession of these events, or processes, and not primarily a collection of material objects. A material object may indeed exist, viz., the quantum mechanical "system," but this is merely some recognizable permanency among the interrelations between the extensive characters of events. This point of view is exactly the opposite of classical materialism, which regards material objects as the real elements of the physical world and events as mere changes among the interrelations between material objects. In the new philosophy, the program of science is to build a systematic description of events, not a history of material objects. In classical physics, as in ordinary life, the methods of observation have little influence on the course of events being observed. Under such circumstances, it is generally possible and convenient to describe the results of our observations in terms of material objects having an existence independent of the observer. But in atomic physics the quantities of energy involved even in the most refined procedures of observation imaginable are still comparable with the energies involved in the events being observed, and the former influence the course of events so drastically that no description of the observations in terms of material objects is possible. Quantum mechanics is a self-consistent mathematical technique for handling this situation: under classical conditions, it agrees with classical mechanics; under the new conditions, it offers a description of the external world of nonparticularized events and processes without assuming the permanent existence of particles.

Although the results of quantum mechanics differ from those of classical mechanics only when dealing with phenomena on atomic dimensions, it is by no means the case that quantum mechanics is unimportant when dealing with bulk matter. As remarked earlier, classical statistics predicts the average behavior of large assemblies of particles, i.e., of bulk matter, in terms of the classical mechanical properties of the individual particles of which the material is supposed to be composed. But it is exactly here, in the properties of the individual systems, that the classical picture is in error. Quantum statistics describes the average behavior of large assemblies in terms of the quantum mechanical properties of the systems of which the assembly is composed. Aside from the fact that the energy states of individual quantum mechanical systems are different from those of classical particles, the most significant difference between quantum and classical statistics is the following: In classical statistics, the particles are permanent and counted as distinguishable from each other, whereas, in quantum statistics, the systems that replace the particles are not permanently distinguishable from each other and not necessarily localized. Two such systems may interact with each other in such a way as to lose their individuality, there being no way of deciding which is which after the interaction ceases. This makes the computation of average behavior fundamentally different in quantum statistics from the classical one. Before proceeding with the exposition of quantum statistics, we must first review some quantum mechanical properties of individual systems.

1.2 The formalism of quantum mechanics. There are many ways of outlining the quantum mechanical prescription for the solution of atomic problems, but we shall choose the one most convenient for our present purpose, which is simply to review as briefly as possible those results of quantum mechanics needed for our study of quantum statistics.

We first have to consider the problem of interest from the classical point of view and set up the Hamiltonian function $H(\mathbf{p},\mathbf{q})$ in classical phase space. Here $\mathbf{p}$ and $\mathbf{q}$ are f-vectors, where f is the number of degrees of freedom of the system. The energy of the classical material particle is then given as a function of its classical variables

$$E = H(\mathbf{p},\mathbf{q}) \tag{1.201}$$

To go over to quantum mechanics, we replace the material object by a function of the co-ordinates $\mathbf{q}$ and time t and replace the algebraic equation (1.201) by a differential equation through the following prescription:

E is replaced by the operator $\qquad i\hbar\partial/\partial t \qquad$ (1.211)

$\mathbf{p}$ is replaced by the operator $\qquad -i\hbar\ \mathbf{grad} \qquad$ (1.212) the gradient operators being with respect to the co-ordinates $\mathbf{q}$. We then obtain the differential equation reading

$$H(-i\hbar \ \mathbf{grad}, \ \mathbf{q})\psi(\mathbf{q},t) = i\hbar(\partial/\partial t)\psi(\mathbf{q},t) \qquad (1.221)$$

If, as is here implied, the classical Hamiltonian is not dependent explicitly on time, we can solve this equation for $\psi(\mathbf{q},t)$ in the form

$$\psi(\mathbf{q},t) = u(\mathbf{q}) \exp(-iEt/\hbar) \qquad (1.222)$$

Putting Eq. (1.222) into (1.221) gives a differential equation for $u(\mathbf{q})$ known as the Schrödinger wave equation:

$$H(-i\hbar \ \mathbf{grad}, \ \mathbf{q})u(\mathbf{q}) = Eu(\mathbf{q}) \qquad (1.223)$$

The function $\psi(\mathbf{q},t)$ represents the system in the following sense: In any small element of volume in $\mathbf{q}$-space, written $\Pi d\mathbf{q}$, the probability that a suitable experiment shall detect the system is equal to the product of ψ and its complex conjugate per unit volume at the point of interest:

$$\text{probability} = \bar{\psi}(\mathbf{q},t)\psi(\mathbf{q},t)\Pi d\mathbf{q} = \bar{u}(\mathbf{q})u(\mathbf{q})\Pi d\mathbf{q} \qquad (1.231)$$

If an experiment is performed to measure the position of the system, the result according to quantum mechanics is the expectation value of the co-ordinate given by the definition

$$\langle \mathbf{q} \rangle = \int \cdots \int \bar{\psi}(\mathbf{q},t)\mathbf{q}\psi(\mathbf{q},t)\Pi d\mathbf{q} \qquad (1.232)$$

Similarly an experiment designed to measure its momentum yields the expectation value of momentum:

$$\langle \mathbf{p} \rangle = -i\hbar \int \cdots \int \bar{\psi}(\mathbf{q},t)\nabla\psi(\mathbf{q},t)\Pi d\mathbf{q} \qquad (1.233)$$

the operator (1.212) being used in place of $\mathbf{p}$ in the integrand. The expectation value of the energy of the system is defined as

$$\langle E \rangle = i\hbar \int \cdots \int \bar{\psi}(\mathbf{q},t)(\partial/\partial t)\psi(\mathbf{q},t)\Pi d\mathbf{q} \qquad (1.234)$$

The integrations in these last three equations are all taken over the entire $\mathbf{q}$-space. If we write Eq. (1.222) into Eq. (1.234) we find that E is actually the same as $\langle E \rangle$ if the functions $u(\mathbf{q})$ are normalized:

$$\int \cdots \int \bar{u}(\mathbf{q})u(\mathbf{q})\Pi d\mathbf{q} = 1 \qquad (1.241)$$

The Schrödinger equation (1.223) is an eigenvalue equation in the sense that it has well-behaved solutions $u(\mathbf{q})$ only for special values of the energy E. The family of solutions corresponding to all possible E values is an orthogonal closed set of functions that can always be normalized to satisfy Eq. (1.241). Let us indicate the family by means of a subscript; $u_n(\mathbf{q})$ then being the eigenfunction corresponding to the energy value E_n, n being in general an integer. Orthogonality means that

$$\int \cdots \int \bar{u}_n(\mathbf{q})u_m(\mathbf{q})\Pi d\mathbf{q} = \delta_{nm} \qquad (1.242)$$

Closure implies that any function, say $v(\mathbf{q})$ may be represented in terms of the members of the closed family:

$$v(\mathbf{q}) = \sum_n a_n u_n(\mathbf{q}) \qquad (1.243)$$

where a_n are constants given by the transform of Eq. (1.243):

$$a_n = \int \cdots \int \bar{u}_n(\mathbf{q}')v(\mathbf{q}')\Pi d\mathbf{q}' \qquad (1.244)$$

The necessary condition that the family be closed is that

$$\sum_n u_n(\mathbf{q}')u_n(\mathbf{q}) = \delta(\mathbf{q}' - \mathbf{q}) \qquad (1.245)$$

the right side being the Dirac *delta*-function.

The student familiar with vector analysis can think of Eq. (1.242) as the scalar product of two complex-valued vectors, the nth and mth in a family, the component of the vector is indicated by $\mathbf{q}$, the number of dimensions being infinite and equal to the entire domain of possible $\mathbf{q}$-values. Similarly, Eq. (2.245) may be thought of as a scalar product of two vectors, but here the different values of $\mathbf{q}$ select different vectors, and their components are indicated by the subscript n. Closure is thus another form of orthogonality. In Eq. (1.243) we think of $v(\mathbf{q})$ as the $\mathbf{q}$th component of the vector v and the right side of the equation as the expansion of the vector in terms of unit vectors, a_n being the nth component of $v(\mathbf{q})$ in the direction of the nth unit vector $u_n(\mathbf{q})$. Equation (1.244) is then exactly the analog of the vector equation giving a_n as the scalar product between u_n and v in function space.

The energy values E_n may not all be different for any given Schrödinger equation (1.223), and the corresponding eigenfunctions $u_n(\mathbf{q})$ can be grouped together—each group corresponding to a single energy level. Such an energy level to which several orthogonal eigenfunctions belong is said to be degenerate.

In working out the statistics of large assemblies of quantum mechanical systems the important items are the entire spectrum of energy eigenvalues and their degeneracy numbers, i.e., the number of distinct eigenfunctions associated with each energy eigenvalue. It is not usually necessary to know the eigenfunctions.

It may be appropriate to remark at this point that the student in the present course is expected to have already experienced the somewhat painful process of becoming acquainted with the mathematical techniques of quantum mechanics, and that this outline is intended merely as a rapid review. It is certainly not intended to be a logical proof or deduction of quantum mechanics from any a priori acceptable basis. No such a priori argument at present exists. To the logically minded student we would commend the thought that quantum mechanics, and with it our present subject, quantum statistics, does not attempt to explain, but only to describe, actually observable events and to predict future events, and that no test of success in this is more strict than success itself.

1.3 The quantum states of several simple systems. Consider first a free mass point confined in the volume of a box. The classical Hamiltonian is

$$H = p^2/2m + V \qquad (1.301)$$

where V is the potential energy, being zero everywhere inside the box and becoming discontinuously infinite at the walls. Using the prescription of § 1.2 the Schrödinger wave equation (1.223) becomes

$$\text{div } \mathbf{grad } u(\mathbf{q}) + (2m/\hbar^2)(E - V)u(\mathbf{q}) = 0 \qquad (1.302)$$

This equation has well-behaved solutions in the box, vanishing on the walls, only if the energy has one of the values

$$E_\mathbf{k} = (\hbar^2/2m)\{(k_1/L_1)^2 + (k_2/L_2)^2 + (k_3/L_3)^2\} \qquad (1.303)$$

where L_1, L_2, L_3 are the linear dimensions of the box, and the vector $\mathbf{k}$ has components $k_j = \pi n_j$, the n's being integers. These eigenvalues are degenerate only because there may exist different sets of numbers n_1, n_2, n_3 leading to the same sum of squares appearing in Eq. (1.303); this kind of degeneracy is called accidental because it depends on the shape of the enclosure. The eigenfunctions corresponding to these eigenvalues are standing waves, and when normalized are:

$$u_\mathbf{k}(x,y,z) = (8/L_1 L_2 L_3)^{1/2} \sin (k_1 x/L_1) \sin (k_2 y/L_2) \sin (k_3 z/L_3) \qquad (1.311)$$

Each sine function in this equation could be written as the difference between two conjugate exponentials, and this is equivalent to analyzing the standing wave into two oppositely moving progressive waves. In place of Eq. (1.311), we may therefore enumerate the wave functions in the form,

$$u_\mathbf{k}(\mathbf{q}) = (1/L)^{3/2} \exp (i\mathbf{k}\cdot\mathbf{q}/L) \qquad (1.312)$$

if the box is cubic, and allow the vector components of $\mathbf{k}$ to take both positive and negative values. Appropriate linear combinations of these functions reduce to Eq. (1.311). For many purposes it is easier to work with the exponential forms than with trigonometrical ones.

Consider next the quantum states of the three-dimensional harmonic oscillator. The potential function is

$$V(x,y,z) = \tfrac{1}{2}K_1 x^2 + \tfrac{1}{2}K_2 y^2 + \tfrac{1}{2}K_3 z^2 \qquad (1.321)$$

and the Schrödinger equation is the same as Eq. (1.302) except for this potential function. Well-behaved solutions exist only when E has one of the eigenvalues:

$$E_n = \sum_j (n_j + \tfrac{1}{2})\hbar(K_j/m)^{1/2} \qquad (1.322)$$

where the vector $\mathbf{n}$ has three components that are positive integers or zero. There is only one function $u_n(x,y,z)$ to each vector $\mathbf{n}$, although there may again be accidental degeneracy. The functions are expressible in terms of the Hermite polynomials.

It is worth noticing that, in the neighborhood of a potential minimum, the first approximation to any potential is just the expression (1.321) plus a constant giving the potential at the minimum. For small enough amplitudes or small enough energies, the result (1.322) is therefore a first approximation to the eigenvalues of any potential problem that has an equilibrium minimum at the origin.

As a third example, consider the quantum states of a symmetrical, rotating body. Here the Laplacian operator appearing in the Schrödinger equation has to be expressed in polar co-ordinates, and the rotational inertia, I, of the body replaces the mass of the particle. The resulting equation is

$$\frac{1}{\sin\theta}\frac{\partial}{\partial\theta}\left[\sin\theta\,\frac{\partial u(\theta,\varphi)}{\partial\theta}\right] + \frac{1}{\sin^2\theta}\frac{\partial^2 u(\theta,\varphi)}{\partial\varphi^2} + \frac{2IE}{\hbar^2}u(\theta,\varphi) = 0 \qquad (1.331)$$

The eigenvalues of this equation are

$$E_j = j(j+1)\hbar^2/2I \qquad (1.332)$$

where j is any positive integer and there are $2j+1$ eigenfunctions to each eigenvalue, so the weight of the jth level is

$$\omega_j = 2j + 1 \qquad (1.333)$$

The eigenfunctions are spherical harmonics.

1.4 Quantum states of assemblies of identical systems. So far we have considered only single systems. We shall also need to understand something of the quantum mechanics of large numbers of systems, and then the foregoing prescription for setting up quantum mechanical procedures has to be modified in the following way. Let the assembly consist of N systems each with f degrees of freedom, so that the configuration of the assembly is specified by Nf variables. Let the wave function for the assembly be a function of all these Nf variables, and be written in the form

$$\psi(\mathbf{q},t) = u(q_1,q_2,\cdots q_N)e^{-iEt/\hbar} \qquad (1.401)$$

where each q_j is an f-vector representing all the co-ordinates of the jth system. The square modulus of this function multiplied by the hypervolume element in Nf-co-ordinate space:

$$\bar{u}(q_1,q_2,\cdots q_N)u(q_1,q_2,\cdots q_N)d\tau_1 d\tau_2 \cdots d\tau_N \qquad (1.402)$$

is interpreted as the probability that a suitable experiment will reveal one system simultaneously in each of the volume elements $d\tau_1$, $d\tau_2$, $\cdots d\tau_N$ in the f-dimensional space of each system.

The Schrödinger wave equation for such an assembly is found by the same kind of prescription as for a single system. We first set up the classical Hamiltonian of the assembly

$$H = H(p_1, p_2, \cdots p_N; \quad q_1, q_2, \cdots q_N) \tag{1.411}$$

as a function of all the co-ordinates and all the momenta. Then we replace each momentum vector by the corresponding gradient operator:

$$p_j \rightarrow -i\hbar \, \mathrm{grad}_j \tag{1.412}$$

where grad_j means the gradient with respect to the co-ordinates of the jth system. The Schrödinger equation is thus

$$H(-i\hbar \, \textbf{grad}, \, \textbf{q})u(\textbf{q}) = Eu(\textbf{q}) \tag{1.413}$$

where **grad** means the whole set of operators grad_j. This is a partial differential equation in which all Nf variables are independent.

Because all the systems in the assembly are the same, it makes no difference in the classical Hamiltonian if any pair of systems is interchanged, or in general if any permutation among the systems is effected. The same remark evidently applies to the differential operator in the Schrödinger equation. However, this in general need not be true of the eigenfunctions $u(q_1, q_2, \cdots q_N)$ in Eq. (1.413); this function may well depend on q_1, for instance, in a different way from its dependence on q_2, so that an interchange of the first two particles or systems alters the function significantly. But because such a permutation does not alter the Hamiltonian differential operator, the new eigenfunction is still a solution of the same equation with the same eigenvalue as before. In general, there may be as many as $N!$ different eigenfunctions with the same eigenvalue—a property that is called exchange degeneracy.

Consider for example an assembly of only two systems, and let $u(q_1, q_2)$ be one wave function corresponding to some energy eigenvalue. Then $u(q_2, q_1)$ is also an eigenfunction with the same eigenvalue, and, unless $u(q_1, q_2)$ itself happens to be symmetrical in the two sets of co-ordinates, these two eigenfunctions are different from each other and, indeed, are orthogonal to each other. Because both are solutions of the same linear differential equation (the same eigenvalue), any linear combination of them is also a solution. For example, either of the following two linear combinations are eigenfunctions with the same eigenvalue as before:

$$u_s(q_1, q_2) = 2^{-\frac{1}{2}}\{u(q_1, q_2) + u(q_2, q_1)\} \tag{1.421}$$

$$u_a(q_1, q_2) = 2^{-\frac{1}{2}}\{u(q_1, q_2) - u(q_2, q_1)\} \tag{1.422}$$

Here evidently u_s is symmetrical in the two systems and does not change when the systems are interchanged, while u_a is antisymmetrical and reverses sign when they are interchanged. Eqs. (1.221) and (1.222), describing the time-dependence of the wave functions, show that any symmetry character of the types here described is conserved during the progress of time: if a pair of systems starts out being symmetrical like (1.421), it will remain in a symmetrical state, etc.

Consider now an assembly of a large number N of almost independent systems, like the particles of an ideal gas, where we ignore the forces acting between them. The classical Hamiltonian of such an assembly is simply the sum of the Hamiltonians for the individual systems; therefore the Hamiltonian operator in the Schrödinger equation splits into the sum of single-system operators:

$$H(1,2,\cdots N) = H(1) + H(2) + \cdots H(N) \tag{1.431}$$

where for brevity we have written numerals $1,2,\cdots N$ to indicate the sets of coordinates $q_1, q_2, \cdots q_N$. The Schrödinger equation (1.413) can then be solved by separation of the variables in the familiar fashion:

$$u(1,2,\cdots N) = u(1)u(2) \cdots u(N) \tag{1.432}$$

and the Schrödinger equation splits into N separate equations, each one involving a single system, all identical in form. Any one of these equations possesses a whole family of eigenfunctions, $u_j(q)$, $j = 1,2,\cdots$, which is usually denumerably infinite in number. Each of the N functions appearing on the right side of Eq. (1.432) must be one member of this family, with, of course, its own appropriate variable. Suppose we arbitrarily choose a particular set of N such eigenfunctions from the family and assign them to the assembly, one to each system, and form the product

$$u(1,2,\cdots N) = u_1(1)u_2(2)u_3(3) \cdots u_N(N) \tag{1.433}$$

If the eigenvalue of the function $u_j(q)$ is E_j in the single-particle wave equation, then the eigenvalue of the combined function (1.433) in the wave equation for the assembly is the sum

$$E = \sum_j E_j \tag{1.434}$$

This eigenvalue is degenerate with respect to the wave function, like (1.433), because we can interchange the factor functions among the systems without altering the total energy. For example, the function

$$u(2,1,\cdots N) = u_2(1)u_1(2)u_3(3) \cdots u_N(N) \tag{1.435}$$

simply assigns the energy E_2 to the first system and E_1 to the second, so the total E is unchanged. Just as we did in the example of two systems, we can now form linear combinations of functions like (1.433) and (1.435) and look for those combinations that are either symmetrical or antisymmetrical in all possible interchanges. Evidently the symmetrical combination is formed by adding all products, such as the two samples already given, that can be formed by permuting the particles among the functions. When the result is normalized we then have

$$u_s(1,2,\cdots N) = (N!)^{-\frac{1}{2}} \sum_P \prod_{j=1}^{N} u_j(Pj) \tag{1.436}$$

where $\sum_P$ means the sum over all permutations P, and Pj means that index obtained from j by the permutation P. There is only one symmetrical combination for a given total energy, hence exchange degeneracy has been removed by this process.

The linear combination that is antisymmetrical in all the systems is most conveniently written in the form of a determinant:

$$u_a(1,2,\cdots N) = (N!)^{-\frac{1}{2}} \begin{vmatrix} u_1(1) & u_1(2) & \cdots & u_1(N) \\ u_2(1) & u_2(2) & \cdots & u_2(N) \\ \cdots & \cdots & \cdots & \cdots \\ u_N(1) & u_N(2) & \cdots & u_N(N) \end{vmatrix} \tag{1.437}$$

This antisymmetrical function can also be written in a more condensed form like that used above for the symmetrical one:

$$u_a(1,2,\cdots N) = (N!)^{-\frac{1}{2}} \sum_P (-1)^P \prod_{j=1}^{N} u_j(Pj) \tag{1.438}$$

where the factor $(-1)^P$ is positive if the permutation P is even, and negative if P is odd.

We note next that, in the symmetrical combination (1.436), it does not matter if some of the particle eigenfunctions are identical with each other; we can still form the symmetrical combination. However, if we did the same thing with the determinant, for example, if the function u_1 were the same as the function u_2, then two rows of the determinant (1.437) would be identical, and so the determinant would vanish identically. This result can be interpreted to mean that an assembly that is described only by antisymmetrical eigenfunctions never has more than one of its member systems in any one single-system eigenstate. This is the Pauli exclusion principle. No such restriction operates if the assembly is described by symmetrical functions.

It was remarked earlier that if a pair of systems starts out in a symmetrical state, it must remain in symmetrical states; the same is true of large assemblies —once an antisymmetrical assembly, always an antisymmetrical assembly. In practice, it is found that the symmetry character of an assembly is a unique property of the kind of system in the assembly. For reasons that are still somewhat obscure, assemblies of electrons, H atoms, and any gas whose molecules contain an odd number of nucleons and therefore having odd spin are always described by antisymmetrical eigenfunctions; while photons, deuterons, He⁴ atoms, and any gas whose molecules contain an even number of nucleons having even or zero spin are always described by symmetrical eigenfunctions. The Pauli exclusion principle operates only on the antisymmetrical kinds, and this is of great importance for quantum statistics.

To appreciate the difference between the two kinds of system let us return to the example of an assembly of just two systems and write down the expression (1.402) for the probability density in the two kinds of symmetry. For the symmetrical case we use Eq. (1.421) and find for the probability density per unit hypervolume in Nf-space:

$$P_s = \bar{u}_s(1,2)u_s(1,2) = \tfrac{1}{2}[\bar{u}(1,2) + \bar{u}(2,1)][u(1,2) + u(2,1)]$$

$$= \tfrac{1}{2}|u(1,2)|^2 + \tfrac{1}{2}|u(2,1)|^2 + Re[\bar{u}(1,2)u(2,1)] \tag{1.441}$$

Similarly for the antisymmetrical case, using Eq. (1.422) we find

$$P_a = \tfrac{1}{2}|u(1,2)|^2 + \tfrac{1}{2}|u(2,1)|^2 - Re[\bar{u}(1,2)u(2,1)] \tag{1.442}$$

The quantities $\tfrac{1}{2}|u(1,2)|^2 + \tfrac{1}{2}|u(2,1)|^2$ are exactly what we would expect if we ignored symmetry questions completely. It is not difficult to see that the other quantity, the real part of $\bar{u}(1,2)u(2,1)$ is large only if the two systems are near each other so that their individual wave functions overlap. Therefore Eq. (1.441) says that the symmetrical assembly tends to favor clustering, the close pair having an anomalously high probability; whereas Eq. (1.442) says that the antisymmetrical assembly tends to avoid clustering, because the close pair has an anomalously low probability. There is an apparent attraction between particles in a symmetrical assembly and an apparent repulsion between those of an antisymmetrical assembly. This result carries over into assemblies of any number of systems. The apparent forces are called "exchange forces"; they are fictitious forces in the sense that they do no work, but the terminology is convenient.

1.5 Spin and symmetry. It is known that all fundamental particles possess properties that are vaguely analogous to intrinsic angular momentum or spin. The complete theory of this would take us too far from our subject, and we summarize only the results to be used later.

The quantum of spin momentum is $\tfrac{1}{2}\hbar$, one half that of ordinary orbital angular momentum, and the spin of any particle is $s\hbar$ where s is some half-integer or integer. The spin s is treated as a new variable, and every eigenfunction is given an extra factor, the spin factor, depending on this spin variable. Every elementary particle,* e.g., electron, proton, neutron, etc., has only two possible spin states, $s = \pm\tfrac{1}{2}$; every complex nucleus has its characteristic spin spectrum, the known nuclei having maximum spins ranging all the way from zero to $s = \tfrac{9}{2}$. The general parity rule mentioned in the last paragraph states that assemblies of particles each having even $2s$ values have eigenfunctions that are symmetrical to the interchanges of particles, while those having odd $2s$ values have assembly eigenfunctions antisymmetrical in the interchange between particles. For a

---

* The status of the meson in this general statement is not clear at the present time; it is considered an elementary particle, but has spin $s = 1$.

given system, s can change only by unity—say from $\frac{1}{2}$ to $-\frac{1}{2}$—to conserve symmetry.

For particles with spin s, there are $2s + 1$ different possible spin factors corresponding roughly to the space-quantization of orbital angular momentum. In the absence of a magnetic field these different states all have the same energy, so their number simply multiplies the degeneracy of the energy levels. For most statistical work this is all that we need to consider. In the theory of assemblies of complex molecules for instance, the spin degeneracies modify the relative weights of the various angular momentum states of the molecule as listed in Eq. (1.333).

Consider a pair of identical atoms, a and b, forming a single diatomic molecule. The angular momentum eigenfunctions corresponding to the energy levels listed in Eq. (1.332) with even j-values are in fact symmetrical for interchanges between the two atoms, while those for odd j-values are antisymmetrical. When these eigenfunctions are multiplied by spin factors, the symmetry of the result depends on the symmetry of the spin factors. If $S_1(a)$ is a spin factor assigned to particle a, we may write an antisymmetrical spin factor for the pair in the form

$$S_1(a)S_2(b) - S_1(b)S_2(a) \tag{1.501}$$

analogous to Eq. (1.422) for ordinary eigenfunctions. There are $2s + 1$ different spin states S, and therefore $s(2s + 1)$ different combinations like (1.501) that are antisymmetrical in the particles. On the other hand we can write two kinds of spin factors that are symmetrical in the particles:

$$S_1(a)S_2(b) + S_1(b)S_2(a) \quad \text{and} \quad S_1(a)S_1(b), \quad \text{etc.} \tag{1.502}$$

There are $s(2s + 1)$ of the first type and $2s + 1$ of the second type, so that in all there are $(s + 1)(2s + 1)$ symmetrical spin factors.

According to our parity rule, a pair of identical particles each with even spin ($2s$ even) must have a combined eigenfunction that is symmetrical between the particles; therefore, their orbital angular momentum eigenfunctions that have even j-values must combine with symmetrical spin factors with even $2s$-values, multiplying the degeneracy weight by the factor $(s + 1)(2s + 1)$:

j even, $2s$ even: $\qquad \omega_{j,s} = (2j + 1)(s + 1)(2s + 1) \tag{1.503}$

On the other hand, their orbital angular-momentum states with odd j-values must combine with antisymmetrical spin factors, multiplying the degeneracy weights by the factor $s(2s + 1)$:

j odd, $2s$ even: $\qquad \omega_{j,s} = (2j + 1)s(2s + 1) \tag{1.504}$

A pair of identical particles each with $2s$ odd must have a combined eigenfunction that is antisymmetrical between the particles; therefore, their even j-values combine with antisymmetrical spin factors, multiplying the weight by $s(2s + 1)$:

j even, $2s$ odd: $\qquad \omega_{j,s} = (2j + 1)s(2s + 1) \tag{1.505}$

while their odd j-values combine with symmetrical spin factors, multiplying the weight by $(s + 1)(2s + 1)$:

$$j \text{ odd, } 2s \text{ odd:} \qquad \omega_{j,s} = (2j + 1)(s + 1)(2s + 1) \qquad (1.506)$$

If the two atoms in a diatomic molecule are not alike, the symmetry of the angular-momentum eigenfunction is of no significance, and the weight of the level is simply multiplied by the product of the two spin degeneracies of the atoms separately, i.e., by $(2s_a + 1)(2s_b + 1)$, where s_a and s_b are the spins of the atoms a and b respectively.

In studying polyatomic molecules the question of spin degeneracy becomes more involved, but, in practice, a useful approximation turns out to be adequate. We note that for any pair of atoms the two possible spin weight factors are $s(2s + 1)$ and $(s + 1)(2s + 1)$, and if s is large, these two numbers will not be very different: an average between them would be approximately $\frac{1}{2}(2s + 1)^2$. Now $(2s + 1)$ is the spin degeneracy of either particle separately, and $\frac{1}{2}$ is the reciprocal of the number of indistinguishable configurations of the pair that can be produced by a simple rotation in space. By analogy we may generalize to any complex polyatomic molecule. Multiply together the spin degeneracies of all the atoms and divide by the number of equivalent configurations produced by simple rotations of the molecule as a whole. The result is approximately the extra degeneracy factor to be attached to each orbital momentum state.

1.6   The matrix formulation of quantum mechanics.   Given the Hamiltonian operator and any closed orthogonal normalized set of functions v_n, we may form the expression

$$H_{nm} = \int \bar{v}_n H v_m d\tau \qquad (1.601)$$

for any pair of subscripts n,m. This set of quantities may be regarded as a matrix, and called the matrix of H on the v-representation. If the v_n happen to be the eigenfunctions u_n of the operator H, then $Hu_n = E_n u_n$ and the matrix elements become

$$H_{nm} = E_m \int \bar{u}_n u_m d\tau = E_m \delta_{nm} \qquad (1.602)$$

On the u-representation, the matrix of H is diagonal, and its diagonal elements are the eigenvalues E_m of the operator H. In general, the v-representation of H is not diagonal, but the following rule of matrix algebra permits us to find the diagonal form of the matrix without knowing the eigenfunctions u_n. We form the matrix $H - \lambda I$, where λ is a scalar unknown, and I is the unit diagonal matrix, and equate the determinant of this to zero:

$$|H - \lambda I| = 0 \qquad (1.603)$$

This is a polynomial expression in powers of λ equated to zero, and the roots of the equation are $\lambda = E_n$, all the eigenvalues of H.

Any physical observable $F(p,q,t)$ for which an operator can be found by the rules of § 1.2 can be expressed in the form of a matrix:

$$F_{nm} = \int \bar{v}_n F v_m d\tau \tag{1.604}$$

This matrix can be diagonalized by the rule (1.603) to yield the eigenvalues of F, and these are interpreted as the possible results of a physical measurement of F.

Any Hermitian matrix (i.e., one composed of complex elements such that $F_{nm} = \bar{F}_{mn}$) can be diagonalized by the rule (1.603), whether or not the operator F from which the matrix is formed by (1.604) can be derived from a classical observable by the rules (1.211) and (1.212). The most significant contribution of the matrix method is in suggesting that any Hermitian matrix may represent an observable, even one without a classical analog, and that, when diagonalized, its diagonal elements are the possible results of measuring this observable. The spin of any elementary particle discussed in the last section is such an observable without classical analog: its matrix is one of the Pauli spin matrices.

The dynamical laws for the time-behavior of nonclassical variables can be set up in terms of the matrix notation without reference to the classical laws of motion. This is done by using the time-dependent wave functions for v_n in Eq. (1.604) and applying Eq. (1.221) in the form:

$$i\hbar \partial v_n/\partial t = Hv_n \tag{1.605}$$

to the equation

$$\partial F_{nm}/\partial t = (\partial/\partial t)\int \bar{v}_n F v_m d\tau$$

The result can be shown to be

$$dF/dt = \partial F/\partial t + (1/i\hbar)(FH - HF) \tag{1.606}$$

where $\partial F/\partial t$ is present only when the component elements of F depend on time explicitly, and $FH - HF$ is the commutator of the two matrices F and H. From the last equation we derive the following theorem: Any matrix that (a) does not depend on time explicitly, and (b) commutes with the Hamiltonian matrix H of the system, represents a constant of the motion of the system. Moreover any two matrices that commute with each other can be diagonalized by one and the same representation. This is interpreted to mean that observables represented by commuting matrices can be simultaneously measured in one and the same operation, while two observables whose matrices do not commute cannot be measured precisely in one simultaneous operation.

As an example of this, matrices can be set up for the generalized co-ordinates and momenta in the classical Hamiltonian dynamics. They are given by

$$Q_{nm} = \int \bar{v}_n q v_m d\tau$$

$$P_{nm} = -i\hbar \int \bar{v}_n (\partial v_m/\partial q) d\tau$$

$$\left. \right\} \qquad (1.607)$$

It can be proved that these matrices satisfy the following commutation rule:

$$QP - PQ = i\hbar I \qquad (1.608)$$

where I is the unit diagonal matrix. Since Q and P do not commute, they cannot be measured simultaneously. This result is equivalent to the Heisenberg uncertainty principle:

$$\Delta p \Delta q = \hbar \qquad (1.609)$$

where Δp and Δq are the minimum possible uncertainties in the result of trying to measure p and q simultaneously in one operation.

Any two matrices P and Q that satisfy Eq. (1.608) can be used as a pair of canonical variables for the quantum mechanical description of a dynamical system. One of the important techniques of the matrix method in quantum mechanics is the search for matrices that satisfy Eq. (1.608) and the subsequent diagonalization of these matrices to obtain the possible results of a physical measurement of either one or the other.

EXERCISES AND PROBLEMS

1. Show that the expectation value of the energy given by Eq. (1.234) is equal to E if the wave function is given by Eq. (1.222).

2. Use Eqs. (1.242) and (1.243) to prove Eq. (1.244).

3. Use Eq. (1.244) to derive Eq. (1.245) and explain the meaning of the Dirac *delta*-function in this result.

4. Verify that the wave functions of Eq. (1.311) are solutions of Eq. (1.302) with the eigenvalues given by Eq. (1.303).

5. Set up wave functions of the form Eq. (1.222) from each of the functions (1.421) and (1.422), substitute into the Schrödinger equation (1.223), and demonstrate that the symmetry of the wave function does not change with time.

6. Show that the normalizing factor $(N!)^{-1/2}$ in Eq. (1.436) reduces the integrated square modulus of the function u_s to unity.

7. Sketch diagrams to illustrate the statement following Eq. (1.442) regarding the real part of the function $\bar{u}(1,2)\, u(2,1)$.

8. Discuss the nuclear spin degeneracy of the molecules of H_2, CO_2, the benzene ring C_6H_6 and ethane $2(H_3C)$.

9. Diagonalize the matrices:

$$\begin{pmatrix} 0 & 1 & 0 \\ 1 & 0 & 1 \\ 0 & 1 & 0 \end{pmatrix} \qquad \begin{pmatrix} 0 & i & 0 \\ -i & 0 & 1 \\ 0 & 1 & 0 \end{pmatrix}$$

and interpret the results in quantum mechanical terms.

10. Diagonalize the Pauli spin matrices:

$$\begin{pmatrix} 0 & 1 \\ 1 & 0 \end{pmatrix} \quad \begin{pmatrix} 0 & -i \\ i & 0 \end{pmatrix} \quad \begin{pmatrix} 1 & 0 \\ 0 & -1 \end{pmatrix}$$

Show that the column vectors $\begin{pmatrix} 1 \\ 0 \end{pmatrix}$ and $\begin{pmatrix} 0 \\ 1 \end{pmatrix}$ are eigenvectors of these matrices.

11. Verify Eq. (1.606). (Hint: see Schiff, *Quantum Mechanics*, § 23.)

12. Verify Eq. (1.608). (Hint: see Schiff, *Quantum Mechanics*, § 12.)

REFERENCES FOR FURTHER STUDY

The Nature of Physical Reality, H. Margenau, McGraw-Hill, 1950.
Quantum Mechanics, L. I. Schiff, McGraw-Hill, 1949.
Fundamentals of Quantum Mechanics, E. Persico, Prentice-Hall, 1950.
Quantum Mechanics of Particles and Wave Fields, A. March, Wiley, 1951.

Chapter II

THE FORMALISM OF STATISTICAL MECHANICS

2.1 The basic postulates. Let us consider an assembly of N identical systems between which there are only extremely small interactions, and let us set up the appropriate wave functions, either Eq. (1.436) or (1.437). In setting up these assembly wave functions, we have a whole spectrum of single-system wave functions $u_j(q)$ from which to choose N factors in the combined wave function. If we know the quantum properties of the individual systems, we know these individual wave functions; hence it is in principle feasible to construct all the possible combined eigenfunctions for the whole assembly. We shall always normalize the combined wave functions to unity so that they represent states with unit probability when integrated over the entire phase space of the assembly.

The basic postulate of quantum statistical mechanics may be stated as follows: If our methods of observation are too coarse to determine the assembly eigenfunction, equal probability has to be assigned to each assembly eigenfunction that is not inconsistent with the data. A great deal of discussion exists in the literature concerning the validity of this and the equivalent classical assumption, and the student is referred to some of this in the suggestions for further reading. Here we shall simply accept it as pragmatically justified. In practice our observations are never able to determine the precise assembly wave function for any piece of bulk matter; the best that we can discover is the distribution-in-energy of the assembly, by which is meant a specification of the number of systems in each possible energy level. As will be seen immediately, a large number of assembly eigenfunctions generally exist that belong to any one distribution-in-energy. Because we assume each assembly eigenfunction has the same a priori probability, the distribution-in-energy that corresponds to the maximum number of assembly eigenfunctions is the most probable distribution-in-energy. The immediate task is therefore to count the number of assembly eigenfunctions corresponding to every possible distribution-in-energy.

In § 1.4 we have described two kinds of assembly eigenfunctions, the symmetrical and the antisymmetrical. Before continuing with the immediate task, it is advisable to include another kind of assembly eigenfunction that is appropriate when the particles forming the assembly are large enough to be mutually distinguishable—unlike the elementary particles. Such an assembly is called a Boltzmann assembly; the results will lead to the Boltzmann statistics, and we wish to include this along with our discussion of quantum statistics. If the particles are mutually distinguishable from each other permanently, the discussion of § 1.4 proceeds in exactly the same way up to the point reached in the Schrödinger equation (1.413). At this point, we are not now permitted to permute the particles, because they are not indistinguishable from each other; even though they may be similar with each other, we can, in principle, put a tag on each particle to identify it from the others. We could therefore—also in principle— decide whether, for example, the correct wave function for a pair of particles was $u(q_1,q_2)$ or $u(q_2,q_1)$, and it is not possible to attach any real meaning to such a combination as Eq. (1.421) or (1.422). We can however take up the discussion around Eq. (1.431) and set up the combined eigenfunction (1.433) for the assembly of distinguishable particles. We can then set up an eigenfunction like (1.435), recalling that this eigenfunction is now actually distinguishable from (1.433), because a permutation among the particles does make a real difference if we have tagged them. The symmetrical combination and the antisymmetrical combination do not have any real meaning in this case. Finally, we can include the Boltzmann assembly in our discussion if we note that there are many more eigenfunctions for the Boltzmann assembly, namely, one for every permutation of the particles among the states u_j, which we may write

$$u_B(P) = \prod_{j=1}^{N} u_j(Pj) \qquad (2.101)$$

—the subscript B for Boltzmann, and P for permutation as before.

In classical Boltzmann statistics, the term "complexion" was used to indicate an assignment of particles to the states u_j, and this term is convenient also with quantum statistics. Each assembly eigenfunction in fact makes exactly such an assignment of particles or systems to the states u_j, so that there is a one-to-one correspondence between the eigenfunctions and the complexions. The basic postulate of quantum statistics is therefore the same as that of the Boltzmann statistics, i.e., that every complexion is equally probable.

Before attempting to count complexions in general, it is desirable to discuss some very simple examples to illustrate the meaning of complexions and the significance of the difference between distinguishable and indistinguishable systems. First consider an assembly of two particles for each of which there are six possible states, and let the particles be completely indistinguishable from each other. The following table displays several distinct complexions of this assembly:

Complexion	State 1	2	3	4	5	6
A	0	1	1	0	0	0
B	0	0	0	0	0	2
C	1	0	1	0	0	0

The numbers in the body of the table indicate how many particles are in the states listed in the top row. Row A represents one complexion where a single particle is in the second state, another in the third state, and no particles in any other state. Each complexion, A, B, or C, etc., is equally probable if we make a random "throw" of the two particles into the field of the six states. The wave functions corresponding to the three complexions listed in the table are of the form:

$$u_A(1,2) = \tfrac{1}{2}\{u_2(1)u_3(2) \pm u_2(2)u_3(1)\}$$

$$u_B(1,2) = u_6(1)u_6(2) \quad\text{or}\quad 0 \tag{2.102}$$

$$u_C(1,2) = \tfrac{1}{2}\{u_1(1)u_3(2) \pm u_1(2)u_3(1)\}$$

The positive sign corresponds to symmetrical, the negative sign to antisymmetrical, wave functions. In the complexion B, there is no antisymmetrical wave function.

Next suppose the particles of the above assembly are actually distinguishable from each other, like a pair of dice that could be colored differently; the side of each die indicates its state by its score mark. Let us call the dice a and b; then we have the following complexions (among many others):

Complexion	State	1	2	3	4	5	6
Ai		0	a	b	0	0	0
Aii		0	b	a	0	0	0
B		0	0	0	0	0	$a+b$
Ci		a	0	b	0	0	0
Cii		b	0	a	0	0	0

The wave functions, for example, corresponding to the complexions Ai and Aii are of the form:

$$u_{Ai} = u_2(a)u_3(b) \quad\text{and}\quad u_{Aii} = u_2(b)u_3(a) \tag{2.103}$$

Comparing the two tables we see that a score of $2+3$ when the particles are distinguishable corresponds to two complexions Ai and Aii, while it is given only by one complexion A when the particles are indistinguishable—the probability is doubled when the particles are distinguishable. One could imagine a device whereby a pair of dice could be made to follow the quantum statistics, and to have complexions as given in the first table. Thus if each die could be made sensitive to the score shown on the other die, and be provided with a mechanism making it jump over to show the same score as the other die had initially, after a brief relaxation time, we could imagine a pair of dice having been thrown to show a score of $2+3$ jumping over to show the score $3+2$, and then jumping back to $2+3$, and so on indefinitely. This kind of exchange process between the two dice would mean that the two complexions Ai and Aii would not exist as separate states of the pair; instead, there would be only a single combined state, like A in the first table. It is often helpful to picture fundamental particles like electrons as making exactly this kind of exchange jump between the states appearing in the wave function of the assembly. In fact, one is obliged to accept this strange picture if one wishes to retain the existence of material particles in the quantum mechanical situation; it is an excellent example of the kind of troubles one is forced into by trying to keep hold of the point of view of classical materialism in discussing quantum mechanics.

2.2   The number of complexions in any distribution-in-energy.   Consider an assembly of N systems. Let each system have a spectrum of possible energy levels ϵ_k and a number of eigenstates ω_k corresponding to the kth energy level. A distribution-in-energy of the assembly is defined by the set of numbers n_k of systems in the kth energy level—all k values to be counted. Following the basic postulate that the assembly eigenfunctions are equally probable, we wish to count how many such assembly eigenfunctions correspond to any particular distribution-in-energy; such a count would measure the a priori probability that the assembly be found in this distribution-in-energy. Clearly the number in question depends on whether we use the Boltzmann unsymmetrized eigenfunctions of Eq. (2.101), the antisymmetrical eigenfunctions of Eq. (1.437), or the symmetrical ones of Eq. (1.436). The statistics resulting from these different methods of counting are called Boltzmann, Fermi-Dirac, or Bose-Einstein statistics respectively; we shall discuss each in turn.

A. The Boltzmann statistical count.   In writing out explicitly the product of individual system eigenfunctions appearing on the right side of Eq. (2.101) as the expression for a Boltzmann complexion, we shall in general find some systems assigned to one and the same eigenfunction, whereas some systems will be assigned to various eigenfunctions that nevertheless belong to the same energy level because of degeneracy. The total number of systems to be assigned to the kth level is of course n_k. The question is: How many different assembly eigenfunctions like Eq. (2.101) can we form that all have the same set of numbers n_k?

In forming the eigenfunctions (2.101), we remarked that the individual systems are in principle distinguishable; hence any permutation of them among the states produces a different eigenfunction, at least insofar as the permutation exchanges systems that are in different states—even the different states belonging to the same energy level. The number of complexions in the distribution-in-energy is therefore found by counting the number of significant permutations of particles among the states consistent with keeping the numbers n_k fixed. To make this count, we may first arrange the N particles in groups containing n_k particles in the kth group, and later assign each group in all possible ways to the ω_k states in the kth level. The number of ways we can arrange N distinguishable particles in groups of n_k does not include the permutations of the members within any one group, so that if X is the desired number, we have

$$N! = Xn_1!n_2! \cdots n_j! \cdots \qquad (2.211)$$

where the number of factors on the right is indefinite. Wherever an energy level contains no particles, the factor 0! is counted as unity. We may read this equation as stating that the total number of permutations $N!$ of particles is equal to X times the permutations that do not count. Thus:

$$X = N! \prod_k (1/n_k!) \tag{2.212}$$

Having thus counted the number of ways we can form the required groups, we now have to count the number of ways in which each such group can be assigned to the ω_k states in each level. Consider first some one level, the kth, and count the number of ways n_k systems can be distributed among the ω_k states belonging to this level. In doing this there is no restriction on the number of systems that can be put into any one state. Thus we can assign each and every system to the level in ω_k different ways, one for each state, and the total number of ways is the product of ω_k for each of the n_k systems, $(\omega_k)^{n_k}$. The same expression holds for every level, and the combination of all possibilities is the product over all the levels. Combining this statement with the number X given in Eq. (2.212) gives the Boltzmann count:

$$C_{\text{Boltz}}\{n_k\} = N! \prod_k (\omega_k)^{n_k}/n_k! \tag{2.213}$$

where $\{n_k\}$ is to be read "the set of numbers like n_k."

B. Bose-Einstein statistical count. For the Bose-Einstein statistics we have to count how many different symmetrical assembly eigenfunctions like Eq. (1.436) can be formed consistent with a given distribution-in-energy. In forming the function (1.436) we note that all the $N!$ permutations of the systems among themselves are contained in the assembly eigenfunction symmetrically, so that it makes no difference to it if we permute the particles. Thus in arranging our systems in the groups n_k, the permutations counted as X in Eq. (2.212) do not count in this case; there is in fact only one way in which N completely indistinguishable systems can be arranged in groups. We are left then with the problem of counting up how many different ways there are of arranging n_k systems in ω_k eigenstates at each energy level—the systems being completely indistinguishable, so that permutations among them are not counted. There is no limit set to the number of systems assignable to any one state. Let the symbols u_j, $j = 1, 2, \cdots \omega_k$ represent the ω_k eigenstates at the kth level, and let the numerals $1, 2, \cdots n_k$ represent the systems in the level. Then the following row of symbols is an abbreviation for the factor appearing in one permutation in the combined wave function (1.436):

$$u_1\ 1\ 2\ u_2\ 3\ u_3\ u_4\ 4\ \cdots\ u_{\omega_k} n_k \tag{2.221}$$

This may be read as stating that in the first eigenstate we have placed the first and second systems; in the second eigenstate, the third system; in the third eigenstate, no system; in the fourth eigenstate, the fourth system; etc.; and in the last eigenstate, the last system. All this is for one particular level, the kth. Let us find how many significantly different expressions like (2.221) we can form. Suppose we keep the symbol u_1 always in its first place; this is the only way to be sure that we shall count only symbols beginning with a u-term, and exclude such meaningless things as $2\ u_1\ 1\ u_3\ \cdots$. All the other symbols, altogether $(n_k + \omega_k - 1)$ of them, are to be freely permuted, forming $(n_k + \omega_k - 1)!$ different expressions; for example, one of these is

$$u_1\ 2\ 1\ u_3\ u_4\ 4\ u_2\ 3\ \cdots\ u_{\omega k}\ (n_k - 1)\ n_k \tag{2.222}$$

In this example we see that system 1 and system 2 are still assigned to the first state; none to the third state; the third to the second state; the fourth to the fourth state; etc.; however, to the last state we have added the $(n_k - 1)$th system. The first four states are no different from before, but the last state, and one unlisted state, have different populations; hence the symmetrical eigenfunction corresponding to (2.222) is different from that corresponding to (2.221). Any permutation among the systems alone (there are $n_k!$ such permutations in this level) makes no difference to the assembly eigenfunction, and any permutation of such groups of symbols as $u_4\ 4$ with $u_2\ 3$, which takes an eigenstate with its total population and exchanges it with another eigenstate and its total population, does not produce a new eigenfunction for the assembly. Thus the number of assembly eigenfunctions equals the total number of permutations $(n_k + \omega_k - 1)!$ divided by the number of permutations that do not count, namely, $n_k!$ permutations among the systems in the level, and $(\omega_k - 1)!$ permutations among the states with their populations, not including the first. Finally, therefore, we have for the Bose-Einstein count:

$$C_{\text{B.E.}}\{n_k\} = \prod_k (n_k + \omega_k - 1)!/[(\omega_k - 1)!n_k!] \tag{2.223}$$

where we have combined the numbers obtained for every level.

C. *Fermi-Dirac statistical count.* The only difference between this and the Bose-Einstein count is that we are not now permitted to put more than one system into any single eigenstate. Again there is only one way of grouping the systems into the numbers n_k, because they are indistinguishable; next we have to count the number of ways we can place n_k systems into ω_k states at the kth level. Clearly no distribution can be considered for which n_k exceeds ω_k, for this would violate the exclusion principle that no more than one system be assigned to each state. We write out a sample factor in the wave function for the kth level, following the same code as for the Bose-Einstein case:

$$u_1\ 1\ u_2\ u_3\ 2\ u_4\ u_5\ u_6\ 3\ u_7\ 4\ \cdots\ u_{\omega_k} n_k \tag{2.230}$$

The number of significantly different expressions of this type is the number of ways we can place n_k integers in ω_k places (right after the u-symbols), with no more than one integer per place. The first integer can be placed in any of the ω_k places; the second then has only $\omega_k - 1$ places to choose; the third, only $\omega_k - 2$

places; etc.; the result is $\omega_k!/(\omega_k - n_k)!$ ways. Having done this, we have inadvertently counted all the permutations among the n_k systems, and these have to be removed. Therefore, combining finally all the energy levels we find for the total Fermi-Dirac count:

$$C_{\text{F.D.}}\{n_k\} = \prod_k \omega_k!/[(\omega_k - n_k)!n_k!] \qquad (2.231)$$

Statistical mechanics is a useful discipline only in the study of assemblies containing large numbers of systems. This is the case simply because we start out the whole work with a statement of ignorance, as we did in § 2.1, viz., that we cannot on the basis of available methods of observation determine the actual quantum states of the individual systems. If the assembly consisted of only a few systems, a very few real observations would indeed give us the states of these individual systems, and there would be no need to resort to statistical methods. Quantum mechanical laws applied to each system separately would predict the behavior of the whole assembly directly. We should perhaps emphasize that the ignorance assumed at the basis of statistics is not the kind of ignorance implied in the Heisenberg uncertainty principle; rather, it is ignorance forced upon us by the sheer immensity of the problem. One cubic centimeter of matter may contain as many as ten billion molecules, and, quite apart from the uncertainty principle, it is just not practicable to write down even a single possible wave function for the assembly—let alone decide which one is correct. For this reason, our formulae are intended to apply only to very large numbers of systems, and this permits us to make some simplifying approximations. In particular, we make repeated use of Stirling's approximation, which states that for any sufficiently large number X the natural logarithm may be written

$$\ln X! = X \ln X - X \qquad (2.241)$$

Taking the logarithms of the numbers C_{Boltz}, $C_{\text{B.E.}}$, and $C_{\text{F.D.}}$ given in this section, and supposing that all the numbers appearing in the formulae are large, we can easily show from Eq. (2.241) that

$$\ln C_{\text{Boltz}}\{n_k\} = \ln N! + \sum_k n_k[\ln (\omega_k/n_k) + 1] \qquad (2.242)$$

$$\ln C_{\text{B.E.}}\{n_k\} = \sum_k [n_k \ln (\omega_k/n_k + 1) + \omega_k \ln (1 + n_k/\omega_k)] \qquad (2.243)$$

$$\ln C_{\text{F.D.}}\{n_k\} = \sum_k [n_k \ln (\omega_k/n_k - 1) - \omega_k \ln (1 - n_k/\omega_k)] \qquad (2.244)$$

The term $\ln N!$ has been left in that form in Eq. (2.242) to facilitate a direct comparison with the other two expressions for B.E. and F.D. statistics, as follows: In case $n_k \ll \omega_k$ for all values of k, then $\lim n_k/\omega_k = 0$:

$$\ln C_{\text{B.E.}}\{n_k\} = \ln C_{\text{F.D.}}\{n_k\} = \ln [C_{\text{Boltz}}\{n_k\}/N!] \qquad (2.245)$$

The common limit of all three statistics given here is called classical statistics.

Equation (2.245) implies that, if we know that in every energy level there are far more eigenstates available than there are systems in them, we may use the Boltzmann statistics, provided we first correct its count by dividing by $N!$. The correction is due essentially to the fact that Boltzmann's count was calculated by assuming the particles as being mutually distinguishable; dividing by $N!$ corrects for this—at least approximately. We shall find later that the conditions required for the validity of this approximation are generally fulfilled for all gases at ordinary laboratory temperatures and sufficiently low densities, but that, at very high densities or extremely low temperatures, the approximation ceases to be valid and it is then necessary to distinguish carefully between the three statistics.

The student may have noticed an apparent contradiction between the assumption that ω_k and n_k be very large numbers and the statement of the exclusion principle that no more than one system be permitted in any one eigenstate, i.e., on the Fermi-Dirac statistics. There is indeed a serious difficulty here because in many problems the eigenstates are not degenerate, $\omega_k = 1$; therefore n_k is either 0 or 1, and Stirling's approximation is obviously wrong. However, in many of these cases we can get around this by bunching large numbers of levels lying very close together in a small energy interval, by going over from a discrete sum to an integral over the energy, and by correctly assuming that the significant numbers are indeed all large. (This question is discussed more fully in § 8.8.)

2.3 The most probable distribution-in-energy. In this section we consider an assembly that not only has a specified number N of systems, but also has a specified total energy E. We wish to calculate which distribution-in-energy, among all those consistent with this total energy, has the maximum number of complexions; according to our basic postulate, this is the most probable distribution-in-energy associated with the given total energy. The distribution numbers n_k must satisfy

$$\sum_j n_j = N \quad \text{and} \quad \sum_j n_j \epsilon_j = E \tag{2.301}$$

where j is taken over all energy levels of the system. To find the most probable distribution numbers, we make variations, dn_j, and set the resulting variation in the number of complexions equal to zero; this will ensure that the number of complexions is either maximum or minimum. When the number C is a maximum, so is its logarithm, and so we make variations in the logarithms of the numbers given in Eqs. (2.242)–(2.244) and for brevity write

$$C = \text{maximum value of } C\{n_k\} \tag{2.302}$$

—omitting the suffix indicating which statistics are being used until we need to differentiate between them. Then we have

$$d \ln C = \sum_i dn_j \partial(\ln C)/\partial n_j = 0 \tag{2.303}$$

The variations dn_j are not here independent because the n's must continue to satisfy the restrictions of Eq. (2.301) after the variations. Indeed, we have two other equations that must be satisfied by the variations dn_j:

$$dN = 0 = \sum_j dn_j \quad \text{and} \quad dE = 0 = \sum_j \epsilon_j dn_j \qquad (2.304)$$

Multiply the first of Eqs. (2.304) by an arbitrary constant $-\alpha$ and the second by another arbitrary constant $-\beta$, add the results to Eq. (2.303), and obtain

$$\sum_j dn_j[\partial(\ln C)/\partial n_j - \alpha - \beta\epsilon_j] = 0 \qquad (2.305)$$

Because α and β are arbitrary, we can treat the variations dn_j in Eq. (2.305) as all independent from each other; α and β constitute two extra variables we can use to prevent Eqs. (2.301) from being violated. This device is known as the method of Lagrange multipliers. In Eq. (2.305), we now note that since all the dn_j are effectively independent, we can choose all but one of them as zero; then in order to satisfy the equation, we shall have to set the coefficient of the non-zero dn_k equal to zero:

$$\partial(\ln C)/\partial n_j = \alpha + \beta\epsilon_j \qquad (2.306)$$

which must be true whatever j we may happen to select.

We now apply this result to each of the statistics in turn, equating C to C_{Boltz}, $C_{\text{B.E.}}$, and $C_{\text{F.D.}}$, respectively, as given in Eqs. (2.242)–(2.244).

A. *Boltzmann's distribution.* Using the Stirling approximation on the term $\ln N!$ in Eq. (2.242),

$$\ln C_{\text{Boltz}} = N \ln N + \sum_j n_j \ln (\omega_j/n_j) \qquad (2.311)$$

To apply Eq. (2.306) to this expression, we need the partial derivatives of N. Note that we are treating all the dn_j as independent, so that the partial derivatives mean that we vary only one n_j—a particular j of interest—keeping all the other n's fixed. Then since $N = \sum_j n_j$, the partial derivatives of N are all unity:

$$\partial N/\partial n_j = (\partial/\partial n_j) \sum_k n_k = 1 \qquad (2.312)$$

The derivative of Eq. (2.311) is therefore

$$(\partial/\partial n_j) \ln C_{\text{Boltz}} = \ln N + \ln \omega_j - \ln n_j \qquad (2.313)$$

and hence Eq. (2.306) yields the result

$$n_j = N\omega_j \exp (-\alpha - \beta\epsilon_j) \qquad (2.314)$$

for every value of j.

These equations give the distribution-in-energy that has a maximum number of complexions, and thus the most probable distribution-in-energy consistent with the given total energy E, expressed in terms of the undetermined multipliers α and β. To complete the solution of the problem, we have to find α and β, and to do this, we make use of the fact that they have to be chosen so as to make sure that the restrictions (2.301) are fulfilled. Putting Eq. (2.314) directly into the left side of the first of Eqs. (2.301), we have

$$N \sum_j \omega_j \exp\left(-\alpha - \beta\epsilon_j\right) = N$$

and this gives one equation between α and β:

$$\sum_j \omega_j \exp\left(-\alpha - \beta\epsilon_j\right) = 1 \tag{2.315}$$

or, alternatively,

$$e^\alpha = \sum_j \omega_j e^{-\beta\epsilon_j} \tag{2.316}$$

Again putting Eq. (2.314) into the second equation (2.301), we find a second equation between α and β:

$$\sum_j \omega_j \epsilon_j \exp\left(-\alpha - \beta\epsilon_j\right) = E/N \tag{2.317}$$

Eliminating α between this and (2.316) yields

$$E/N = \sum_j \omega_j \epsilon_j e^{-\beta\epsilon_j} / \sum_j \omega_j e^{-\beta\epsilon_j} \tag{2.318}$$

In any particular problem where the energy levels ϵ_j and their degeneracies ω_j are known, Eqs. (2.318) and (2.316) enable us to compute the constants α and β, and so from Eq. (2.314), to find the most probable distribution-in-energy.

B. *Bose-Einstein distribution.* Writing Eq. (2.243) for $\ln C$ in Eq. (2.306):

$$\partial \ln C_{\text{B.E.}}/\partial n_j = \alpha + \beta\epsilon_j$$

leads almost immediately to

$$\ln\left(n_j + \omega_j\right) - \ln n_j = \alpha + \beta\epsilon_j$$

and taking the exponential of this equation we find for the most probable distribution-in-energy:

$$n_j = \omega_j/[\exp\left(\alpha + \beta\epsilon_j\right) - 1] \tag{2.321}$$

The undetermined multipliers α and β are to be found again by putting this equation into the restrictions (2.301). This yields

$$N = \sum_j \omega_j/[\exp\left(\alpha + \beta\epsilon_j\right) - 1] \tag{2.322}$$

and

$$E = \sum_j \omega_j \epsilon_j/[\exp\left(\alpha + \beta\epsilon_j\right) - 1] \tag{2.323}$$

These two equations can, in principle, be solved for α and β, and, putting their solutions into Eq. (2.321), we obtain the most probable distribution-in-energy for the Bose-Einstein statistics.

C. Fermi-Dirac distribution. Again using Eq. (2.244) for $\ln C_{\text{F.D.}}$ in Eq. (2.306) we easily find

$$\ln (\omega_j - n_j) - \ln n_j = \alpha + \beta \epsilon_j$$

which gives the result

$$n_j = \omega_j / [\exp (\alpha + \beta \epsilon_j) + 1] \tag{2.331}$$

Putting this into the restrictions (2.301) yields two equations

$$N = \sum_j \omega_j / [\exp (\alpha + \beta \epsilon_j) + 1] \tag{2.332}$$

$$E = \sum_j \omega_j \epsilon_j / [\exp (\alpha + \beta \epsilon_j) + 1] \tag{2.333}$$

Solving these for α and β, we can, in principle, use the results in Eq. (2.331) to find the most probable distribution-in-energy for the Fermi-Dirac statistics.

Inspection of Eqs. (2.321) and (2.331) shows that the two distributions approach the same limit when $n_j/\omega_j \to 0$, viz.:

$$n_j/\omega_j \to 0: \qquad n_j = \omega_j \exp (-\alpha - \beta \epsilon_j) \tag{2.341}$$

This is because the only way that Eqs. (2.321) and (2.331) can give a very small value to n_j/ω_j is by the factor $\exp (\alpha + \beta \epsilon_j)$ becoming much greater than unity. The reader should note the difference between the result (2.341) and the Boltzmann distribution (2.314); it is left as an exercise to prove that the corrected Boltzmann statistics ($N!$ removed) lead just to the result (2.341) which we now call the classical distribution-in-energy. The Boltzmann distribution (2.213) is applicable to assemblies in which the systems are mutually distinguishable; the classical distribution, to assemblies in which they are not distinguishable. The parameters α and β for the classical distribution are found by putting Eq. (2.341) into Eq. (2.301), solving for α and β:

$$N = \sum_j \omega_j \exp (-\alpha - \beta \epsilon_j) \tag{2.342}$$

$$E = \sum_j \omega_j \epsilon_j \exp (-\alpha - \beta \epsilon_j) \tag{2.343}$$

Putting the results into Eq. (2.341) gives the most probable classical distribution. (Actual examples of these procedures will be given later.)

2.4   The Darwin-Fowler method. There exists a much more powerful method —due originally to C. G. Darwin and R. H. Fowler—of deriving the results given in this chapter without the use of the Stirling approximation. The method also provides an advanced mathematical technique for handling the applications discussed later in our work. We, however, shall not use this technique; its details are unnecessarily difficult for the student who has not had more mathematical training than is needed for a complete understanding of the more useful results of statistical mechanics. In this section, we present the basic ideas of the Darwin-Fowler method and show how it leads to the same results as we have just derived.

First we specify the states of a system by the energy values ϵ_s, having first in principle removed all degeneracies—every state being indicated separately, even if its energies are numerically equal. Next we write down a symbol:

$$x^{n_s} z^{n_s \epsilon_s} \tag{2.401}$$

which is to be read "there may be n_s systems in the sth state, and their energy total is $n_s \epsilon_s$." We then sum symbols like the above over all allowed values of n_s starting from zero:

$$1 + xz^{\epsilon_s} + x^2 z^{2\epsilon_s} + \cdots \tag{2.402}$$

and in reading this expression we begin by saying "there may be no systems at all in the sth state, or there may be one system in this state, or there may be two systems $\cdots$." It is essential to read the $+$ sign as "or," not as "and," in order to understand the logic of this method. In the Fermi-Dirac statistics, we stop at the two alternatives, zero and one system in any one state; in the Bose-Einstein statistics, we continue indefinitely. These alternative possibilities regarding the sth state are to be combined with the similar alternatives for all the states available to the systems, and, as will appear shortly, the appropriate way of making this combination is to multiply together the several sums:

$$\prod_s \sum_{n_s} x^{n_s} z^{n_s \epsilon_s} \tag{2.403}$$

This product combines symbolically all possible assignments of the systems to the various energy states. If the product is actually worked out, we get a power series in x and in z. The combined coefficient of all terms containing x^N equals the number of individual terms (possible assignments) consistent with the total number of systems being equal to N, while the coefficient of all terms containing z^E automatically equals the total number of possible assignments consistent with a total energy equal to E. We translate the words "possible assignments" to read "complexions," assume equal probability, and find it apparent that this device is a general way of deducing results like Eqs. (2.213), (2.223), and (2.231). From the theory of residues in complex variables, it is known that the coefficient in a power series can be obtained in the form of a contour integral in the complex plane:

$$C(N,E) = \frac{1}{(2\pi i)^2} \oint\oint \frac{dx\,dz}{x^{N+1} z^{E+1}} \prod_s \sum_{n_s} x^{n_s} z^{n_s \epsilon_s} \tag{2.404}$$

where we have to set up a complex plane for both x and z independently. The number $C(N,E)$ is the number of complexions corresponding to given total number N and total energy E, and is the coefficient of the term $x^N z^E$ in the double power series covering all possible assignments.

In looking for the average value of any function, for example, the average population of the kth state, we regard the number of complexions accompanying any particular value of the population or other function as a measure of its probability. Let n_k be a particular value of the population of the kth state, and write down all the possible assignments in which the population has this fixed value—there is just one term in the sum over assignments to the kth state, but a complete sum over all other states:

$$x^{n_k} z^{n_k \epsilon_k} \prod_{s \neq k} \sum_{n_s} x^{n_s} z^{n_s \epsilon_s} \tag{2.405}$$

The coefficient of $x^N z^E$ in this expression gives the probability of finding the particular value n_k for the population of the kth state. Write this coefficient symbolically as $C(N,E,n_k)$; then the weighted mean value of all possible n_k values is given by $\bar{n}_k$, where

$$\bar{n}_k C(N,E) = \sum_{n_k} n_k C(N,E,n_k) \tag{2.406}$$

which in turn is equal to the coefficient of $x^N z^E$ in the following expression:

$$\sum_{n_k} n_k x^{n_k} z^{n_k \epsilon_k} \prod_{s \neq k} \sum_{n_s} x^{n_s} z^{n_s \epsilon_s} \tag{2.407}$$

The first sum in this expression can be written as $x(\partial/\partial x) \sum_{n_k} x^{n_k} z^{n_k \epsilon_k}$, so that, finally, Eq. (2.407) becomes

$$\bar{n}_k C(N,E) = \frac{1}{(2\pi i)^2} \oint\oint \frac{dx\,dz}{x^{N+1} z^{E+1}} \{\text{extra factor}\} \prod_{s} \sum_{n_s} x^{n_s} z^{n_s \epsilon_s} \tag{2.408}$$

where the extra factor is

$$x(\partial/\partial x) \ln\left\{ \sum_{n_k} x^{n_k} z^{n_k \epsilon_k} \right\} \tag{2.409}$$

Comparing the integrals in Eqs. (2.408) and (2.404), we see that the extra factor is all that distinguishes them. Darwin and Fowler proved that, if N is very great, the integrand in Eq. (2.404) has a sharp maximum at the real axis as we move round a circle in the complex plane; that this maximum is sharpest when the circle is taken to pass through the minimum of the integrand along the real axis, i.e., at the saddle point; and that the extra factor in (2.408) varies very slowly in the neighborhood of this saddle point. The ratio between the two integrals, which is what one needs in Eq. (2.408) to find $\bar{n}_k$, is therefore essentially equal to the extra factor evaluated at the minimum of the integrand in Eq. (2.404):

$$\bar{n}_k = \bar{x}(\partial/\partial\bar{x}) \ln\left\{ \sum_{n_k} \bar{x}^{n_k} \bar{z}^{n_k \epsilon_k} \right\} \tag{2.410}$$

where $\bar{x}$ and $\bar{z}$ are the values of x and z that minimize the following expression, which is the logarithm of the integrand in (2.404) when $d \ln x$ and $d \ln z$ are taken as the variations instead of dx and dz:

minimize:
$$-N \ln x - E \ln z + \sum_s \ln \left\{ \sum_{n_s} x^{n_s} z^{n_s \epsilon_s} \right\} \tag{2.411}$$

We omit any discussion of several fine points involved in this argument; these may be found in the references for further reading.

Applying these methods to Fermi-Dirac statistics, the sum over n_k is restricted to two terms, $n_k = 0$ and 1. Equation (2.410) then yields

$$\bar{n}_k = \bar{x}\bar{z}^{\epsilon_k}/(1 + \bar{x}\bar{z}^{\epsilon_k}) \tag{2.412}$$

while maximizing (2.411) with respect to x yields the equivalent to $N = \sum_k n_k$, and maximizing the same expression with respect to z yields, simply, $E = \sum_k \epsilon_k n_k$. Comparing these results with Eqs. (2.331)–(2.333), we see at once that they are identical, provided only that $\bar{x}$ is identified with $e^{-\alpha}$ and $\bar{z}$ with $e^{-\beta}$.

Applying the same method to the Bose-Einstein statistics, where the sum goes over all n_s values without limit, we note that

$$\sum_n x^n z^{n\epsilon} = (1 - xz^\epsilon)^{-1} \tag{2.413}$$

for each energy level. The differentiations involved in Eqs. (2.410) and (2.411) then go through in an elementary fashion, and it is left as an exercise for the student to verify that the results coincide with Eqs. (2.321)–(2.323).

The chief contribution of this discussion from our present point of view is to prove that the results derived in terms of the Stirling approximation are in fact valid on much less restrictive conditions than are required by that approximation. All that is needed is for the total number N to be large; it is not essential for all the individual numbers n_k to be large, as it was with the Stirling approximation. In fact the method of Darwin and Fowler indicates further that, even if the number N were not large enough, the only consequence would be to reduce the sharpness of the maximum probability. In other words, the values indicated by Eqs. (2.331), etc., are still the most probable distribution numbers, but the mean deviation from these most probable values may be increased in smaller populations. Actually it is a very familiar fact, not only in the field of theoretical physics, but also in everyday affairs, that statistical results have meaning only in large populations, and the larger the population, the greater the reliability of the statistical results. We may therefore conclude that the results of this chapter are valid wherever the statistical method can be legitimately used. We can hardly ask for more in developing a statistical theory.

EXERCISES AND PROBLEMS

1. Draw up a chart showing all the complexions of an assembly of three coins, each of which is allowed only two states, and write down the corresponding wave function forms for (a) Boltzmann and (b) Bose-Einstein statistics. What would happen if the Fermi-Dirac statistics were assumed in this problem?

2. Fill in the steps leading from Eq. (2.241) to Eqs. (2.242)–(2.244). Verify Eq. (2.245).

3. Verify the steps leading from Eq. (2.306) to Eqs. (2.321) and (2.331).

4. Omit the term $\ln N!$ from Eq. (2.242), which then applies to the classical corrected Boltzmann statistics; follow through the steps that now replace Eqs. (2.311) and (2.314); and show that the final result coincides with Eq. (2.341), derived from the Fermi-Dirac and Bose-Einstein statistics in the classical limit.

5. Verify that maximizing the expression (2.411) with respect to x and z results in the relations $N = \sum_k n_k$ and $E = \sum_k \epsilon_k n_k$.

6. Deduce Eqs. (2.321) and (2.323) from Eqs. (2.413) as outlined in the text.

7. Suppose N independent indistinguishable systems form an assembly such that, at most, p systems can be assigned to a single quantum state. Use the method of Darwin and Fowler to show that the most probable distribution-in-energy is

$$n_k = \omega_k/[e^{(\epsilon_k - \mu)/kT} - 1] - (1 + p)\omega_k/[e^{(1+p)(\epsilon_k - \mu)/kT} - 1]$$

where $1/kT$ corresponds to β and $-\mu/kT$ to α in the notation of the present section. Check that this result reduces respectively to the Fermi-Dirac and Bose-Einstein results when $p = 1$ or infinity.

REFERENCES FOR FURTHER STUDY

Introduction to Statistical Mechanics, R. W. Gurney, McGraw-Hill, 1949.
Statistical Physics, L. Landau and E. Lifshitz, Oxford, 1938.
The Principles of Statistical Mechanics, R. C. Tolman, Oxford, 1938.
Statistical Mechanics, J. E. Mayer and M. G. Mayer, Wiley, 1940.

Chapter III

STATISTICAL INTERPRETATION OF THERMODYNAMICS

3.1 The thermodynamic state of an assembly. The thermodynamic state of an assembly is described by macroscopic variables: pressure p, temperature T, volume V, total energy E, and number of systems N. The number N is not a variable if the assembly is a homogeneous aggregation of a given number of particles. There exist well-defined prescriptions for the measurement of the thermodynamic variables p, T, V, and E. It is found that any two of these can be regarded as independent, hence the thermodynamic state of a homogeneous thermodynamic assembly is two-dimensional—there are two degrees of freedom. Between any three of the variables, there exists a functional relationship that may be called the equation of state of the assembly. These remarks apply, however, only as long as the assembly is in a state of internal equilibrium, and the equation of state is the condition of equilibrium of the assembly.

In statistical mechanics, we interpret the state of equilibrium as the most probable state: an assembly is in equilibrium when it is in the most probable distribution-in-energy allowed by the various restrictions imposed on the assembly. The equivalence of the concept of maximum probability and thermodynamic equilibrium is ensured by the work of § 2.3, where the two arbitrary constants that determine the most probable distribution-numbers n_j, i.e., α and β, can be regarded as representing the two degrees of freedom of the assembly. Before developing this connection between statistics and thermodynamics, it is desirable to review some thermodynamic formulae that will be useful later.

If E and V are taken as independent variables, it is found that there exists a function $S(E,V)$ of E and V called the entropy of the assembly, such that its first variation is given by

$$dS = (p/T)dV + (1/T)dE \qquad (3.101)$$

The entropy being a single-valued function of E and V, its differential is an exact one: the change in entropy as one moves about the E,V plane is independent of the path and depends only on the end points—like the potential function in a conservative field of force. Provided the assembly is in internal equilibrium, i.e., in the most probable distribution-in-energy, the pressure p and temperature T are functions only of E and V; therefore Eq. (3.101) is sufficient to define the entropy S to within an arbitrary constant. An alternative form of Eq. (3.101) is

$$p/T = \partial S(E,V)/\partial V \quad 1/T = \partial S(E,V)/\partial E \tag{3.102}$$

These equations permit us to calculate p and T as functions of E and V when we know the entropy as a function of E and V to within an arbitrary constant.

If p and T are taken as the independent variables, a different function exists, known as the Gibbs free energy, $F(T,p)$, such that

$$dF = V dp - S dT \tag{3.111}$$

is an exact differential. If we know the Gibbs free energy as a function of p and T to within an arbitrary constant, we can find S and V as a function of p and T through the relations:

$$V = \partial F(T,p)/\partial p \quad S = -\partial F(T,p)/\partial T \tag{3.112}$$

If T and V are the independent variables, we have the Helmholtz free energy, $A(T,V)$, such that

$$dA = -S dT - p dV \tag{3.121}$$

and

$$S = -\partial A(T,V)/\partial T \quad p = -\partial A(T,V)/\partial V \tag{3.122}$$

Finally, with p and S as independent variables, we have the enthalpy $H(S,p)$ such that

$$dH = T dS + V dp \tag{3.131}$$

and

$$T = \partial H(S,p)/\partial S \quad V = \partial H(S,p)/\partial p \tag{3.132}$$

Any one of the four functions $S(E,V)$, $F(T,p)$, $A(T,V)$, or $H(S,p)$ may be used as a potential function, depending on which pair of independent variables happens to be convenient in describing the thermodynamic state of the assembly. The four equations (3.101), (3.111), (3.121), (3.131) are simply alternative statements of essentially the same principle, namely, that there exists a single-valued function of the state variables of a thermodynamic assembly.

Up to this point, we have limited the discussion to homogeneous assemblies having a fixed number of systems in them. It often happens that we shall be interested in calculating how an assembly adjusts its population between two or more different phases. In other words, we wish to know the equilibrium or most probable number of systems in each of several different phases, each phase having its own spectrum of energy levels and its own distribution-in-energy. A first example of this occurs in Chapter V. In discussing any one of these competing phases, we have to include not only the two state variables needed for a homogeneous assembly but must also regard the number N in the phase as a variable. With three independent variables, the total variation of each state function becomes the sum over three partial variations instead of two. Thus, for instance, the generalization of Eq. (3.101) and of (3.111) may be written

$$TdS = dE + pdV + T(\partial S/\partial N)_{VE}dN \qquad (3.141)$$

$$dF = Vdp - SdT + (\partial F/\partial N)_{pT}dN \qquad (3.142)$$

If we add these equations, we obtain

$$dF + d(ST) = d(pV) + dE + (\partial F/\partial N)_{pT}dN + T(\partial S/\partial N)_{VE}dN \qquad (3.143)$$

In the particular case that $dN = 0$, this equation can be integrated to give

$$F = pV + E - ST + \text{constant} \qquad (3.144)$$

an equation that is accepted as the definition of F, even when N is not fixed, so that Eq. (3.142) leads simply to

$$\mu \equiv (\partial F/\partial N)_{pT} = -T(\partial S/\partial N)_{VE} \qquad (3.145)$$

The quantity μ, the free energy per molecule, is called the chemical potential of the phase, and it can be shown that two phases are in equilibrium when they have the same chemical potential.

The second law of thermodynamics may be stated in terms of any one of the potential functions. In terms of entropy, it may be stated as follows: Consider two similar thermodynamic assemblies initially isolated from each other and in possibly different thermodynamic states, each with its own entropy. The assemblies are then put into thermal contact; they disturb each other thermally and eventually settle down into a new equilibrium state for the mixture as a whole. If the two parts were initially in the same state, the final entropy is exactly the sum of the two parts, but otherwise the final entropy is greater than the sum of the two initial parts. This law suggests a close connection between entropy and probability: If the combined assembly can go over into a more probable state than that formed by simply juxtaposing the two initial states, it will do so, the final probability is greater, and every real change is toward greater probability. While the combinatory rule for probabilities is multiplicative, that for entropy is additive, because entropy is an extensive function. It will be seen in § 3.4 that entropy is identified with the logarithm of the probability.

3.2 Identification of the temperature. In order to find the thermodynamic interpretation of the parameters α and β from the classical distribution formulae (2.341) and (2.343), it is necessary to consider some particular assembly in which we know the energy levels and their degeneracies. Consider, then, an ideal gas of N particles of mass m in a cubic box of side L and with energy states listed in Eq. (1.303):

$$\epsilon_n = (h^2/8mL^2)(n_1{}^2 + n_2{}^2 + n_3{}^2) = h^2n^2/8mL^2 \qquad (3.201)$$

where n is the magnitude of the vector (n_1, n_2, n_3). There is one eigenfunction to each set of positive integers n_1, n_2, n_3. In a three dimensional diagram of n-space, there is one eigenfunction to each lattice point, meaning one eigenfunction per unit volume in the space inside the positive axes. When the numbers n_j are all large, as required for the formulae of the last chapter, we can imagine a spherical shell of thickness small compared with its radius, yet containing a large number of lattice points, and we can equate the number of eigenfunctions associated with the n-vectors ending in the shell, $\omega(n)dn$, to the volume of the shell in n-space:

$$\omega(n)dn = \tfrac{1}{2}\pi n^2 dn \tag{3.202}$$

From Eq. (3.201), we have

$$d\epsilon = \tfrac{1}{4}(h^2/mL^2)ndn \tag{3.203}$$

Then from Eqs. (3.203) and (3.201), we can show that the number (3.202) may be written in the form:

$$\omega(n)dn = 2\pi(2m)^{3/2}(L/h)^3\epsilon^{1/2}d\epsilon = \omega(\epsilon)d\epsilon \tag{3.204}$$

In the light of this relation, we rewrite Eq. (2.341) in the form:

$$n(\epsilon)d\epsilon = \omega(\epsilon)e^{-\alpha-\beta\epsilon}d\epsilon \tag{3.205}$$

and Eqs. (2.342) and (2.343) in an integral form:

$$N = \int_0^\infty \omega(\epsilon)e^{-\alpha-\beta\epsilon}d\epsilon \tag{3.206}$$

$$E = \int_0^\infty \epsilon\omega(\epsilon)e^{-\alpha-\beta\epsilon}d\epsilon \tag{3.207}$$

Writing Eq. (3.204) into Eq. (3.206) we obtain immediately

$$N/L^3 = (2\pi m/\beta)^{3/2}/(h^3e^\alpha) \tag{3.208}$$

(Pierce's Tables #496), while doing the same thing with Eq. (3.207) gives

$$E/L^3 = (3/2\beta)(2\pi m/\beta)^{3/2}/(h^3e^\alpha) \tag{3.209}$$

(Pierce's Tables #481). Eliminating α from between these last two we find

$$\beta = 3N/2E \tag{3.210}$$

showing that $1/\beta$ is two-thirds of the mean kinetic energy per particle. The student will recognize this as equal to kT, where k is the Boltzmann constant of kinetic theory and T is the kinetic theory temperature:

$$\beta = 1/kT \tag{3.211}$$

3.3   Equation of state of the ideal gas.   To find the equation of state of any assembly it is necessary to find the pressure, for example, as a function of V and T. This can be done in the following way: Consider a virtual change in volume δV of the assembly and the corresponding changes in the energy levels:

$$\delta \epsilon_j = (\partial \epsilon_j / \partial V) \delta V \tag{3.301}$$

By a virtual change, we mean that the distribution-in-energy, defined by the set of numbers $\{n_j\}$, is not to be disturbed by the change, which implies that the assembly remains in the most probable distribution-in-energy and that its entropy remains unaltered, as will be seen from Eq. (3.402). The increase in energy under these circumstances is equal to $-p\delta V$ from Eq. (3.101), and, therefore,

$$p\delta V = - \sum_j n_j (\partial \epsilon_j / \partial V) \delta V \tag{3.302}$$

Now from Eq. (3.201) we have for each energy level or given n-vector that ϵ is proportional to $1/L^2$ or to $V^{-\frac{2}{3}}$, so

$$\partial \epsilon_j / \partial V = -2\epsilon_j / 3V$$

and Eq. (3.302) becomes simply

$$p = 2E/3V \tag{3.303}$$

Combining this with Eq. (3.210), we find

$$pV = N/\beta \tag{3.304}$$

Comparing this with the perfect gas law, $pV = NkT$, we see that Eq. (3.211) again is true, with T now identified with the perfect gas scale of Kelvin.

3.4   Statistical definition of entropy.   In the last two sections, we have appealed to earlier definitions of temperature in terms of kinetic theory of gases. Here we shall by-pass such an argument by making a different approach, viz., by setting up a statistical definition of entropy and then applying the general thermodynamic equations (3.102) to deduce the temperature and pressure of the ideal gas.

The accepted definition of entropy in terms of statistical concepts that best fits the known properties of entropy is the equation,

$$S = k \ln C \tag{3.401}$$

and this is true whatever statistical count is used for the number of complexions C—Boltzmann, Bose-Einstein, Fermi-Dirac, or the classical limit of the last two. In the classical limit, Eq. (2.245) leads to

$$S = k \sum_j n_j \{ \ln (\omega_j / n_j) + 1 \} \tag{3.402}$$

Putting Eq. (2.341) for the most probable classical distribution-in-energy into this equation we find

$$S = k \sum_j n_j(1 + \alpha + \beta\epsilon_j) = k\beta E + k(1 + \alpha)N \qquad (3.403)$$

Using Eqs. (3.208) and (3.210) in this to eliminate α and β, we obtain

$$S = \tfrac{5}{2}kN + kN \ln \{(V/N)(4\pi mE/3Nh^2)^{3/2}\} \qquad (3.404)$$

This expresses S as a function of E and V for the ideal gas in the classical limit. Applying the second thermodynamic Eq. (3.102) to this yields

$$1/T = (\partial S/\partial E)_V = (3Nk/2)(\partial \ln E/\partial E) = 3Nk/2E \qquad (3.405)$$

Putting this back into Eq. (3.210) gives, at once, the same result as before:

$$\beta = 1/kT \qquad (3.406)$$

Again from the first Eq. (3.102), we have

$$p/T = (\partial S/\partial V)_E = Nk(\partial \ln V/\partial V) = Nk/V \qquad (3.407)$$

The fact that our proposed definition of entropy, Eq. (3.401), leads to the correct equation of state for the ideal gas in the classical limit is taken as sufficient confirmation of that definition, at least for the present. It is to be observed that, according to the second law of thermodynamics, entropy is defined only to within an arbitrary constant, through the differential relation (3.101), whereas in statistical mechanics, the definition of entropy given in Eq. (3.401) goes further than that. If we accept Eq. (3.406) or Eq. (3.211) as the statistical definition of temperature, then Eq. (3.401) automatically satisfies Eq. (3.101), the thermodynamic definition of entropy, while at the same time fixing the arbitrary constant of entropy. This reasoning has been carried through in the foregoing only for the ideal classical gas, but we shall accept Eq. (3.211) and Eq. (3.401) as valid for all assemblies and work out the consequences of this assumption.

3.5 Identification of the chemical potential. Having identified β as $3N/2E$ in Eq. (3.210), we can substitute this value into Eq. (3.208) to obtain

$$\alpha = \ln \{(V/N)(4\pi mE/3h^2N)^{3/2}\} \qquad (3.501)$$

and, comparing this with the expression (3.404) for entropy, we see that

$$\alpha = (1/k)(\partial S/\partial N)_{VE} \qquad (3.502)$$

This, compared with Eq. (3.145), yields

$$\alpha = -\mu/kT = -F/NkT \qquad (3.503)$$

relating the parameter α to the chemical potential or free energy per molecule.

It is convenient here to reiterate the equations for the most probable distribution-in-energy for the various statistics in terms of μ and T instead of the parameters α and β:

Boltzmann $$n_j/\omega_j = N e^{-(\epsilon_j - \mu)/kT} \tag{3.510}$$

Bose-Einstein $$n_j/\omega_j = \{e^{(\epsilon_j - \mu)/kT} - 1\}^{-1} \tag{3.511}$$

Fermi-Dirac $$n_j/\omega_j = \{e^{(\epsilon_j - \mu)/kT} + 1\}^{-1} \tag{3.512}$$

Classical $$n_j/\omega_j = e^{-(\epsilon_j - \mu)/kT} \tag{3.513}$$

3.6 Validity of the classical approximation. It was pointed out in connection with Eq. (2.341) that the classical approximation could be used when $n_j/\omega_j \ll 1$ for all values of j, and that this requires

$$e^{(\epsilon_j - \mu)/kT} \gg 1 \tag{3.601}$$

We see from Eq. (3.405) that kT is of the same order of magnitude as the mean energy per particle, and so of the same order of magnitude as the energy eigenvalue ϵ_j. To satisfy Eq. (3.601), we need the exponent to be at least about 4, so that μ must be negative and roughly several times kT in magnitude. Looking back at Eqs. (3.501) and (3.502) we see that this requires

$$\ln \{(V/N)(2\pi m kT/h^2)^{3/2}\} > 3 \tag{3.602}$$

where we have used Eq. (3.405) to express E in terms of T. In most gases N/V is of the order 10^{20}, and m is about 10^{-24} times the atomic weight. If we are interested in temperatures above 100 °K, these values do in fact satisfy the condition (3.602), so the classical approximation is valid. If, however, the atomic weight is small, e.g., of hydrogen or helium, and if T is of the order of a few degrees Kelvin, the condition (3.602) is violated, and classical statistics is not valid. If m is the mass of an electron, the condition (3.602) is violated even at ordinary laboratory temperatures, and the statistics of electrons must be handled in terms of the Fermi-Dirac formalism. If for N/V we use the numerical density of protons inside heavy nuclei, we find the degeneracy temperature has the order of magnitude 10^{10} °K. This means that any liquid drop model for the nucleus must treat the assembly of protons as being practically at absolute zero of temperature, unless the temperature is high enough to produce thermonuclear reactions; even then it may be necessary to include full corrections for quantum degeneracy.

3.7 The second and third laws of thermodynamics. The statistical interpretation of entropy leads to a slight but very significant modification of the second law of thermodynamics. Whereas the purely formal statement of the second law says that the entropy of an isolated system (here called assembly rather than system) can never decrease, we must now qualify this with a "hardly ever." The decrease in entropy would mean a change from a most probable condition to a less probable one, and while this is not likely, it is not impossible. Stated more explicitly, we may say that by comparing the probabilities of various distributions-in-energy in the neighborhood of the most probable one, we shall find a Gaussian form of probability curve about the maximum. It can be shown that the sharpness of this Gaussian curve is in general greater for assemblies containing larger numbers of systems (we shall see this in some detail in Chapter XV). It is indeed a common experience; the statistical computations of insurance groups are useful and valid only because of the large numbers of individuals co-operating for security. Any small selection of individuals may easily exhibit wild departures from the most probable behavior, but the average behavior of a large number will depart only very slightly from the average behavior, or most probable behavior, of the whole assembly. The thermodynamic behavior of an assembly is just the average behavior of a large number of systems, and the larger the number of systems, the sharper is the meaning of "hardly ever." The number of individuals required to make insurance statistics successful is only of the order of some tens of thousands; the number of particles in any ordinary quantity of matter is of the order 10^{20}, so the probability maximum predicted by quantum statistics is even fantastically sharper than that in successful insurance statistics—our "hardly ever" is as good as the classical "never."

Indeed the new statement, although it seems weaker than the classical one, actually implies much more. The methods we shall develop for calculating statistical averages yield, *pari passu*, the average departures or mean deviations from the said averages. This leads us naturally to regard spontaneous fluctuations of thermodynamic variables about their mean values as natural characteristics of the equilibrium state, rather than as paradoxical departures from that state. Statistical equilibrium consists of a whole pattern of states distributed about the most probable one. This picture modifies the concept of a "reversible process." In classical thermodynamics we are supposed to constrain a system to move with infinite slowness through a succession of equilibrium states, the process then being reversible through the same succession of equilibrium states. If the process were carried out at finite speed, we would have to force small departures from equilibrium in order to effect the changes; then, if the reverse process were effected, the necessary small departures from equilibrium would cause hysteresis between the "up" and "down" paths. This in fact leads to an admission that a truly reversible process is at best an idealized abstraction. On the new statistical picture, the situation is entirely different. We do not have to force small departures from equilibrium to cause changes; small departures from the most probable state already occur as spontaneous fluctuations, and all we have to do is to take advantage of those fluctuations tending in the desired direction and resist those tending in the wrong directions. Hysteresis between the up and down paths then does not need to be greater than the normal fluctuations occurring on either path, and the two cannot be resolved. In this sense a statistically reversible process is in fact possible at finite speed, depending only on the magnitude and frequency of the fluctuations characteristic of any equilibrium state.

As already mentioned in § 3.4, the statistical interpretation of entropy removes the arbitrary constant that remained in classical thermodynamics. Concerning this arbitrary constant, Nernst postulated, as a result of extensive observations of actual thermodynamic assemblies at very low temperature, that the entropy of all materials would reduce to the same level as T approached absolute zero, and, on the basis of this, he proposed to establish an absolute zero of entropy at the absolute zero of temperature. Unfortunately, there were exceptions to Nernst's observations that could not be explained at that time, and also there was, and of course still is, the practical difficulty that no actual measurements can ever be carried near enough to 0 °K to afford perfect surety that the limiting entropy had in fact been reached. Nernst's law therefore remained controversial until statistical mechanics provided a theoretical value for absolute entropy. It is now possible to calculate the chemical constants without actually measuring entropy right down to 0 °K and, also, to explain the earlier apparent exceptions to Nernst's law. The third law of thermodynamics has thus become a direct corollary of the statistical definition of entropy. Further details of this very interesting topic will be found in the texts suggested for further reading; here we confine ourselves to a brief word of caution.

The classical formulae based on Eq. (2.245) cannot be used to discuss the approach to absolute zero; in particular, Eqs. (4.207) and (4.208), for the free energy and entropy of an ideal gas, become invalid at temperatures where quantum degeneracy becomes important. The classical formulae, if applied at the limit $T = 0$, would give entropy minus infinity, and this is a spurious result. We shall find later that the low-temperature behavior of an ideal gas always makes S approach zero if the proper quantum statistics are used. Thus with Fermi-Dirac statistics, it is found that at $T = 0$ all the lowest energy states are filled to capacity, while the others remain empty:

$$n_j = \omega_j, \quad j = 1, 2, \cdots k; \quad n_j = 0, \quad j > k$$

where k is determined by $\sum_{j=1}^{k} n_j = N$. Putting these values into Eq. (2.231), for the number of complexions, we find

$$C_{\mathrm{F.D.}}(T = 0) = \prod_{j=1}^{k} \{\omega_j!/0!\omega_j!\} \prod_{j>k} \{\omega_j!/\omega_j!0!\} = 1$$

The entropy is then the logarithm of unity, which is zero. In the Bose-Einstein statistics, it is found that all the systems go into the single lowest state at $T = 0$; then it is easy to see from Eq. (2.223) that $C = 1$, and therefore entropy again vanishes at absolute zero temperature.

EXERCISES AND PROBLEMS

1. Verify Eq. (3.204) for the density-in-energy.

2. Derive Eqs. (3.208) and (3.209).

3. An assembly consists of 1,000 particles shared between two nondegenerate energy levels, $\epsilon_1 = 1$ and $\epsilon_2 = 2$ units. Find the most probable distribution-in-energy in classical statistics when the total energy is 1,200 units. Find the temperature and entropy of the assembly if the unit of energy is equal to 1.37×10^{-16} erg (kT at 1 °K).

4. Consider Problem 3 in Bose-Einstein statistics. Suppose that the energy levels are 100-fold degenerate and compare the results with the nondegenerate case.

5. Formulate and solve a problem like that in Problem 3 which has a meaning in Fermi-Dirac statistics.

6. If the nucleus of Pb isotope mass 204 has a cross section of one barn, 10^{-24} cm^2, find the temperature above which the nucleons within the nucleus could be treated as a classical assembly.

REFERENCES FOR FURTHER STUDY

Statistical Mechanics, R. H. Fowler, Cambridge, 1936; especially Chapters 6, 7, and 20.
Statistical Thermodynamics, R. H. Fowler and E. A. Guggenheim, Cambridge, 1939.
Textbook of Thermodynamics, P. S. Epstein, Wiley, 1937; especially Chapter 13.

Chapter IV

THE PARTITION FUNCTION IN CLASSICAL STATISTICS

4.1 The partition function. In this chapter we shall consider either (a) assemblies of independent indistinguishable systems in the classical limit, where the formula (2.341) gives the most probable distribution-in-energy, or (b) assemblies of distinguishable systems where the formula of Boltzmann, Eq. (2.314), applies.

A. Indistinguishable systems. Summing Eq. (2.341) over all subscripts gave us Eq. (2.342), and this can be written in the form:

$$N = Qe^{\mu/kT} \tag{4.101}$$

where

$$Q = \sum_j \omega_j e^{-\epsilon_j/kT} \tag{4.102}$$

The quantity Q, which is a function of T explicitly, and a function of V through the eigenvalue spectrum, is called the partition function of the systems of which the assembly is composed. The partition function is a purely mechanical entity in the sense that it can be computed as a function of T and V as soon as we know the quantum mechanical properties of any one system. It is found to be possible, and at the same time convenient, to express all the thermodynamical and statistical properties of the assembly in terms of the partition function of the member systems. It must, however, be emphasized at the outset that this program is valid only in the classical limit or with Boltzmann statistics.

Taking the logarithm of Eq. (4.101) yields

$$\mu = kT(\ln N - \ln Q) \tag{4.103}$$

Recalling Eq. (3.145) we may say that μ for a homogeneous assembly is simply the free energy per system or particle; but F is an extensive function in a homogeneous assembly, so that the total free energy F of the assembly is just N times the free energy per particle. Thus Eq. (4.103) leads at once to

$$F = NkT(\ln N - \ln Q) \tag{4.104}$$

Equations (3.112) then give the equation of state of the assembly indirectly. Incidentally, the zero of free energy is usually regarded as arbitrary, and Eq. (4.104) gives essentially the difference between the free energy at the temperature T and the free energy at absolute zero temperature.

Independently of Eq. (3.112) we shall prove that

$$p = NkT(\partial \ln Q/\partial V)_T \tag{4.111}$$

and derive the equation of state directly. To do this we put Eq. (4.102) in the right side of (4.111) and obtain

$$p = (NkT/Q)(\partial Q/\partial V)_T = -(N/Q) \sum_j \omega_j(\partial \epsilon_j/\partial V)e^{-\epsilon_j/kT} \tag{4.112}$$

Multiply this sum by $e^{\mu/kT}$, and multiply the Q in the denominator by the same quantity, making use of Eq. (4.101) in the denominator, and of Eq. (3.513) in the sum; the result is

$$p = - \sum_j n_j(\partial \epsilon_j/\partial V) \tag{4.113}$$

which is precisely the same expression as that derived for pressure in Eq. (3.302), thus verifying Eq. (4.111). This equation is essentially the equation of state, expressing p as a function of T and V.

We can also express entropy S in terms of the partition function through Eqs. (3.112) and (4.104):

$$S = -Nk \ln (N/Q) + NkT(\partial \ln Q/\partial T)_p \tag{4.114}$$

It is left as an exercise to check that this result agrees with Eq. (3.402) in the example of the classical gas, where $pV = NkT$. The energy E can be expressed in terms of Q if we divide Eq. (2.342) into Eq. (2.343) and make use of the definition of Q in Eq. (4.102) to write

$$E/N = (1/Q) \sum_j \omega_j\epsilon_je^{-\epsilon_j/kT} = (kT^2/Q)(\partial Q/\partial T)_V$$

so that

$$E = NkT^2(\partial \ln Q/\partial T)_V \tag{4.115}$$

The heat capacity at constant volume, C_v, is obtained from this by using the definition

$$C_v = (\partial E/\partial T)_V \tag{4.116}$$

The heat capacity at constant pressure, on the other hand, is derivable from the total heat or enthalpy H of Eq. (3.131), instead of from the total energy E. First we obtain H in terms of Q. It is easy to verify that, to within an arbitrary constant, Eq. (3.131) leads to

$$H = F + ST = F - T(\partial F/\partial T)_p = -T^2(\partial/\partial T)(F/T)_p \tag{4.121}$$

where we have made use of Eq. (3.112). Then from Eq. (4.104), remembering that $Nk \ln N$ is a constant, we obtain at once

$$H = NkT^2(\partial \ln Q/\partial T)_p \qquad (4.122)$$

This gives the heat capacity through

$$C_p = (\partial H/\partial T)_p \qquad (4.123)$$

The foregoing formulae enable us to calculate the thermodynamic properties of any classical assembly of independent systems when we know the quantum mechanical properties of the systems, i.e., when we can compute their partition functions. Although the statistics are restricted to being classical, the partition function must be evaluated by quantum mechanics, and we shall see immediately how this materially alters the predictions of the classical analysis of the thermodynamic behavior of assemblies.

B. *Distinguishable systems.* The definition (3.401) of entropy applied to Boltzmann statistics of distinguishable systems, making use of Eq. (2.242), yields

$$S = k \ln C_{\text{Boltz}} = k\{N \ln N + \sum_j n_j \ln (\omega_j/n_j)\} \qquad (4.131)$$

and then the Boltzmann distribution Eq. (2.314) gives

$$S = k \sum_j n_j(\alpha + \beta\epsilon_j) = Nk\alpha + Ek\beta \qquad (4.132)$$

We accept the former interpretation of β in Eq. (3.406) and so write the last result as

$$NkT\alpha = ST - E \qquad (4.133)$$

However, it is easy to verify that the Helmholtz free energy A is given by Eq. (3.121) to within an arbitrary constant:

$$A = E - TS \qquad (4.134)$$

so that Eq. (4.203) leads to the identification of α with the Helmholtz free energy per particle:

$$\alpha = -A/NkT \qquad (4.135)$$

Thus in the Boltzmann statistics, the Helmholtz free energy plays the same role as the Gibbs free energy plays in the classical statistics, as shown in Eq. (3.503).

We can now reverse the reading of Eq. (4.135), applying the definition of Q to the left side, viz., Eq. (4.102). Thus from the Boltzmann expression (2.316) and (4.102) we have

$$Q = e^\alpha \qquad (4.136)$$

Combining the last two equations thus gives

$$A = -NkT \ln Q \qquad (4.137)$$

Eq. (3.122) then permits us to evaluate the entropy and pressure:

$$S = Nk \ln Q + NkT(\partial \ln Q/\partial T)_V \qquad (4.138)$$

and

$$p = NkT(\partial \ln Q/\partial V)_T \qquad (4.139)$$

in terms of the partition function. The thermodynamic relations

$$E = A + TS \quad \text{and} \quad H = E + pV \qquad (4.140)$$

then in turn lead to formulae for the heat capacity in terms of Q. The first is in fact identical with Eq. (4.115). The second leads to

$$H = NkT^2\{(\partial \ln Q/\partial T)_V + (V/T)(\partial \ln Q/\partial V)_T\} \qquad (4.141)$$

Although this looks quite unlike Eq. (4.122), it is easy to show that the two forms are equivalent for the classical ideal gas.

The identity of results for the pressure, energy, enthalpy, and heat capacities in terms of the partition function, as between the classical limit of quantum statistics and the Boltzmann statistics, can lead to some confusion if their essential differences are not kept in mind. Note first that the entropy Eq. (4.208) for the Boltzmann statistics is not the same as that given in Eq. (4.114) for the classical limit. The equations of the present section (B) on distinguishable systems are exact for all temperatures, not only being valid for high ones. The equations (A) on indistinguishable systems are valid only in the classical limit, sufficiently high temperatures or low densities. If we are not concerned with the absolute value of entropy, the difference does not matter; but it is better to keep Boltzmann statistics explicitly for distinguishable systems alone, and always make the distinction between Boltzmann and classical statistics, so that at very low temperatures there will be no confusion.

4.2 Partition function for the ideal monatomic gas. We transform the summed form of Q in Eq. (4.102) into an integral

$$Q = \int \omega(\epsilon)e^{-\epsilon/kT}d\epsilon \qquad (4.201)$$

and make use of Eq. (3.204) giving the number of energy states in any energy range for the ideal gas. The resulting integral was already evaluated in § 3.2 in connection with Eq. (3.206), and evidently we have

$$Q = V(2\pi mkT/h^2)^{3/2} \qquad (4.202)$$

This form of Q expressed as a function of T and V allows us to use the Eqs. (4.112) and (4.115) for p and E:

$$p = NkT(\partial \ln Q/\partial V)_T = NkT/V \qquad (4.203)$$

$$E = NkT^2(\partial \ln Q/\partial T)_V = 3NkT/2 \qquad (4.204)$$

yielding

$$C_v = (\partial E/\partial T)_V = 3Nk/2 \qquad (4.205)$$

all of which are familiar classical results. Also from Eq. (4.104), Eq. (4.202) gives

$$F = NkT\{\ln (N/V) - \tfrac{3}{2}\ln T - \ln [(2\pi mk/h^2)^{3/2}]\} \tag{4.206}$$

In order to make use of this last expression in the thermodynamic formulae (3.112), we have to express it instead in terms of p and T, eliminating V between Eqs. (4.203) and (4.206):

$$F = NkT\{\ln p - \tfrac{5}{2}\ln T - \ln [k^{5/2}(2\pi m/h^2)^{3/2}]\} \tag{4.207}$$

Eq. (3.112) then immediately yields

$$S = -Nk\{\ln p - \tfrac{5}{2}\ln T - \tfrac{5}{2} - \ln [k^{5/2}(2\pi m/h^2)^{3/2}]\} \tag{4.208}$$

The same result could have been obtained by expressing Q in terms of p and T

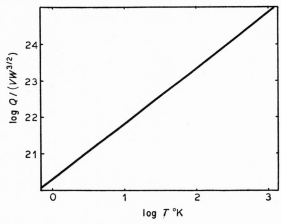

FIG. 4.21. Universal curve for partition function of ideal gas. W is the atomic weight and V the volume of the gas.

and thereby eliminating V between Eqs. (4.202) and (4.203), and by using Eq. (4.114):

$$Q = (NkT/p)(2\pi mkT/h^2)^{3/2} \tag{4.211}$$

Making use of this form of Q and Eq. (4.112) also gives the enthalpy:

$$H = NkT^2(\partial \ln Q/\partial T)_p = 5NkT/2 \tag{4.212}$$

and hence the heat capacity at constant pressure:

$$C_p = (\partial H/\partial T)_p = 5Nk/2 \tag{4.213}$$

All the above results are of course familiar properties of the ideal gas in kinetic theory and serve merely to confirm the present statistical procedures. However, the two results given in Eqs. (4.207) and (4.208) call for special comment: they contain more information than the classical results of thermodynamics, viz., a precise statement of the previously arbitrary constant appearing in the thermodynamic expressions for F and S. As remarked in the discussion of the third law of thermodynamics, this so-called chemical constant had to be estimated by extrapolation down to 0 °K on the assumption that all substances approached the same entropy at absolute zero temperature.   Kinetic theory gave no prediction of the value of the chemical constant. Statistical theory predicts that the chemical constants have the value:

$$I = \ln \left[k^{5/2} (2\pi m/h^2)^{3/2} \right] \qquad (4.214)$$

a result that has been well confirmed by comparison with experiment. In order to emphasize the importance of this advance in understanding the chemical constants by means of the quantum mechanical partition function, we give here the classical mechanical calculations and point out where they fail.

In the classical mechanical description of a system, we set up a phase space of $2f$ dimensions, where f is the number of degrees of freedom of the system, as discussed in § 1.1. This phase space may now be imagined divided into equal cells each having $2f$ dimensions, and each having the same definite size g^f, where g is the area in any one p-q plane section. Liouville's theorem in classical analytical dynamics proved that a random uniform distribution of systems in this phase space, moving according to the Hamiltonian equations of motion, remains uniformly distributed in phase space for all time. This, combined with the ergodic theorem that every system will pass through every point in phase space given sufficient time, leads to the basic hypothesis of classical statistics: that every cell in phase space is a priori equally probable. This is the classical equivalent to the quantum hypothesis that every quantum state is equally probable. The major difference resulting from this is that in the classical theory no definite magnitude could be assigned to the cell size, g; the cells in phase space are used instead of the quantum states.

For the ideal monatomic gas, $f = 3$ and the cells of phase space are six dimensional hypervolumes:

$$d\tau = dq_1 dq_2 dq_3 dp_1 dp_2 dp_3 \qquad (4.215)$$

The number of cells of size g^3 in such a volume element is

$$\omega(\epsilon)d\epsilon = d\tau/g^3 \qquad (4.216)$$

where $d\epsilon$ is the energy range corresponding to the element of momentum through the expression

$$\epsilon(p) = (p_1{}^2 + p_2{}^2 + p_3{}^2)/2m \qquad (4.217)$$

The partition function obtained from the integral form, Eq. (4.201), is

$$Q = g^{-3} \iiint dq_1 dq_2 dq_3 \iiint_{-\infty}^{\infty} \exp\left[- (p_1{}^2 + p_2{}^2 + p_3{}^2)/2mkT\right] dp_1 dp_2 dp_3$$

$$(4.218)$$

The configuration integral simply equals the volume of the enclosure, and the momentum integrals can be carried out separately (Pierce's Tables #492):

$$Q = V(2\pi mkT/g^2)^{3/2} \tag{4.219}$$

Comparing this with Eq. (4.202), we see that the classically arbitrary quantity g is replaced by Planck's constant h in quantum mechanics. The quantum theory thus has the effect of limiting the minimum size of cells in phase space, one cell per quantum state. In classical mechanics, there was no reason for such a limit to g; one would in fact have expected to allow g to approach zero indefinitely. The fact that Nernst's theorem seemed to give a definite size to the phase cell was entirely mysterious in classical theory. Putting g instead of h in the chemical constant Eq. (4.214) and then letting g go to zero would give a negative infinite value to the chemical constant.

4.3 Most probable distribution-in-momentum: kinetic theory. Because in practice it is not possible to follow the motion of individual atoms, the most probable distribution-in-energy n_j of Eqs. (3.510)–(3.513) can be interpreted as giving a measure of the probability of finding an atom in the jth state. Normalizing to unity for the total probability of finding an atom in some state, we may assert that

$$\rho_j = n_j/N$$

is the probability, on inspecting an atom in the assembly, of finding it to be in the jth state. In terms of a continuous spectrum, the probability would be written in the form:

$$\rho(\epsilon) = n(\epsilon)/N$$

For classical statistics we then have

$$\rho(\epsilon) = \omega(\epsilon)e^{-\epsilon/kT} \div \int \omega(\epsilon)e^{-\epsilon/kT}d\epsilon = \omega(\epsilon)e^{-\epsilon/kT}/Q \tag{4.301}$$

For Bose-Einstein or Fermi-Dirac statistics it is rather

$$\rho(\epsilon) = \omega(\epsilon)/N[e^{(\epsilon-\mu)/kT} \mp 1] \tag{4.302}$$

where μ has to be determined so that the integrated probability is unity.

If it is assumed that the assembly is isotropic in momentum space, all directions of motion associated with any one energy value are equally probable. The statistical weights of the states may be written

$$\omega(\epsilon)d\epsilon = Vdp_1dp_2dp_3/h^3$$

and the classical probability of finding the atom with momentum vector **p** within the element $dp_1dp_2dp_3$ is $\rho(\mathbf{p})$ where

$$\rho(\mathbf{p}) = \exp(-p^2/2mkT)/\int \cdots \int \exp(-p^2/2mkT)dp_1dp_2dp_3$$

leading to the well-known Maxwell distribution function:

$$\rho(\mathbf{p}) = (2\pi m k T)^{-3/2} e^{-p^2/2mkT} \tag{4.303}$$

The relation between $\rho(\mathbf{p})$ and $\rho(\epsilon)$ is evidently

$$\rho(\epsilon)d\epsilon = (V/h^3)\rho(\mathbf{p})dp_1 dp_2 dp_3 \tag{4.304}$$

This distribution function is the basis of classical kinetic theory. Thus, for example, the mean speed of atoms in an ideal gas is derived from

$$m\bar{v} = \int \cdots \int p\rho(\mathbf{p})dp_1 dp_2 dp_3$$

which results in

$$\bar{v} = 2(2kT/\pi m)^{1/2} \tag{4.305}$$

The mean square speed is similarly found from

$$m^2\overline{v^2} = \int \cdots \int p^2\rho(\mathbf{p})dp_1 dp_2 dp_3$$

resulting in

$$\overline{v^2} = 3kT/m \tag{4.306}$$

The root mean square deviation of the speed defined by

$$(\overline{v^2} - \bar{v}^2)^{1/2}/\bar{v}$$

derived from Eqs. (4.305) and (4.306) turns out to be 0.419; the speed is thus not very sharply defined, no matter how large the assembly may be. This is not in conflict with the statement made in § 3.7 about the sharpness of the most probable value of a thermodynamic variable, because the speed of an atom in an assembly is not regarded as a thermodynamic variable.

We shall not pursue the development of classical kinetic theory further; there are many excellent treatments available. Instead, we shall point out briefly how this subject may be generalized to fit the quantum statistics. Expanding the square bracket reciprocal in Eq. (4.302) in a power series, one derives at once the following expression for the probability in momentum space for either Bose-Einstein or Fermi-Dirac ideal gas:

$$\rho(\mathbf{p}) = (V/Nh^3) \sum_j (\pm 1)^j e^{j\mu/kT} \exp\left(-jp^2/2mkT\right) \tag{4.307}$$

where the factor (V/h^3) comes from the comparison between $\rho(\epsilon)$ and $\rho(\mathbf{p})$ in Eq. (4.304), and the parameter μ is to be determined from the normalizing condition, $\int \cdots \int \rho(\mathbf{p})dp_1 dp_2 dp_3 = 1$. The mean speed in the Bose-Einstein gas (positive sign in the last equation) is to be found from

$$m\bar{v}_{\text{B.E.}} = \int \cdots \int p\rho(\mathbf{p})dp_1 dp_2 dp_3$$

and Eq. (4.307) for $\rho(\mathbf{p})$. The result is

$$\bar{v}_{\text{B.E.}} = (2\pi/m)(V/Nh^3)(2mkT)^2 \sum_j (1/j)^2 e^{j\mu/kT} \tag{4.308}$$

The sum $\sum_j 1/j^2 = 1.645$. The properties of a Bose-Einstein gas will be discussed at length in Chapter VIII; it will be shown there, for instance, that the free energy parameter μ becomes practically zero at a temperature T_0 where

$$N/V = 2.612(2\pi mkT_0/h^2)^{3/2} \tag{4.309}$$

and at this temperature the Bose-Einstein gas begins to condense into its lowest state. The mean speed at this temperature can be compared with that of a classical gas at the same temperature as given in Eq. (4.305),

$$T = T_0: \qquad\qquad \bar{v}_{\text{B.E.}} = 0.63\bar{v}_{\text{class}} \tag{4.310}$$

The mean square speed of the Bose-Einstein gas atoms is also readily evaluated in the same way as for the classical gas, using instead the probability function of Eq. (4.307). If Eq. (4.309) is used to eliminate V/N and the temperature taken to equal T_0 we find

$$T = T_0: \quad \overline{v^2}_{\text{B.E.}} = (3kT_0/m) \sum_j (1/j)^{5/2} / \sum_j (1/j)^{3/2} = 0.5134\,(3kT_0/m) \tag{4.311}$$

The root mean square deviation turns out to be 0.725 at T_0, which is even larger than in the classical gas.

Some very interesting anomalies in the kinetic theory behavior of the Bose-Einstein gas have been derived by this generalization.[*]

4.4 The partition function for internal degrees of freedom. In the foregoing discussions of the ideal gas, we have treated the atoms of the gas as single mass points with no energy other than that of translation. In fact even single atoms have internal energy states due to electrons, and it is not correct to ignore these without proof that they actually do not affect the calculation, and to correct for the neglect if they do.

In any system with internal degrees of freedom, the Hamiltonian can be expressed exactly as the sum of two parts, one of which is the kinetic energy of the whole mass moving with the center of mass, the other, the energy relative to the center of mass. We are here assuming there is no potential due to external forces; hence the Schrödinger equation solves by separation of the variables cor-

---

[*] S. Chapman and T. G. Cowling, *The Mathematical Theory of Non-Uniform Gases*, Cambridge, 1952; especially Chapter 17.
  W. Band, *Phys. Rev.*, **75** (1949), pp. 1937–1946; *ibid.*, **76** (1949), pp. 558–564; *ibid.*, **79** (1950), pp. 589–592.

responding to the center of mass on the one hand, and to the positions relative to the center of mass on the other. The factor depending only on the center of mass is identical with that for a single mass point already discussed. It will have eigenvalues ϵ_j and weights ω_j precisely as before. The factor in the wave function depending on the internal variables relative to the center of mass will have eigenvalues ϵ'_n and weights ω'_n, n being an integer indicating the member of the internal energy spectrum. The total energy of the system will contain one energy from each of ϵ_j and ϵ'_n:

$$\epsilon_{jn} = \epsilon_j + \epsilon'_n \qquad (4.401)$$

The statistical weight or degeneracy of such an energy level as ϵ_{jn} is the combined weight of the two levels appearing in Eq. (4.401), because to each internal wave function there correspond ω_j wave functions for the external states. Thus we may write for the weight of ω_{jn} the product:

$$\omega_{jn} = \omega_j \omega'_n \qquad (4.402)$$

The partition function for such a system, following the defining Eq. (4.102), is generalized to the present problem to read

$$Q = \sum_n \sum_j \omega_{jn} \exp\left[-(\epsilon'_n + \epsilon_j)/kT\right] \qquad (4.403)$$

Writing Eq. (4.402) into this we have simply

$$Q = Q_{\text{c.m.}} Q_{\text{int}} \qquad (4.404)$$

where $Q_{\text{c.m.}}$ is identical in form with Eq. (4.102) and

$$Q_{\text{int}} = \sum_n \omega'_n \exp\left(-\epsilon'_n/kT\right) \qquad (4.405)$$

The lowest internal energy state may be arbitrarily set at $\epsilon'_0 = 0$, provided we regard any internal energy remaining at this lowest state as a zero-point energy of the spectrum ϵ_j. If then the next internal energy ϵ'_1 is far greater than kT, the series in Eq. (4.405) reduces practically to its first term:

$$Q_{\text{int}} \doteq \omega'_0 \exp\left(-\epsilon'_0/kT\right) = \omega'_0 \qquad (4.406)$$

This is in fact usually true for electronic energy levels, the excitation energy for electrons being much greater than the thermal energy of the atom. The complete partition function (4.403) thus reduces to

$$Q = \omega'_0 \sum_j \omega_j \exp\left(-\epsilon_j/kT\right) \qquad (4.407)$$

if, as suggested, we include ϵ'_0 as the zero-point energy of ϵ_j. This partition function differs from that of a single mass point, Eq. (4.102), merely in the numerical factor ω'_0, the statistical degeneracy of the lowest internal level, or the number of eigenfunctions corresponding to this level. If the quantum mechanical problem were solved completely, this number ω'_0 would already be included in ω_j, so the internal energies actually have no effect on the partition function when the lowest energy of excitation is large compared with kT. Moreover, with the exception of entropy and free energy, all the thermodynamic variables depend only on the derivatives of the logarithm of Q, so that complete neglect of the factor ω'_0 would make no difference except to the chemical constants. A term $Nk \ln \omega'_0$ must be added to these constants. At very high temperatures it may no longer be legitimate to neglect the internal partition function.

4.5 Partition function for diatomic molecules. Taking the logarithm of Eq. (4.404) we find

$$\ln Q = \ln Q_{\text{c.m.}} + \ln Q_{\text{int}} \tag{4.501}$$

Now all the thermodynamic functions are expressed in terms of the logarithm of Q and its derivatives, so that this equation implies that the center of mass motion and the internal degrees of freedom make additive contributions to all

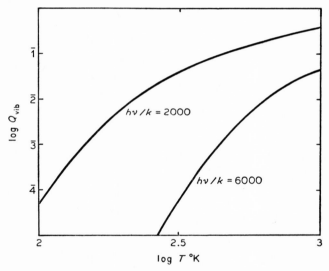

Fig. 4.51. Vibration partition functions. The frequency $\nu = 6000k/h$ corresponds roughly to the hydrogen molecule.

the thermodynamic functions. We can speak of the translational (center of mass motion) heat capacity and the internal heat capacity, the total heat capacity being the sum of these.

A diatomic molecule can have rotational energy of motion about its axis of symmetry only by virtue of its electronic states, and for the reasons given at the close of the last section, we neglect these entirely. The diatomic molecule can, however, have energy of rotation about any axis perpendicular to its axis of symmetry. The wave mechanical problem separates into two sets of variables, the radial distance between the two atoms, and the angles of the axes. Unlike the H atom problem with electronic eigenfunctions, the radial problem in the diatomic molecule yields quantum numbers that do not have any relation with the possible values of angular momentum. The two sets of quantum levels are entirely independent, and it is found that the oscillatory energies are

$$\epsilon'_n = h\nu(n + \tfrac{1}{2}) \tag{4.502}$$

where ν is the frequency of the oscillators; see Eq. (1.322). The angular motion gives energy levels:

$$\epsilon'_j = j(j + 1)h^2/8\pi^2 I \tag{4.503}$$

where I is the rotational inertia of the molecules; see Eq. (1.332). Here n and j are any integers. The oscillator levels are not degenerate, but the rotator levels are, due to space quantization:

$$\omega_j = 2j + 1 \tag{4.504}$$

See also Eq. (1.333). From the discussion of spin and symmetry in § 1.5, we also know that spin degeneracy needs to be taken into account. For the moment we may write this in as a weight factor $\sigma(j)$ and elaborate in detail at a more convenient place. The internal partition function is therefore

$$Q_{\text{int}} = \sum_n \sum_j \sigma(j)(2j + 1) \exp\left[-(\epsilon'_j + \epsilon'_n)/kT\right] = Q_{\text{vib}}Q_{\text{rot}} \tag{4.505}$$

where

$$Q_{\text{vib}} = \sum_n \exp\left[-h\nu(n + \tfrac{1}{2})/kT\right] \tag{4.506}$$

and

$$Q_{\text{rot}} = \sum_j \sigma(j)(2j + 1) \exp\left[-j(j + 1)\hbar^2/2IkT\right] \tag{4.507}$$

Taking the logarithm of Eq. (4.505) again leads to an additive rule

$$\ln Q_{\text{int}} = \ln Q_{\text{vib}} + \ln Q_{\text{rot}} \tag{4.508}$$

so that the vibrational states and the rotational states make their own additive contributions to the thermodynamic functions. The problem yet entails summing the series in Eqs. (4.506) and (4.507), in order that the heat capacities can be obtained from the general relations (4.116) and (4.115), or (4.123) and (4.122). Thus we have

$$C_{\text{vib}} = (\partial/\partial T)[NkT^2(\partial \ln Q_{\text{vib}}/\partial T)_V] \tag{4.511}$$

Summing the geometrical series in Eq. (4.506), we find

$$\ln Q_{\text{vib}} = -\tfrac{1}{2}h\nu/kT - \ln(1 - e^{-h\nu/kT})$$

Expanding the logarithm as a series, and differentiating this series term by term, we find

$$C_{\text{vib}} = Nk(h\nu/kT)^2 \sum_n ne^{-nh\nu/kT} \tag{4.512}$$

$$= Nk(h\nu/kT)^2[1 - e^{-h\nu/kT}]^{-2}e^{-h\nu/kT} \tag{4.513}$$

At sufficiently high temperatures, the exponential in Eq. (4.513) can be expanded in a power series that converges rapidly, and the whole series in square brackets can be raised to the power of minus two by the binomial theorem, giving, finally, the following result:

$$T \gg h\nu/k: \qquad C_{\text{vib}} = Nk[1 - \tfrac{1}{12}(h\nu/kT)^2 + \text{smaller terms}] \qquad (4.514)$$

This approaches the classical limit Nk at sufficiently high temperatures. At the other extreme, very low temperatures, we can use Eq. (4.512) directly, noting that the exponential terms rapidly become very small with an increasing value of n, and indeed for low enough temperature, we can retain only the first term of the series in Eq. (4.512) and neglect the rest:

$$T \to 0: \qquad C_{\text{vib}} = Nk(h\nu/kT)^2 e^{-h\nu/kT} \qquad (4.515)$$

Writing Q_{rot} in Eq. (4.511) in place of Q_{vib} yields C_{rot}. Here we have to include the spin degeneracy factor $\sigma(j)$. For two unlike atoms this factor is $(2s_a + 1)(2s_b + 1)$ and is independent of j. Equation (4.507) cannot be summed in closed form; the best we can do is to compute the first few terms of the series. Write

$$\theta_r = h^2/8\pi^2 IK \qquad (4.521)$$

then Eq. (4.507) may be written as

$$Q_{\text{rot}} = (2s_a + 1)(2s_b + 1)(1 + 3e^{-2\theta_r/T} + 5e^{-6\theta_r/T} + 7e^{-12\theta_r/T} + \cdots) \qquad (4.522)$$

The spin factor has no effect on the heat capacity. We can evaluate the reciprocal of this series by the binomial theorem and multiply the result into the temperature derivative of the series to find $\partial \ln Q/\partial T$. The process is straightforward and can be carried out to any desired accuracy to give a series expansion

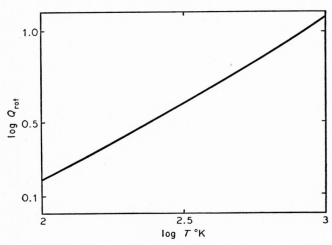

FIG. 4.52. Rotational partition function for hydrogen molecule.

for C_{rot}. At lower temperatures the series converges more rapidly, and at very low temperatures we can neglect all but the first term of the series:

$$T \rightarrow 0: \qquad C_{rot} = (3N/kT^2)(\hbar^4/I^2)e^{-\hbar^2/IkT} = 3Nk(\theta_r/T)^2 e^{-\theta_r/T} \qquad (4.523)$$

The high temperature behavior of C_{rot} cannot be obtained directly from Eq. (4.522), because that series converges too slowly at high T. Instead the sum (4.507) has to be evaluated by the Euler-Maclaurin sum formula before the temperature derivative of the logarithm is evaluated. The final result turns out to be

$$T \gg h\nu/k: \qquad C_{rot} = Nk[1 + \tfrac{1}{45}(\theta_r/T)^2 + \text{smaller terms}] \qquad (4.524)$$

The rotational heat capacity crosses the classical value at some definite temperature and approaches it asymptotically from above at very high T.

Evidently the rotational heat capacity is a function only of the ratio θ_r/T, and the function is the same for all heteronuclear diatomic molecules. The temperature scale factor θ_r is generally only a few degrees Kelvin; for example, CO has a scale $\theta_r = 2.77$ °K; for HCl it is 15.2 °K, and for HD, about 56 °K. The deviation from classical behavior becomes measurable only at temperatures lower than about three times θ_r, as Eq. (4.524) shows. The rotational inertia I of the molecule is proportional to the mass, and so θ_r is greatest for the smallest molecules. It is only for the smallest masses that the substances are still gaseous when they begin to deviate, and the deviation has in fact been observed only in HD among the heteronuclear compounds.

By contrast with the rotational heat capacity, the vibrational term C_{vib} is hardly excited at all at ordinary temperatures, because the temperature scale factor θ_v is generally several thousand degrees; thus for CO, $\theta_v = 3070$ °K, and for HD, it is about five thousand degrees. In general θ_v increases with decreasing mass, and in particular, among the isotopes of a single element, θ_v is proportional to $1/m^{1/2}$. At the temperature where C_{rot} is becoming classical, the value of C_{vib} is still practically negligible; hence the heat capacity of a gas behaves as follows: Starting at low temperatures the heat capacity is purely translational and equal to $3Nk/2$; as T increases through values around θ_r, the heat capacity increases to $5Nk/2$, the classical rotational contribution Nk becoming practically complete when T is a few times θ_r; at still higher temperatures, the vibrational heat capacity begins to appear, and the total rises to $7Nk/2$ when T is larger than θ_v. Because of the great difference between θ_r and θ_v it is usually possible to separate the rotational and vibrational heat capacities completely, and hence to obtain quite accurate estimates of θ_v. Recently very comprehensive tables have been published * giving values of C_{vib} for atomic vibration frequencies from 100 cm^{-1} to 3,600 cm^{-1}.

There are two kinds of error that can spoil the simplicity of the foregoing situation. The first is due to the fact that the forces between atoms are not

* P. Torkington, *J. Chem. Phys.* **18** (1950), p. 1373.

strictly simple harmonic ones, except for vanishingly small amplitudes. This anharmonicity can be taken care of approximately by a more precise discussion of the quantum mechanical problem. The second difficulty is more interesting from the point of statistical mechanics, and it arises in the following way: The easiest method for measuring the heat capacity of a gas is generally by means of the velocity of sound transmission, but this method sometimes gives a heat capacity less than that predicted by the theory at high temperatures, where the C_{vib} term should appear. On the other hand, static measurements of the heat capacity using direct calorimetric methods give the results predicted by the theory. This discrepancy can be understood if it is admitted that the equilibrium distribution of energy among the rotational and vibrational modes of the molecule's motion takes more time to adjust itself than the period of the sound wave. The energy in the sound wave then does not have time to excite the vibrational modes which therefore fail to exert their full effect on the heat capacity. The absorption of the sound wave in the gas becomes strong if the period of the wave is adjusted to equal the relaxation time for equilibrium adjustments with the vibrational modes of molecular motion; in this way an estimate of the relaxation time can be made.

We return now to the discussion of homonuclear diatomic molecules, like H_2, D_2, O_2, etc. As discussed in § 1.5, here the spin factor depends on j, and moreover, the dependency on j is a function of the spin s. If s is odd as in hydrogen, the factor is $\sigma = s(2s + 1)$ when j is even, and $(2s + 1)(s + 1)$ when j is odd. For H_2, with $s = \frac{1}{2}$, the partition function (4.507) should be

$$Q_{rot} = 1 + 5e^{-6\theta_r/T} + 8e^{-20\theta_r/T} + \cdots + 3\{3e^{-2\theta_r/T} + 7e^{-12\theta_r/T} + \cdots\} \quad (4.525)$$

If this partition function is used to calculate the heat capacity of H_2, the result is quite different from the observed heat capacity when plotted as a function of temperature. The reason for this is again concerned with a time factor. Statistics based on Eq. (4.525) of course assume that equilibrium is established among all the states included in the expression, and this means we assume frequent transitions between all the states enumerated—in particular between symmetrical and antisymmetrical rotation states, which in turn implies transitions between different spin states. If collisions can dissociate the H_2 molecule into two H atoms, they can result very quickly in a new molecule with different rotational and spin states, but collisons of this violence are very rare at ordinary temperatures. Ordinarily, spin states can only be changed by magnetic fields. Therefore we may conclude that it is very difficult to establish an equilibrium distribution between symmetrical and antisymmetrical rotation states. The gas H_2 may behave rather as a mixture of two different species, one with symmetrical rotational eigenfunctions, and the other with antisymmetrical ones. The symmetrical species is called *ortho*-hydrogen, the antisymmetrical one is *para*-hydrogen. The partition functions for these two species are to be written separately:

$$Q_{\text{para}} = 1 + 5e^{-6\theta_r/T} + 9e^{-20\theta_r/T} + \cdots \Big\}$$
$$Q_{\text{ortho}} = 3\{3e^{-2\theta_r/T} + 7e^{-12\theta_r/T} + \cdots \quad \Big\} \tag{4.526}$$

The equilibrium between two species is properly the subject of a later chapter, where it is shown that the ratio of the numbers of particles in the two species is equal to the ratio of their partition functions—see Eq. (6.321). At moderately high temperatures the two series in Eq. (4.526) are roughly equal, except for the factor 3, so that hydrogen gas will ordinarily have *ortho*-hydrogen and *para*-hydrogen roughly in the ratio 3 to 1. We then find the separate heat capacities from the two partition functions and obtain the heat capacity of the mixture from the simple law of mixtures:

H_2:
$$C_{\text{rot}} = \tfrac{1}{4}C_{\text{para}} + \tfrac{3}{4}C_{\text{ortho}} \tag{4.527}$$

and this is found to agree excellently with the data.

Heavy hydrogen is another example. We note that D_2 is a pair of identical particles each with even spin, so the spin degeneracy factors are interchanged compared with those for H_2. Also since $s = 1$, the partition functions for the two species for deuterium are:

$$Q_{\text{ortho}} = 6\{1 + 5e^{-6\theta_r/T} + 9e^{-20\theta_r/T} + \cdots \Big\}$$
$$Q_{\text{para}} = 3\{3e^{-2\theta_r/T} + 7e^{-12\theta_r/T} + \cdots \quad \Big\} \tag{4.528}$$

The relative concentrations are now two to one instead of three to one, and the law of mixtures gives

D_2:
$$C_{\text{rot}} = \tfrac{1}{3}C_{\text{para}} + \tfrac{2}{3}C_{\text{ortho}} \tag{4.529}$$

The temperature scale factors involved are, for H_2, $\theta_r = 85.4\ °K$ and for D_2, $\theta_r = 42\ °K$; the range of temperatures where the comparison is significant lies between about 25 °K and 150 °K.

4.6 Interpretation of rotation spectra. The rotation spectrum to be expected from a diatomic molecule is derived from Eq. (4.502) and the Bohr principle that the frequency of an emitted spectral line equals the energy emitted per quantum jump divided by Planck's constant:

$$\nu = (\epsilon_{j'} - \epsilon_j)/h \tag{4.601}$$

All transitions $j' \rightarrow j$ are not allowed; a selection rule operates which requires $j' - j = 1$ for a possible transition. Thus the possible frequencies of the rotational spectrum are

$$\nu = k\theta_r[j(j + 1) - (j - 1)j] = 2jk\theta_r \tag{4.602}$$

where j is the quantum number associated with the initial level. A line is associated with each value of j, and they are equally spaced in frequency at intervals $2k\theta_r$. A rotational transition $j \rightarrow j - 1$ may occur in conjunction with some other transition, either vibrational or electronic, and the quantum emitted then contains both contributions. Bohr's principle operates with the result that the emitted frequency is the sum of the rotational and nonrotational terms:

$$\nu(j) = \nu(0) + 2jk\theta_r \qquad (4.603)$$

where $\nu(0)$ is the frequency in the absence of the rotational transition. The quantum number j can be either positive or negative in this general case, a negative j meaning that the rotational transition involves an absorption of some of the quantum that would have been emitted by the nonrotational transition.

The intensities of spectral lines are proportional to the transition probabilities in any one molecule, and to the relative populations of the molecules that happen to be in the initial states on average. The transition probabilities present a purely quantum mechanical problem that we shall not discuss, but the mean relative populations in the initial states can be calculated by our statistical formulae.

In general we may, from Eq. (4.301), assert that the mean population in any state is generally proportional to $\omega_j e^{-\epsilon_j/kT}/Q$, and in this case the number in the jth rotational state must be proportional to

$$(2j + 1)e^{-j(j+1)\theta_r/T}/Q_{\text{rot}} \qquad (4.604)$$

Generally to produce a spectrum at all, the temperature has to be pretty high, even greater than θ_r, so that the partition function can be evaluated by means of an integration approximation, with the result:

$$Q_{\text{rot}} \doteq \int_0^\infty (2j + 1)e^{-j(j+1)\theta_r/T}dj = T/\theta_r \qquad (4.605)$$

and so the probability of finding a molecule in the jth rotational state is

$$\rho(j) = (T/\theta_r)(2j + 1)e^{-j(j+1)\theta_r/T} \qquad (4.606)$$

This quantity should give some idea of the relative intensities of the rotational spectral lines, although of course the factor depending on transition probabilities has been omitted. It has a characteristic "shape" in its dependence on j, having a maximum at

$$2j_{\max} + 1 = (2T/\theta_r)^{1/2} \qquad (4.607)$$

starting from T/θ_r at $j = 0$ and approaching zero for large values of j. A negative value of j indicates absorption, and this must be proportional to the population in the lower energy state corresponding to $j - 1$. This characteristic intensity pattern makes rotation spectra rather easily recognizable, and their evenly spaced lines provide an accurate way of calculating, from Eq. (4.603), the characteristic temperature θ_r.

The interpretation of atomic and molecular spectra constitutes of course a vast subject in itself, and it would be quite out of order to attempt even an outline here.

4.7 Effects of magnetic and electric fields. A complete discussion of the statistical theory of the magnetic properties of matter would carry us too far afield; we restrict ourselves to the construction of a few appropriate partition functions and their immediate applications.

The electrons in an atom or molecule have a total angular momentum $\sqrt{j(j + 1)}\ \hbar$ due to a combination of orbital and spin momenta, where j may be an integer or a half-integer. In the state specified by j, there are $2j + 1$ different orthogonal eigenfunctions which are degenerate in the absence of a magnetic field: compare Eq. (1.333). In the presence of a magnetic field the angular momentum suffers "space quantization," and the component of angular momentum parallel to the field is restricted to the values $m_j\hbar$, where m_j can take only the $2j + 1$ values between $+j$ and $-j$ at integral intervals. If j is a whole integer, the m_j values are also integers, while if j is a half-integer, the m_j values are all half-integers. The magnetic moment of the atom due to its electrons is at the same time restricted to have a component along the field equal to $gm_j\mu_0$, where μ_0 is the Bohr magneton $e\hbar/2mc$, and g is the numerical Landé factor, which depends on the way the spin and orbital angular momentum are combined to produce the total angular momentum. In the state specified by m_j, the energy of the atom in the magnetic field H is $-gm_j\mu_0H$, and this may be added to the energy existing in the absence of the magnetic field, provided it is small enough to be treated as a first-order perturbation. The partition function then takes the form:

$$Q = \sum_n \sum_l \sum_{m_j=-j}^{+j} \sigma \exp \{-E_{n,l} + gm_j\mu_0H\}/kT \qquad (4.701)$$

where σ is the nuclear spin degeneracy factor and n and l are the orbital quantum numbers; the relation between l and j depends on the individual case under discussion. If the ground state of the electron (lowest values of n and l) is taken as the zero of energy, and if the first excited state has an energy considerably greater than kT, we may drop the sum over n and l and the partition function reduces to

$$Q = \sum_{m_j=-j}^{+j} \sigma \exp (gm_i\mu_0H/kT) \qquad (4.702)$$

At very high temperatures this approximation would be invalid, but magnetic effects are generally negligible then, because the exponent $gm_j\mu_0H/kT$ is very small. Even at ordinary temperatures and ordinary magnetic fields, this exponent is considerably smaller than unity, and a convenient approximation can be used to evaluate the partition function. Expanding the exponential as far as the second order term and summing over m_j, we find

$$Q = \sigma(2j + 1) + (\sigma/6)j(j + 1)(2j + 1)(g\mu_0H/kT)^2 + \cdots \qquad (4.703)$$

The appropriate free energy for this system is $A = -NkT \ln Q$. The contribution of the magnetic fields to the free energy is $-N\bar{\mu}H$, where $\bar{\mu}$ is the mean magnetic moment per atom in the direction of the field. Therefore, the latter can be found from

$$N\bar{\mu} = -(\partial A/\partial H)_{T,V} \tag{4.704}$$

Using Eqs. (4.137) and (4.703) in this equation leads to

$$\bar{\mu} = g^2\mu_0^2 j(j+1)H/3kT \tag{4.705}$$

where we have neglected terms of higher order in $\mu_0 H/kT$. The susceptibility $N\bar{\mu}/H$ then varies inversely with T, a form of Curie's law. At very low temperatures a different approximation becomes appropriate. Thus if $\mu_0 H \gg kT$, then those terms in the partition function (4.702) with the highest positive values of m_j dominate the sum. Taking only the two top terms we then get

Low T: $$Q = \sigma e^{jg\mu_0 H/kT}(1 + e^{-g\mu_0 H/kT}) \tag{4.706}$$

To a good approximation the free energy is now

$$A = NkT \ln \sigma + Njg\mu_0 H + NkTe^{-g\mu_0 H/kT} \tag{4.707}$$

The mean magnetic moment given by Eq. (4.704) is now

$$\bar{\mu} = jg\mu_0 - g\mu_0 He^{-g\mu_0 H/kT} \tag{4.708}$$

showing that this moment reaches a saturation value $jg\mu_0$ as T approaches zero, independent of the magnetic field H.

The entropy change due to the magnetic field is of great interest. This is to be derived from Eq. (4.138). In the absence of a magnetic field, the partition function (4.702) reduces to the constant $\sigma(2j+1)$ and the entropy is

$H = 0$: $$S = Nk \ln \sigma + Nk \ln (2j+1) \tag{4.709}$$

In the present approximation, this entropy remains even when T goes to zero; it represents the randomness of nuclear spin orientation (the σ-term) and the randomness of electronic angular momentum orientation (the j-term). The status of this result with respect to the third law of thermodynamics will be clarified in a moment. In the presence of a magnetic field H, we use Eq. (4.706) for the partition function, and Eq. (4.138) for the entropy of a dilute paramagnetic gas:

$H \neq 0$: $$S = Nk \ln \sigma + Nk(1 + g\mu_0 H/kT)e^{-g\mu_0 H/kT} \tag{4.710}$$

If $\mu_0 H/kT$ is made large enough—large fields and low temperatures, the temperature-dependent part of this expression may be made as small as we please. Comparing the limiting value, $Nk \ln \sigma$ with that obtained in the absence of H, Eq. (4.709), we see that the magnetic field has practically removed the entropy $Nk \ln (2j+1)$, representing the removal of disorder by aligning the magnetic moments up parallel to the field.

A similar effect is the basis of a technique of reaching temperatures below 1 °K by magnetic cooling. Provided a substance is available that can readily exchange energy between its electronic spin angular momentum states and its atomic lattice vibrations, it can be magnetized isothermally to receive the saturation magnetic moment $\bar{\mu}$, like that given in Eq. (4.708), heat being extracted from the cryostat to remove the entropy. The specimen is then thermally isolated and the magnetizing field removed. On demagnetizing, the entropy of the orbital states tends to return to the higher value indicated in Eq. (4.709), but it can do this only by absorbing thermal energy from the vibrational energy of the lattice, thus reducing the temperature of the material. Using this technique, temperatures estimated to be within 10^{-3} °K of absolute zero have been reported.

There remains the question of reconciling the apparent nonzero entropy remaining at 0 °K with the third law of thermodynamics. This comes about from the fact that even in a dilute paramagnetic gas there are electric perturbing fields that can produce small (usually entirely negligible) Stark effects on the orbital angular momentum states. The $2j + 1$ such states, treated as identical in the approximation leading to Eq. (4.709) for the entropy, are in fact very slightly different in energy, even in the absence of any external field.* Instead of writing $Q = \sigma(2j + 1)$, we should have

$$Q = \sum_{m_j = -j}^{+j} \sigma \exp\left[-\epsilon(m_j)/kT\right]$$

where $\epsilon(m_j)$ are extremely small energies compared with kT when T is of the order 1 °K. To a first approximation, and at all ordinary temperatures this Q is indeed almost exactly equal to $\sigma(2j + 1)$. But if we push T down toward zero, there must come a point where kT is comparable with $\epsilon(m_j)$, no matter how small these energies are. Before T actually becomes zero, the value of Q becomes essentially $Q = \sigma \exp(-\epsilon_m/kT)$, where ϵ_m is the lowest of the energies $\epsilon(m_j)$; as T goes to zero, the exponential vanishes and we are left with an entropy $Nk \ln \sigma$, the term $Nk \ln(2j + 1)$ having disappeared from (4.709). This persistent term $Nk \ln \sigma$ due to nuclear spin can also be seen to disappear; actually there must be small magnetic interactions between adjacent nuclear spins, and this will split the energies and remove the degeneracy. A sum over states of very low energy will then replace σ, leading again to an entropy that goes to zero at 0 °K, with the nuclear spins aligned throughout the crystal. In fact this persistent entropy of spin, $Nk \ln \sigma$, still present at temperatures no higher than 10^{-3} °K, represents in principle a possibility of still further magnetic cooling. Because the energy differences are much smaller, the temperatures involved will be much lower and higher magnetic fields may be required to reach them. There is also the problem that nuclear spins do not ordinarily interact readily with the lattice vibrations, so that it may be difficult for the nuclear spins to extract heat from the lattice during demagnetization. While there are hopeful signs that this technique may eventually be achieved, it remains at the moment a very stimulating speculation.

* In a solid the crystalline electric field produces large differences in energy and the levels are not even approximately degenerate.

4.8   Einstein's theory of crystalline solid.   To a very rough approximation, a crystal can be considered as made up of atoms at fixed lattice points, and thermal energy of the crystal can, to this approximation, be regarded as due to independent vibrations of the atoms about these fixed lattice points.   Each atom is in a similar field of force that is approximately independent of the motion of neighboring atoms, and the atoms are permanently distinguishable from each other because they are attached to their respective lattice points.   The Boltzmann statistics are applicable to this assembly.   A more exact theory must take into account the coupling between neighboring atoms, but this refinement will not be discussed until a later section.   The present approximation is due to Einstein and is sometimes called a lattice gas model because the atoms behave independently.

Each atom is treated as a mass point with three degrees of freedom in a potential field approximating that of a three-dimensional harmonic oscillator.   Generalizing Eq. (4.506) to three dimensions, and using Eq. (1.322) for the energies:

$$Q = \sum_{n_1} \sum_{n_2} \sum_{n_3} \exp\left\{-(\epsilon_0 + n_1 h\nu_1 + n_2 h\nu_2 + n_3 h\nu_3)/kT\right\} \qquad (4.801)$$

where

$$\epsilon_0 = \tfrac{1}{2}h(\nu_1 + \nu_2 + \nu_3) \qquad (4.802)$$

is the zero point energy of the atoms.   Each series sums separately and so

$$Q = e^{-\epsilon_0/kT} \prod_{s=1,2,3} \left\{1 - e^{-h\nu_s/kT}\right\}^{-1} \qquad (4.803)$$

or

$$\ln Q = -\epsilon_0/kT - \sum_{s=1,2,3} \ln\left\{1 - e^{-h\nu_s/kT}\right\} \qquad (4.804)$$

Using Eq. (4.115–16) then gives

$$E = N\epsilon_0 + \sum_s N h\nu_s \left\{e^{h\nu_s/kT} - 1\right\}^{-1} \qquad (4.805)$$

and then

$$C_v = Nk \sum_s (h\nu_s/kT)^2 e^{h\nu_s/kT} \left\{e^{h\nu_s/kT} - 1\right\}^{-2} \qquad (4.806)$$

At very high temperatures the exponential $e^{h\nu_s/kT}$ approaches $1 + h\nu_s/kT$ and the heat capacity becomes approximately

$$kT \gg h\nu_s: \qquad C_v = 3Nk + \sum_s Nk h\nu_s/kT \qquad (4.807)$$

This approaches the classical value $3Nk$ at sufficiently high temperatures.   At low temperatures the exponential in the denominator of Eq. (4.806) becomes much greater than unity and we have

$$kT \ll h\nu_s: \qquad C_v = Nk \sum_s (h\nu_s/kT)^2 e^{-h\nu_s/kT} \qquad (4.808)$$

This has a limiting value zero at 0 °K in agreement with the third law of thermodynamics.   The observed behavior of crystals is not too badly represented by

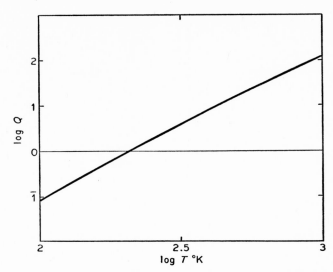

FIG. 4.81. Partition function of Einstein crystal. Einstein frequency ν about 4.16 $\times$ 10^{12} per sec.

this result, at least it is a great improvement over the classical theory which predicted a constant value at all temperatures. Quantitatively however it is not possible to find a single value for each of the frequencies ν_s to give an accurate agreement with the observed heat capacity over the whole temperature range. It is worth noting that the improvement over the classical theory is not due to quantum statistics—we have used the Boltzmann statistics only; it is due only to the quantum mechanical treatment of the energy spectrum of the oscillators representing the atoms in the crystal.

4.9 Assemblies with prescribed momentum. In previous sections we have prescribed the total number and total energy of the assembly, and found the most probable distribution-in-energy under these restrictions. We are naturally free to prescribe any of the constants of the motion that can occur in the assembly, in particular the total momentum. To do this it is not sufficient to enumerate the energy levels, because there are many different momentum states to each energy level; we need to consider a distribution-in-momentum rather than a distribution-in-energy, and start our discussion again from the beginning.

Let the vector **p** denote momentum, and n_p the number of systems with momentum **p**. Then all the arguments of § 2.2 in counting equally probable states in a given distribution-in-energy can be translated into equivalent arguments on counting the number of equally probable states in a given distribution-in-momentum; all we have to do is to read "momentum" for "energy," and substitute n_p for n_k, ω_p for ω_k, and so forth. Equations (2.213), (2.223), and (2.231) immediately go over into the proper counts for the respective statistics and the given distribution-in-momentum.

There are now three restrictions to be applied: total number, total energy, and total momentum are all prescribed so that

$$N = \sum_p n_p \quad \mathbf{P} = \sum_p n_p\mathbf{p}, \quad E = \sum_p n_p\epsilon(\mathbf{p}) \tag{4.901}$$

where $\mathbf{P}$ is the total momentum of the assembly, and $\epsilon(\mathbf{p})$ is the energy of a system whose momentum is $\mathbf{p}$. In an ideal gas $\epsilon(\mathbf{p}) = p^2/2m$.

To determine the most probable distribution-in-momentum, we proceed as in § 2.3, but with the additional restriction of requiring an arbitrary vector multiplier which we may write $\boldsymbol{\gamma}$:

$$\delta(\ln C - \alpha N - \beta E - \boldsymbol{\gamma} \cdot \mathbf{P}) = 0 \tag{4.902}$$

Following the same method as in § 2.3 the resulting distribution is for (a) Boltzmann statistics

$$n_p = N\omega_p \exp (-\alpha - \beta\epsilon_p - \boldsymbol{\gamma} \cdot \mathbf{p}) \tag{4.903}$$

and for (b) Bose-Einstein (upper sign) or Fermi-Dirac (lower sign):

$$n_p = \omega_p\{\exp (\alpha + \beta\epsilon_p + \boldsymbol{\gamma}\cdot\mathbf{p}) \mp 1\}^{-1} \tag{4.904}$$

It cannot be assumed offhand that the physical interpretations of the parameters α and β are identical with those found before. Instead, we have to substitute the results (4.903) into (4.901) and adjust the parameters accordingly. In the classical limit we find

$$N = e^{-\alpha} \sum_p \omega_p \exp (-\beta\epsilon_p - \boldsymbol{\gamma}\cdot\mathbf{p}) \tag{4.905}$$

and the similar expressions for E and $\mathbf{P}$. The eigenfunctions for a particle in a box actually number one to each momentum state, the number of these states in a unit cell in phase space is $1/h^3$ so the proper weight factor is

$$\omega_p = (V/h^3)dp_1dp_2dp_3 \tag{4.906}$$

where V is the volume of the box. Remembering that $\boldsymbol{\gamma}\cdot\mathbf{p} = \sum_j \gamma_j p_j$ is a scalar product, the sum (4.905) becomes an elementary integral:

$$N = e^{-\alpha}V(2\pi m/h^2\beta)^{3/2}e^{1/2m\boldsymbol{\gamma}^2} \tag{4.907}$$

Similarly we find

$$E = e^{-\alpha}V(2\pi m/h^2\beta)^{3/2}e^{1/2m\boldsymbol{\gamma}^2}\{3/2\beta + \tfrac{1}{2}m(\boldsymbol{\gamma}/\beta)^2\} \tag{4.908}$$

and

$$\mathbf{P} = -(m\boldsymbol{\gamma}/\beta)e^{-\alpha}V(2\pi m/h^2\beta)^{3/2}e^{1/2m\boldsymbol{\gamma}^2} \tag{4.909}$$

Divide Eq. (4.909) by (4.907) and we have

$$\mathbf{P} = -Nm\boldsymbol{\gamma}/\beta \tag{4.910}$$

showing that the ratio $-\boldsymbol{\gamma}/\beta$ is the mean drift velocity causing the prescribed momentum $\mathbf{P}$.   Again dividing Eq. (4.908) by (4.907) we have

$$E/N = 3/2\beta + \tfrac{1}{2}m(\boldsymbol{\gamma}/\beta)^2 \tag{4.911}$$

This shows that $\beta = 1/kT$ as before if T is linked with the mean kinetic energy of random motion relative to the center of mass.   Then if we write $\mathbf{v} = \mathbf{P}/Nm$ for the mean drift velocity, Eq. (4.910) yields

$$\boldsymbol{\gamma} = -\mathbf{v}/kT \tag{4.912}$$

for the interpretation of the new vector parameter, and the energy is

$$E/N = 3kT/2 + \tfrac{1}{2}mv^2$$

Finally for the parameter α we find from Eq. (4.907)

$$e^\alpha = (V/N)(2\pi mkT/h^2)^{3/2}e^{\frac{1}{2}mv^2/kT} \tag{4.913}$$

and comparing this with Eqs. (3.208) and (3.503) where we found the chemical potential, we see that α is not now identical with the previous parameter, but instead,

$$\alpha = -\mu/kT + \tfrac{1}{2}mv^2/kT \tag{4.914}$$

Summarizing, we can express the most probable distribution-in-momentum in the form:

classical statistics: $n_{\mathrm{p}} = \omega_{\mathrm{p}} \exp\,(\mu - \epsilon_{\mathrm{p}} + \mathbf{v}\cdot\mathbf{p} - \tfrac{1}{2}mv^2)/kT \tag{4.915}$

with the obvious generalizations for Bose-Einstein and Fermi-Dirac statistics. In particular we may set $\mathbf{v} = 0$, so that the prescribed momentum is zero; the distribution-in-momentum reduces to

$$n_{\mathrm{p}} = \omega_{\mathrm{p}} \exp\,(\mu - \epsilon_{\mathrm{p}})/kT \tag{4.916}$$

formally identical with the distribution-in-energy, but with a different physical interpretation; this result coincides with the distribution used in § 4.4.

We can, incidentally, prove that the distribution (4.915) is derivable from (4.916) by a simple co-ordinate transformation to a system of co-ordinates moving relative to the center of mass of the assembly.   Rewrite Eq. (4.916) in primed co-ordinates:

$$n_{\mathrm{p}} = \omega_{\mathrm{p}} \exp\,(\mu' - \epsilon'_{\mathrm{p}})/kT \tag{4.917}$$

taking the primed system at rest with the center of mass of the assembly.   Transfer to an unprimed system moving to the left with speed $\mathbf{v}$, such that

$$\mathbf{u} = \mathbf{u}' + \mathbf{v}$$

and

$$\epsilon'_{\mathrm{p}} = \tfrac{1}{2}mu'^2 = \tfrac{1}{2}mu^2 - m\mathbf{v}\cdot\mathbf{u} + \tfrac{1}{2}mv^2 \tag{4.918}$$

writing

$$\mathbf{p} = m\mathbf{u} \quad \text{and} \quad \mu' = \mu \tag{4.919}$$

and writing (4.918) into (4.917), we see at once that Eq. (4.915) results.   The chemical potential is an invariant during the transformation. A discussion of Bose-Einstein assemblies from the present point of view leads to interesting practical consequences, and these will be discussed in a later chapter.

EXERCISES AND PROBLEMS

1. Check that the expression (4.114) for the entropy is equivalent with Eq. (3.402) in the classical gas, where we know $pV = NkT$.

2. Show that to within an arbitrary constant Eq. (3.131) gives (4.121).

3. Show that to within an arbitrary constant Eq. (3.121) gives (4.134).

4. Compare the two expressions for enthalpy given in Eqs. (4.122) and (4.134); show that they are equivalent for the ideal classical gas.

5. Derive the formulae (4.305) and (4.306) for the mean speed and mean square speed, and check the numerical value of the root mean square deviation of the mean speed in an ideal gas.

6. Derive Eq. (4.307) and Eq. (4.308) for the mean speed in a Bose-Einstein gas and check the relation (4.310) between Bose-Einstein and classical gas at T_0.

7. Verify the developments for heat capacity given in Eqs. (4.514), (4.523), and (4.524).

8. Develop in detail a formula for the heat capacity of H_2 as a function of temperature using Eq. (4.526) for the partition function, and compare with the one derived from the wrong partition function (4.525).

9. Consider a two-dimensional monolayer gas in a square of side L. Show that the density of translational states is $\omega(\epsilon) = 2\pi m L^2/h^2$. Find the partition function and derive the equation of state in the form $SL^2 = NkT$, where S is the force in dyne/cm on the boundary. What is the heat capacity of the monolayer?

10. Prove Eq. (4.605).

11. Interpret Eq. (4.606) for negative values of j.

12. Plot the probability $\rho(j)$ as a function of j for the following temperatures: $T = 18\theta_r$, $24\frac{1}{2}\theta_r$, and $32\theta_r$. Include negative j-values and sketch the spectrum.

13. Derive Eqs. (4.703) and (4.705).

14. Write out in detail the steps involved in deriving Eqs. (4.903), (4.904), and (4.909) for the most probable distribution-in-momentum.

15. Write out the Bose-Einstein and Fermi-Dirac modifications of the distribution-in-momentum of a classical gas given in Eq. (4.915).

16. Use the formalism of classical statistics and the partition function to find the density of an ideal gas in the presence of a uniform gravitational field of strength g dyne/cm. Check the result with an elementary discussion based on hydrostatics and Boyle's law.

17. Find the partition function and mean energy per particle if it has nondegenerate energy levels given by $E_n = n^p h\nu$, where p is any parameter.

18. The heat capacity of copper is about 2 cal/mol deg at 60 °K, and about 5 cal/mol deg at 160 °K. Use the Einstein model to find the atomic vibrational frequency best agreeing with this data. Do the same for silver, assuming 2 cal/mol deg at 37 °K and 5 cal/mol deg at 118 °K.

REFERENCES FOR FURTHER STUDY

Statistical Mechanics, J. E. Mayer and M. G. Mayer, Wiley, 1940; Chapters 5, 6, 7, 11. *Introduction to Statistical Mechanics*, G. S. Rushbrooke, Oxford, 1949.

Chapter V

EQUILIBRIUM BETWEEN PHASES

5.1 Two gaseous phases: mobile monolayer. In this chapter we consider only phases that can all be treated as assemblies of independent systems. The equilibrium between a liquid and its vapor cannot be so treated with any great accuracy, and the discussion of that problem is postponed until the theory of interacting systems has been developed.

In the present section we consider a two-dimensional gas in equilibrium with a three-dimensional gas—a situation that corresponds to a gas being adsorbed on the surface of a neutral liquid. We shall call the two-dimensional gas the film and omit the adjective "three-dimensional" from the other phase. Let the energy of a particle in the film be ϵ_{fj}, where j takes all integral values to represent the entire spectrum of energy levels in the film; and let ϵ_{gr} be the energy levels of a particle in the gas, r taking all integral values. The degeneracy weights are written ω_{fj} and ω_{gr} respectively. First consider an arrangement in which there are N_f particles in the film, N_g in the gas, the total number in the whole assembly, gas plus film, being

$$N = N_f + N_g \tag{5.101}$$

and suppose there are n_{gr} particles in the rth energy level of the gas, n_{fj} in the jth level in the film. The total number of complexions having the same numbers n_{gr} and n_{fj}, i.e., the same distribution-in-energy, is

$$C = N_f! \prod_j \{(\omega_{fj})^{n_{fj}}/n_{fj}!\} N_g! \prod_r \{(\omega_{gr})^{n_{gr}}/n_{gr}!\} \tag{5.102}$$

This number is derived in the same way as Eq. (2.213), by counting the number of complexions in each phase separately and multiplying them together. This number has to be multiplied by the number of ways in which we can choose N_f particular particles from the total N to assign to the film, the remaining N_g going to the gas. This number is simply

$$N!/N_f!N_g! \tag{5.103}$$

Multiplying Eqs. (5.103) and (5.102) gives the total number of complexions when the particles are distinguishable:

$$C_{\text{Boltz}} = N! \prod_{j,r} (\omega_{fj})^{n_{fj}}(\omega_{gr})^{n_{gr}}/n_{fj}!n_{gr}! \tag{5.104}$$

In practice we need instead the classical limit for the statistics when the particles are indistinguishable, and as discussed in Eq. (2.245), this is obtained by dividing C_{Boltz} by $N!$:

$$C_{\text{class}} = \prod_{j,r} (\omega_{fj})^{n_{fj}}(\omega_{gr})^{n_{gr}}/n_{fj}!n_{gr}! \tag{5.105}$$

The most probable distribution-in-energy is again given by that set of numbers n_{fj} and n_{gr} that maximizes the logarithm of C under the restrictions that the total number N remains fixed and the total energy E is given:

$$N = \sum_j n_{fj} + \sum_r n_{gr} \tag{5.106}$$

$$E = \sum_j n_{fj}\epsilon_{fj} + \sum_r n_{gr}\epsilon_{gr} \tag{5.107}$$

These two restrictions call for two Lagrangian multipliers exactly as for the single phase in § 2.3. Thus we require the following three variations to vanish:

$$d \ln C_{\text{class}} = \sum_j dn_{fj}(\partial \ln C_{\text{class}}/\partial n_{fj}) + \sum_r dn_{gr}(\partial \ln C_{\text{class}}/\partial n_{gr}) = 0 \tag{5.111}$$

$$dN = \sum_j dn_{fj} + \sum_r dn_{gr} = 0 \tag{5.112}$$

$$dE = \sum_j dn_{fj}\epsilon_{fj} + \sum_r dn_{gr}\epsilon_{gr} = 0 \tag{5.113}$$

Multiplying Eq. (5.112) by α and Eq. (5.113) by β and subtracting the two resulting equations from Eq. (5.111), we obtain

$$\sum_j dn_{fj}\{\partial \ln C/\partial n_{fj} - \alpha - \beta\epsilon_{fj}\} + \sum_r dn_{gr}\{\partial \ln C/\partial n_{gr} - \alpha - \beta\epsilon_{gr}\} = 0 \tag{5.114}$$

In this expression we are free to make independent variations of all the quantities dn_{fj} and dn_{gr} so the entire set of coefficients can be equated to zero separately:

$$\partial \ln C_{\text{class}}/\partial n_{fj} = \alpha + \beta\epsilon_{fj} \tag{5.115}$$

$$\partial \ln C_{\text{class}}/\partial n_{gr} = \alpha + \beta\epsilon_{gr} \tag{5.116}$$

for every value of j,r. Evidently the expression for $\ln C_{\text{class}}$ obtained from Eq. (5.105) splits into two parts, film and gas, and these parts survive the differentiations in Eq. (5.115) and (5.116); the film part alone appears in Eq. (5.115) and the gas part alone in Eq. (5.116). These two equations then become identical with the equations that one would derive for each phase separately; the significant point is that the same parameters α and β must be used in both phases. Because the two factors in C_{class}, or the two additive parts in $\ln C_{\text{class}}$, are the same as for single separate phases, the most probable distribution-in-energy derived from Eqs. (5.115) and (5.116) are the same as for the separate phases, the deduction being the same as that of Eqs. (2.341) and (2.306):

$$n_{fj} = \omega_{fj} e^{-\alpha - \beta \epsilon_{fi}}, \quad n_{gr} = \omega_{gr} e^{-\alpha - \beta \epsilon_{gr}} \tag{5.117}$$

Considering either phase separately, we can repeat the argument of § 3.2 and § 3.5 to identify the parameters α and β. The fact that one and the same pair of parameters α and β apply to both phases means therefore that *the assembly as a whole is in equilibrium when the two phases have the same temperature and the same chemical potential.*

It is convenient to introduce the partition function for each phase separately, defined in the same way as for a single homogeneous assembly, as in Eq. (4.102):

$$Q_f = \sum_j \omega_{fj} e^{-\epsilon_{fi}/kT}, \quad Q_g = \sum_r \omega_{gr} e^{-\epsilon_{gr}/kT} \tag{5.121}$$

In terms of these partition functions, the distributions (5.117) allow Eq. (5.101) to be put in the form:

$$N = e^{\mu/kT}(Q_f + Q_g) \tag{5.122}$$

while the two parts separately give

$$N_f = Q_f e^{\mu/kT}, \quad N_g = Q_g e^{\mu/kT} \tag{5.123}$$

The ratio of these equations gives the relative numbers in the two phases:

$$N_f/N_g = Q_f/Q_g \quad \text{and} \quad N_f/N = Q_f/(Q_f + Q_g) \tag{5.124}$$

The thermodynamic variables like E, p and S are derivable from the separate phase partition functions just as for single homogeneous assemblies, as discussed in detail in § 4.1 and § 4.2, and there is no point in repeating the formulae here.

5.2 Adsorption isotherm for mobile monolayer. As the simplest particular example of the general theory of the last section, we discuss now the adsorption of a gas on the surface of a liquid where the adsorbed particles have an energy of adsorption W below the energy of a free particle at rest. We may take the energy of a free particle at rest as the zero of energy; therefore the lowest energy of an adsorbed particle is $-W$. The kinetic energy of adsorbed particles in the mobile film start from this zero-point, and the energy levels of the film are therefore

$$\epsilon_{fk} = \hbar^2 k^2/2mA - W \tag{5.201}$$

—compare Eq. (1.303). In the sum over states involved in calculating the partition function Q_f the factor $e^{W/kT}$ is common throughout the sum; hence the final result is the same as in Problem 4.9 except for this extra factor:

$$Q_f = A(2\pi mkT/h^2)e^{W/kT} \tag{5.202}$$

The partition function for the gas is the same as before:

$$Q_g = V(2\pi mkT/h^2)^{3/2} \tag{5.203}$$

so that the equilibrium equation (5.124) becomes

$$N_f/N_g = (A/V)(2\pi mkT/h^2)^{-\frac{1}{2}}e^{W/kT} \qquad (5.204)$$

This may be expressed in a more useful form by using the ideal gas law to eliminate V. In fact the equation of state for the gas follows at once from Q_g just as it did in § 4.2:

$$p = N_gkT(\partial \ln Q_g/\partial V)_T = N_gkT/V \qquad (5.205)$$

so that Eq. (5.204) becomes

$$N_f/A = (p/kT)(2\pi mkT/h^2)^{-\frac{1}{2}}e^{W/kT} \qquad (5.206)$$

giving the density of the film as a function of pressure in the gas and temperature of the whole assembly. Alternatively, we can introduce the linear pressure of the film, as in Ex. 4.9, and write

$$S_f = N_fkT(\partial \ln Q_f/\partial A)_T = N_fkT/A \qquad (5.207)$$

so that Eq. (5.206) can also be written in the form

$$S_f/p_g = (2\pi mkT/h^2)^{-\frac{1}{2}}e^{W/kT} \qquad (5.208)$$

The reduction of surface tension due to adsorption, measured by S_f, is therefore proportional to the pressure of the parent gas, the constant of proportionality being a given function of T. The adsorption isotherm is a straight line through the origin with slope depending strongly on temperature.

5.3 Langmuir's isotherm. Here we consider a monolayer formed from a parent gas on the surface of a solid. We suppose that there exists on the solid a number X of sites at which a single particle can be adsorbed in an energy state below that of a free particle at rest. We further suppose that there is only one quantum state of adsorption at each site, a simplification that can easily be removed without making any essential difference to the isotherm. Let there be N_f particles adsorbed on the solid and N_g particles in the gas, the total $N = N_f + N_g$ being fixed. The number of ways in which the subdivision can be effected is

$$N!/N_f!N_g! \qquad (5.301)$$

The number of ways N_f particles can be assigned to X sites, no more than one to a site, is

$$X!/(X - N_f)! \qquad (5.302)$$

because the particles are still to be regarded as distinguishable at this stage of the classical calculation. The number of complexions of N_g particles is

$$N_g! \prod_j \omega_{gi}{}^{n_{gi}}/n_{gj}! \qquad (5.303)$$

as in Eq. (5.102), where the symbols have the same meaning as there. The total number of complexions for the combined assembly is the product of all the three numbers just calculated divided by $N!$ to correct for the indistinguishability of the particles:

$$C_{\text{class}} = \{X!/N_f!(X - N_f)!\} \prod_j \omega_{gj}{}^{n_{gi}}/n_{gj}! \tag{5.304}$$

It remains to maximize the logarithm of this number by varying the numbers n_{gj} and the number N_f while keeping N and E fixed:

$$N = N_f + \sum_j n_{gj} = \text{constant} \tag{5.311}$$

$$E = -N_fW + \sum_j n_{gj}\epsilon_{gj} = \text{constant} \tag{5.312}$$

The logarithm of C is the sum of the logarithms of two parts, one part depending on the film, the other on the gas:

$$\ln C_{\text{class}} = \ln C_f + \ln C_g$$

where

$$\ln C_f = \ln \{X!/N_f!(X - N_f)!\} \tag{5.313}$$

and C_g is exactly the same as before for the ideal gas. We follow through the same reasoning as that from Eq. (5.111) to (5.116):

$$d \ln C_{\text{class}} = dN_f(\partial \ln C_f/\partial N_f) + \sum_j dn_{gj}(\partial \ln C_g/\partial n_{gj}) = 0 \tag{5.314}$$

while at the same time,

$$dN = dN_f + \sum_j dn_{gj} = 0 \tag{5.315}$$

$$dE = -WdN_f + \sum_j dn_{gj}\epsilon_{gj} = 0 \tag{5.316}$$

Multiplying the dN-equation by α and the dE-equation by β as before, subtracting from Eq. (5.314) and removing the now independent variations:

$$\partial \ln C_f/\partial N_f = \alpha - W\beta \tag{5.317}$$

$$\partial \ln C_g/\partial n_{gj} = \alpha + \beta\epsilon_{gj} \tag{5.318}$$

for every value of j. Equation (5.318) is identical with that obtained before for the ideal gas, and leads again to the same interpretation of α and β, and to the same distribution-in-energy of the gas. The two equations that result from this, needed in the sequel are Eqs. (4.101) and (4.303):

$$N_g = Q_g e^{\mu/kT}, \quad p = N_g kT/V \tag{5.320}$$

Using the Stirling approximation on Eq. (5.313), we can reduce Eq. (5.317) to

$$\ln (X - N_f) - \ln N_f + (\mu + W)/kT = 0 \tag{5.323}$$

which gives immediately

$$N_f = (X - N_f) \exp (\mu + W)/kT \tag{5.324}$$

Eliminating μ between Eq. (5.320) and this last result gives

$$N_f/(X - N_f) = (N_g/Q_g)e^{W/kT} \tag{5.325}$$

It is usual to write

$$\theta = N_f/X \tag{5.326}$$

for the fraction of sites occupied by the adsorbed film, to make use of the ideal gas equation (5.320), and to express the isotherm Eq. (5.325) as

$$\theta/(1 - \theta) = L(T)p \tag{5.327}$$

where $L(T)$ is a function of temperature only:

$$L(T) = (1/kT)(2\pi mkT/h^2)^{-3/2}e^{W/kT} \tag{5.328}$$

Langmuir deduced this isotherm in the form (5.327) from pure thermodynamics

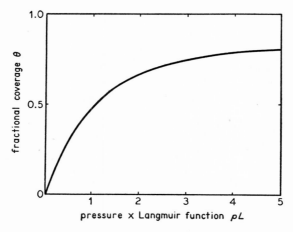

FIG. 5.31.   Universal form of Langmuir isotherm.

but it requires the full statistical argument to find the explicit form Eq. (5.328) for the Langmuir function $L(T)$.

For practical applications, Eq. (5.327) may be written in the equivalent form:

$$p/V_f = 1/(V_mL) + p/V_m \tag{5.329}$$

where V_f is the volume of gas at NTP adsorbed in the film (proportional to N_f), and V_m is the volume of gas at NTP needed to saturate the film (proportional to X). Experimental data yield a plot of p/V_f against p, which, according to the theory, ought to be a straight line; the gradient of this line gives V_m, and the function L can be found from the intercept.

Some interesting work on adsorption of hydrocarbon gases on charcoal done recently will serve as an example.*   Seven different hydrocarbon gases were

* M. A. Nay and J. L. Morrison, *J. Canadian Research*, 27B, 1949, p. 205.

used, as well as a number of different charcoals, while nitrogen was included for comparison.

The table below gives some of the results on one of the charcoals; values of V_m are in millimoles of gas per gram of adsorbent, and A is the area per molecule in the film in square Angstroms:

gas	V_m	A	gas	V_m	A
N_2	9.98	16.2	C_2H_6	7.35	25.9
C_2H_2	8.39	19.8	C_3H_8	5.47	36.0
C_2H_4	8.20	23.1	n-C_4H_{10}	4.55	42.1
CH_4	9.76	19.4	iso-C_4H_{10}	4.02	47.4

The plots were all straight lines, their gradients increasing with increasing molecular weights; this indicated that each adsorbed molecule occupied more than one site. For the larger molecules, the apparent area per adsorbed molecule appears to be about three times that occupied by a nitrogen molecule. The statistics appropriate to this situation have been worked out by J. K. Roberts.* It is of course possible that the concept of definite localized sites on the solid surface is too simple, and indeed experimental evidence from electron microscopic studies might be expected to throw some light on this question.

5.4 Critical phenomena in monolayers on solids. The Langmuir isotherm predicts a continuously increasing adsorption with increasing pressure in the parent gas. In many actual cases there is observed, however, a discontinuous increase in adsorption at a critical pressure, which may be explained in terms of mutual attractions between the adsorbed particles. Any rigorous treatment of such interactions properly follows a discussion of dependent systems in general (see Chapter VII). Here instead, we resort to a very crude approximation by smoothing out the interactions between adsorbed particles in such a way that each particle can still be regarded as independent of its individual neighbors. This is done by letting the energy of adsorption W depend only on the total number adsorbed:

$$W = W_0 + \tfrac{1}{2}\theta W_1 \qquad (5.401)$$

where W_0 and W_1 are constants, and θ is the ratio N_f/X as in the previous section. The factor $\tfrac{1}{2}$ is inserted to cancel a factor 2 arising later, giving a neater form to the final result. The energy of the whole film is

$$E_f = -N_f W_0 - \tfrac{1}{2}N_f{}^2 W_1/X \qquad (5.402)$$

and this replaces $-N_f W$ in Eq. (5.312). This nonlinear dependence of E on population N_f is an example of what are known as co-operative phenomena (the general discussion of such phenomena is given in Chapter XII).

Following through the same steps as in § 5.3 finally leads to replacing the exponent W/kT by the exponent $(W_0 + \theta W_1)/kT$, differentiation of $N_f{}^2$ in the

* J. K. Roberts, *Cambridge Philos. Soc. Proc.*, **34**, 1938, p. 577.

energy having removed the factor $\frac{1}{2}$. The isotherm becomes

$$\theta/(1 - \theta) = L(T)pe^{\theta W_1/kT} \tag{5.403}$$

where $L(T)$ is the same function of T as in Eq. (5.328). To examine the nature of this isotherm, we may take the logarithm and plot the graph of

$$\ln L(T)p = \ln \theta - \ln (1 - \theta) - \theta W_1/kT = G(\theta) \tag{5.411}$$

as a function of θ for various values of T. The Langmuir isotherm is obtained if we put $W_1 = 0$, and is monotone increasing. In general the curve behaves

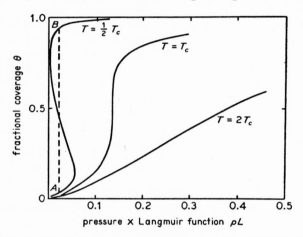

Fig. 5.41. Critical monolayer adsorption. The curves are plotted from Eq. (5.403) for three different temperatures. When T is less than T_c there is a phase change between the points A and B.

instead very much like the van der Waals isotherm for an imperfect gas. We look for the roots of the equation

$$\partial G(\theta)/\partial \theta = 0 \tag{5.412}$$

giving the positions on the θ-axis where $G(\theta)$ has a maximum or a minimum. The solutions of Eq. (5.412) are in fact

$$\theta = \frac{1}{2} \pm \frac{1}{2}(1 - 4kT/W_1)^{1/2} \tag{5.413}$$

At temperatures lower than T_c given by

$$kT_c = \frac{1}{4}W_1 \tag{5.414}$$

the curve $G(\theta)$ is therefore S-shaped. Experimentally we can arrange for the pressure, and therefore the function $G(\theta)$, to increase continually, so the S-shaped curve means that the ratio θ must jump discontinuously from a value just below the lower root of Eq. (5.413) to a value just above the higher root. Just where this jump occurs can be stated only after the theory of the two phases within the film has been developed, and this is possible only after studying the theory of interacting systems and treating the condensed film as a two-dimensional liquid phase.

5.5 Multilayer adsorption, the BET isotherm. According to the Langmuir isotherm, the monolayer fills up only for extremely high—in fact, infinite— pressure in the parent gas. If the parent gas is at a temperature below its critical point, it will condense into the liquid phase at the saturated vapor pressure, and obviously the film must change its character at this point if not before. The question is, what is the nature of the transition in the film corresponding to the saturation of the parent gas? In practice, it is found that a gradual, though comparatively rapid, increase in thickness of the film sets in well before the pressure of the parent gas saturates, indicating a multilayer adsorption process. The film becomes practically identical with a layer of the liquid phase as the pressure approaches saturation, with no apparent discontinuity in the process.

We shall discuss in some detail a very crude but highly useful theory of this process due to Brunauer, Emmett, and Teller.* Write B for the number of sites on the solid surface, and W_1 for the energy of adsorption on each site. Assume that the energy of adsorption on any site is independent of whether or not any neighboring site is occupied—in other words, we neglect interaction between adsorbed particles. Let each adsorbed particle itself become a site for possible further adsorption, write W_L for the energy of adsorption on top of an adsorbed particle, and again assume this to be independent of the presence of neighboring particles similarly adsorbed. Particles adsorbed on top of the first layer constitute the second layer; each particle in the second layer likewise becomes the site of adsorption in the third layer, etc. The energy of adsorption in any layer above the first is assumed equal to W_L and independent of the layer depth, also independent of the population in the layer, and in fact equal finally to the energy of evaporation from the liquid phase.

These assumptions are obviously extremely questionable and quite unrealistic, but they form a basis from which an exact calculation of an adsorption isotherm can be carried through; whereas, if neighbor interactions are included along with dependence of adsorption energy on layer depth, the calculation of an isotherm becomes practically impossible.

The picture of the multilayer film on the BET model is somewhat like the skyline of a big city: the higher layers begin to form before the first one is completely filled; the layers correspond to stories, the first layer to ground level. For example, there may be X_1 particles adsorbed directly on the solid, leaving $B - X_1$ unoccupied sites, X_2 particles adsorbed on top of these X_1 particles and counted as the population of the second layer, etc., with X_r particles ad-

---

* S. Brunauer, P. H. Emmett, and E. Teller, *J. Am. Chem. Soc.*, **60**, 1938, p. 309.

sorbed in the rth layer, r being any integer. The total number adsorbed, say A, is

$$A = \sum_{r=1}^{n} X_r \qquad (5.501)$$

where the sum is taken up to some number n that is at least as great as the tallest "skyscraper" in the film. It can be greater than this because all X_r with $r > n$ are zero anyway. To be quite certain, we may even let n go to infinity; the series will converge to the correct sum.

We first count up all the possible complexions on the assumption that all the particles are distinguishable from each other, and correction is made at the last step by removing the factor $N!$ in the classical fashion. The number of ways in which we can choose A particles out of the total N, leaving N_g in the parent gas is

$$N!/N_g!A! \qquad (5.502)$$

Out of the A adsorbed particles we have to assign X_1 to the first layer, X_2 to the second layer, etc.; the number of ways this can be done is

$$A!/(X_1!X_2! \cdots X_n!) \qquad (5.503)$$

The number of ways X_1 particles can be assigned to B sites is

$$B!/(B - X_1)! \qquad (5.504)$$

The number of ways X_2 particles can be assigned to the sites on top of the X_1 particles is similarly

$$X_1!/(X_1 - X_2)! \qquad (5.505)$$

and so on to the nth layer where the number of ways of assigning X_n particles to their sites on top of X_{n-1} particles is likewise

$$X_{n-1}!/(X_{n-1} - X_n)! \qquad (5.506)$$

Finally, the number of ways we can assign N_g particles to the states in the parent gas with a specified distribution-in-energy $\{n_{gj}\}$ is the Boltzmann count:

$$N_g! \prod_j \omega_{gj}{}^{n_{gj}}/n_{gj}! \qquad (5.507)$$

The total number of complexions is the product of all these numbers Eqs. (5.502)–(5.507), divided by $N!$ for the classical limit:

$$C = \frac{B! \prod_j \omega_{gj}{}^{n_{gj}}/n_{gj}!}{(B - X_1)!(X_1 - X_2)! \cdots (X_{n-1} - X_n)!X_n!} \qquad (5.508)$$

The statistical problem is to find the numbers X_r and n_{gj} that give a maximum value to $\ln C$, under the restrictions implied by a given total number and given total energy:

$$N = N_f + N_g = \sum_r X_r + \sum_j n_{gj} \tag{5.511}$$

$$E = \sum_j n_{gj}\epsilon_{gj} - X_1 W_1 - (A - X_1)W_L \tag{5.512}$$

We treat the set of equations (5.508), (5.511), and (5.512) in exactly the same way as we did Eqs. (5.105)–(5.107), obtaining

$$(\partial/\partial X_r)\{\ln C_f - \alpha \sum_j X_j + \beta(X_1 W_1 + \sum_{j \neq 1} X_j W_L)\} = 0 \tag{5.513}$$

$$(\partial/\partial n_{gj})\{\ln C_g - \alpha \sum_j n_{gj} - \beta \sum_j n_{gj}\epsilon_{gj}\} = 0 \tag{5.514}$$

where the terms C_f and C_g are those factors in Eq. (5.508) that come from the film and gas respectively. Clearly the last equation is identical with what one obtains classically with a gas treated separately from the film, and leads once again to the identification of α and β in terms of the chemical potential and temperature of the gas phase:

$$\alpha = -\mu/kT, \quad \beta = 1/kT$$

and again yields the ideal gas equations

$$pV = N_g kT \tag{5.515}$$

and

$$N_g = V(2\pi mkT/h^2)^{3/2}e^{\mu/kT} \tag{5.516}$$

Putting $r = 1$ in Eq. (5.513) and using the Stirling approximation on the logarithms of the factorials in C_f, we find

$$\ln (B - X_1) - \ln (X_1 - X_2) - \alpha + \beta W_1 = 0$$

or

$$(B - X_1)/(X_1 - X_2) = \exp \{-(\mu + W_1)/kT\} \tag{5.517}$$

Similarly for $1 < r < n$ we find from Eq. (5.513) that

$$(X_{r-1} - X_r)/(X_r - X_{r+1}) = \exp \{-(\mu + W_L)/kT\} \tag{5.518}$$

while for $r = n$, the last term, we have

$$(X_{n-1} - X_n)/X_n = \exp \{-(\mu + W_L)/kT\} \tag{5.519}$$

Equations (5.517)–(5.519) constitute n equations in n unknowns X_r and can be solved by suitable algebraic manipulation, as follows: Let

$$\theta = \exp (\mu + W_L)/kT \tag{5.520}$$

and

$$c = \exp (W_1 - W_L)/kT \tag{5.521}$$

Multiply together all the first r equations from (5.517) and (5.518), noting that the denominator of each equation cancels the numerator of the next equation, with only the rth denominator surviving, to give

$$(B - X_1)/(X_r - X_{r+1}) = 1/c\theta^r \tag{5.522}$$

This equation is true for all values of r, except $r = n$, when we have to multiply all the n equations to obtain

$$(B - X_1)/X_n = 1/c\theta^n \tag{5.523}$$

We rewrite Eqs. (5.522) and (5.523) in the forms

$$1 \leq r < n: \qquad X_r - X_{r+1} = c(B - X_1)\theta^r \tag{5.524}$$

$$X_n = c(B - X_1)\theta^n \tag{5.525}$$

Now add up all these equations to obtain

$$X_1 = c(B - X_1) \sum_{r=1}^{n} \theta^r \tag{5.526}$$

Next multiply each of Eqs. (5.524) and (5.525) by the corresponding value of r, obtaining

$$1 \leq r < n: \qquad r(X_r - X_{r+1}) = c(B - X_1)r\theta^r$$

$$nX_n = c(B - X_1)n\theta^n \tag{5.527}$$

Add all these equations together and obtain

$$A = X_1 + X_2 + \cdots X_n = c(B - X_1) \sum_{r=1}^{n} r\theta^r \tag{5.528}$$

As long as θ is less than unity, we can let n go to infinity and have both the series in Eqs. (5.526) and (5.528) convergent, the results being

$$\sum_{r} \theta^r = \theta/(1 - \theta) \quad \text{and} \quad \sum_{r} r\theta^r = \theta/(1 - \theta)^2 \tag{5.529}$$

Solving Eq. (5.526) for X_1 gives

$$X_1 = cB \left(\sum_{r} \theta^r \right)/(1 + c \sum_{r} \theta^r) \tag{5.530}$$

so that

$$B - X_1 = B/(1 + c \sum_{r} \theta^r) \tag{5.531}$$

Putting this last equation into Eq. (5.528) we find

$$A = B \left(\sum_{r} r\theta^r \right)/(1/c + \sum_{r} \theta^r)$$

and so from Eq. (5.529) we finally derive

$$(B/A)\theta/(1 - \theta) = 1/c + \theta(1 - 1/c) \tag{5.532}$$

This equation gives the ratio A/B as a function of θ, and it is now only necessary to associate θ with the pressure of the parent gas.

We note first that if we make θ approach unity, for example, by making $\mu = -W_L$ in Eq. (5.520), then Eq. (5.532) would require an infinite value for A/B, which means the film would then have an infinite number of layers. Since there are only a finite number of particles in the assembly, this of course is a mathematical idealization only; physically we interpret this result by regarding

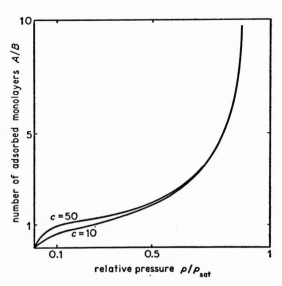

Fig. 5.51. The B.E.T. isotherm. The curves are drawn from Eq. (5.532) for two different values of c, representing two different energies of adsorption.

$\theta = 1$ as the value corresponding to saturation of the gas and the onset of condensation in the film, which then becomes a layer of bulk liquid phase. Next we note that from the definition of θ, Eq. (5.520), and the properties of the gas given by Eqs. (5.515) and (5.516):

$$\theta = (p/kT)(2\pi mkT/h^2)^{-3/2}e^{W_L/kT} \tag{5.533}$$

This shows that at constant temperature—over any isotherm—θ is exactly proportional to the pressure. Therefore, since it equals 1 at saturation, we must have

$$\theta = p/p_{sat} \tag{5.534}$$

The equation (5.532) is therefore just the required isotherm which gives the relative amount adsorbed A/B in equivalent number of layers as a function of θ, the relative pressure of the gas. In making use of this isotherm we measure the amount adsorbed, A, and the relative pressure, θ, and plot the quantity:

$$Y(\theta) = (\theta/A)/(1 - \theta) \tag{5.535}$$

against θ. If the theory is workable we shall find that

$$Y(\theta) = 1/cB + \theta(c - 1)/cB \tag{5.536}$$

is a straight line with gradient $(c - 1)/cB$ and intercept $1/cB$. By measuring the gradient and intercept, we thus find the two constants c and B. From B and the number of particles per square centimeter in the liquid phase surface—assumed equal to the number per square centimeter in the film—we can estimate the area of adsorbing surface. In many examples this procedure does indeed give areas that work out the same for a given adsorbate independently of the gas used, so the method has been accepted as a semi-standard way of measuring the surface areas of solids when more direct methods fail, e.g., powdered crystals, etc. However there are many difficulties involved. Some recent work by Harris and Emmett [*] will serve to illustrate. They investigated the physical adsorption of nitrogen, toluene, benzene, ethyl iodide, hydrogen sulfide, water vapor, carbon disulfide, and pentane gases on various solids: Pyrex glass spheres, ground Pyrex glass, reduced iron, synthetic ammonia catalysts, and silver. Generally the data fitted well with the theoretical isotherms, but the computed areas for any one solid were found to depend quite strongly on the kind of gas used as adsorbate. The following table illustrates the results. Nitrogen gas was used as an arbitrary standard, and the other areas are expressed in terms of that found with N_2, taken as unity.

RELATIVE AREAS OF SOLID ADSORBING SURFACES

Adsorber	Adsorbate			
	N_2	C_2H_5I	C_6H_6	$C_6H_5CH_3$
Glass spheres	1	0.97	0.80	0.72
Porous glass	1	0.40	0.53	0.53
Iron	1	0.70	0.65	0.57

There is little doubt that the discrepancies are due in part to the elongated shape of the heavier molecules, hence on adsorption they tend to lie flat and occupy more space in the film than they would in the surface of a bulk liquid phase. This poses the same theoretical problem that was raised near the end of § 5.3, viz., an adsorbed molecule can occupy more than one site.

Application of the BET isotherm has been extended to the case of adsorption of soluble organic compounds in aqueous solutions.[†] The solute behaves like a gas when sufficiently dilute, and the general BET theory may be accepted.

[*] B. L. Harris and P. H. Emmett, *J. Phys. Col. Chem.*, **53** (1949), p. 811.
[†] R. S. Hansen, Y. Fu, and F. E. Bartell, *J. Phys. Col. Chem.*, **53** (1949), p. 1141.

Caution is needed in interpreting the adsorbing areas derived from the theory because the first monolayer may contain both solute and solvent molecules.

A still more complicated situation is indicated in some work on the adsorption of nitrogen oxides on silica gel and on rutile powder.* The adsorption isotherms of nitrogen tetroxide molecules appear to follow the Langmuir isotherm without multilayer effects, but mixtures of nitrogen dioxide and tetroxide follow the BET isotherm with multilayer effects. The heat of adsorption increases with increased number of layers, in contrast with the normal behavior in simple adsorbate systems. This can be interpreted as due to an associative equilibrium within the film between the various molecules present.

At low coverage the film is largely NO_2 and the energy of dissociation is involved in the heat of adsorption; at high coverage the film is mostly N_2O_4 and the heat of adsorption does not involve dissociation. The statistics of this situation would involve the theory of dissociative equilibria, discussed in the next chapter.

5.6 Sublimation from an Einstein crystal. As a final example, we can study the phase equilibrium between a vapor and a solid crystal below the triple point, where no liquid phase is present. If we use the Einstein model for the crystal we can treat the atoms in the crystal as independent of each other, therefore the theory of the present chapter is adequate. Let there be N_g atoms in the gas and N_s atoms in the solid, the total number being fixed at

$$N = N_g + N_s \qquad (5.601)$$

In the Einstein model, we have to think of N_s fixed centers of equilibrium at lattice points that are mutually distinguishable. We start by counting complexions, as if the atoms were also distinguishable, and correct for this at the end by removing the factor $N!$. The number of ways we can select N_s atoms from among N, putting them into their respective lattice points and leaving N_g in the gas phase, is

$$N!/N_g! \qquad (5.602)$$

Having assigned the atoms to their lattice points, we have to assign each to their energy levels in the lattice field (harmonic oscillator states), n_{sj} of them to the jth level with degeneracy ω_{sj}, the Boltzmann count for this being given by Eq. (2.213):

$$N_s! \prod_j (\omega_{sj})^{n_{sj}}/n_{sj}! \qquad (5.603)$$

We also have to assign the atoms in the gas to their energy levels, with a similar Boltzmann count:

$$N_g! \prod_r (\omega_{gr})^{n_{gr}}/n_{gr}! \qquad (5.604)$$

The total number of complexions corresponding to the distribution-in-energy

* L. H. Reyerson and J. E. Wertz, *J. Phys. Col. Chem.*, **53** (1949), p. 234.

specified by the sets of numbers n_{sj} and n_{gr} is the product of the three numbers (5.602)–(5.604) divided by $N!$ thus:

$$C_{\text{class}} = N_s! \prod_{j,r} (\omega_{sj})^{n_{si}}(\omega_{gr})^{n_{gr}}/(n_{sj}!n_{gr}!) \tag{5.605}$$

Again we vary the numbers n_{sj} and n_{gr} to maximize the logarithm of C under the restrictions of fixed N and fixed E. The part of C depending on the solid is identical in form with that of the Boltzmann statistics, § 2.2A, while that for the gas is the classical ideal expression. Otherwise the argument is exactly the same as in § 5.1, and evidently we shall obtain

$$n_{sj} = N_s\omega_{sj} \exp\left(-\alpha - \beta\epsilon_{sj}\right) \tag{5.606}$$

$$n_{gr} = \omega_{gr} \exp\left(-\alpha - \beta\epsilon_{gr}\right) \tag{5.607}$$

The last equation at once identifies α and β in terms of μ and T as before, so we can sum both equations to yield

$$N_s = N_sQ_se^{\mu/kT}, \quad N_g = Q_ge^{\mu/kT} \tag{5.608}, (5.609)$$

where Q_s and Q_g are the partition functions for the solid and gas, referred to one and the same zero of energy. It is usually more convenient to compute the partition function of the solid with respect to the lowest energy of an atom in the solid as the zero, and that of a gas with respect to a free atom at rest as having zero energy. If the energy of sublimation from the lowest state in the solid to the lowest state in the gas is written as W, then the above partition function Q_s is greater than the partition function Q_{s0}, referred to the lowest state in the solid:

$$Q_s = Q_{s0}e^{W/kT} \tag{5.610}$$

Dividing Eq. (5.608) into (5.609) we have

$$N_g = (Q_g/Q_{s0})e^{-Wk/T} \tag{5.611}$$

If in this we use the partition function (4.211) for the ideal gas and express everything in terms of pressure we find

$$p/kT = (2\pi mkT/h^2)^{3/2}(1/Q_{s0})e^{-W/kT} \tag{5.612}$$

This is the pressure of the gas when in equilibrium with the solid phase described by the Einstein model and the partition function Q_{s0}. It is true for any model of the crystal so long as the atoms of the crystal are independent of each other, and we use the appropriate partition function Q_{s0}. In particular, suppose there is just one energy state at each lattice point in the solid, like the sites for adsorption in the last sections. One state means $Q_{s0} = 1$, since it is the zero of energy for the crystal. Eq. (5.612) becomes equivalent to Eqs. (5.533) and (5.534), the pressure in Eq. (5.612) replacing the saturated vapor pressure of Eq. (5.534),

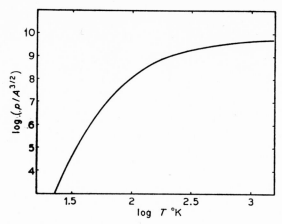

Fig. 5.61. Sublimation pressure of Einstein crystal. The curve is plotted from Eq. (5.612) with $h\nu/k = 200°$, $w/k = 250°$, and $m = $ mass of H atom; A is the atomic weight of the crystal; p is in dynes/cm².

and our present W replacing W_L. The BET isotherm is thus essentially the equilibrium between a gas and a solid, the solid film growing into an Einstein crystal as the layers increase in number. Incidentally this discussion shows how we could generalize the BET isotherm to the case where an adsorbed particle has more than one state—the partition function Q_{s0} for the adsorbed states would have to be included exactly as in Eq. (5.612).

EXERCISES AND PROBLEMS

1. Derive Eq. (5.323).

2. Develop the generalization of § 5.3 when the adsorbed particles occupy two adjacent sites.

3. Gaseous helium is adsorbed on charcoal at 20 °K. The volume adsorbed per gram of charcoal is measured in cc at NTP and the pressure is measured in millimeters of Hg; the following data are found:

pressure	100	200	400	600
volume	180	220	250	280

Discuss these data in terms of the Langmuir isotherm. Find the energy of adsorption and the volume that would fill one layer. If the film has an area of 16 sq. Angstroms per atom, find the area per gram of charcoal. Why is the BET isotherm unsuitable for a discussion of this experiment?

4. Derive the isotherm Eq. (5.403) in the manner outlined in the text and verify Eq. (5.413).

5. Nitrogen is adsorbed on anatase powder at −195.8 °C. The volume in cubic centimeters at NTP adsorbed per gram of powder is plotted against the ratio between the pressure and the saturated vapor pressure of nitrogen with the following results:

p/p_{sat}	0.05	0.10	0.15	0.20	0.30	0.50	0.70	0.90
volume	2.8	3.2	3.5	3.8	4.5	5.7	7.0	11.0

Use the BET isotherm to find the volume adsorbed in filling the first monolayer and calculate the area of the powder, assuming 14 sq. Angstroms per atom. Discuss the validity of the BET theory in general in the light of this experiment.

6. In setting up Eqs. (5.529) we allowed n, the number of adsorbed layers to go to infinity. Many layers will then appear as mathematically containing a small fraction of one particle; discuss the validity of this step in the argument.

7. Derive Eqs. (5.517) and (5.518) from Eq. (5.513).

8. Discuss the generalization of the Langmuir isotherm that results if we allow the adsorbed atoms to have one vibrational degree of freedom with a classical frequency ν; compare the result with the sublimation pressure of an Einstein crystal having three equal vibrational frequencies.

REFERENCES FOR FURTHER STUDY

The Physics and Chemistry of Surfaces, N. K. Adam, Oxford, 1940.
Physical Adsorption, S. Brunauer, Princeton, 1943.

"Note on the Equation of State of Linear Macromolecules in Monolayers," S. J. Singer, *J. Chem. Phys.*, **16** (1948), p. 872.
"The Heat of Adsorption of Diatomic Molecules," A. R. Miller, *Proc. Cambridge Phil. Soc.*, **43** (1947), p. 323.
"Structural Model of Low Pressure Physical Adsorption," M. A. Cook, D. H. Pack, and A. G. Oblad, *J. Chem. Phys.*, **19** (1951), p. 367.
"Statistical Thermodynamics of Sorption of Vapors by Solids," M. Dole, *J. Chem. Phys.*, **16** (1948), p. 25.
"Monolayers Adsorbed on Metal Surfaces," A. R. Miller, *J. Chem. Phys.*, **16** (1948), p. 841.
"Physical Adsorption on Non-Uniform Surfaces," G. Halsey, *J. Chem. Phys.*, **16** (1948), p. 931.
"Statistical Mechanics of Adsorption," T. L. Hill, *J. Chem. Phys.*, **14** (1946), pp. 263 and 441; **16** (1948), p. 181; **17** (1949), pp. 520 and 772.
"Anomalous Adsorption of Helium at Liquid Helium Temperatures," W. Band, *Phys. Rev.*, **76** (1949), p. 441.
"Condensation Coefficient and Adsorption," H. M. Cassel, *J. Chem. Phys.*, **17** (1949), p. 1000.
"The Assumptions of the B.E.T. Theory," W. G. McMillan and E. Teller, *J. Phys. Col. Chem.*, **55** (1951), p. 17.
"Heat Capacity of Multimolecular Layers of Adsorbed Argon," J. A. Morrison and L. E. Drain, *J. Chem. Phys.*, **19** (1951), p. 1063.
"Role of Surface Tension in Multilayer Gas Adsorption," W. G. McMillan and E. Teller, *J. Chem. Phys.*, **19** (1951), p. 25.
"Approximate Adsorption Isotherms for a Mixture of Two Isotopes," W. Band and E. B. Emery, *J. Phys. Col. Chem.*, **56** (1952), p. 384.

Chapter VI

CHEMICAL AND DISSOCIATIVE EQUILIBRIUM

6.1 Dissociative equilibrium in a diatomic gas. In § 4.5 we discussed the partition function and heat capacity of a diatomic gas. Here we consider the more general problem where the diatomic gas can dissociate into separate atoms, and the whole assembly is a mixture of diatomic and monatomic systems. The statistical problem is to find the most probable concentrations of these two parts.

Let there be N atoms altogether, and let N_1 of these be unassociated, N_2 pairs being present, so that

$$N = N_1 + 2N_2 \qquad (6.101)$$

The number of ways, X, in which the N atoms can be distributed into these two sets of states does not include the $N_1!$ permutations among the free atoms, or the $N_2!$ permutations among the molecules, or the $(2!)^{N_2}$ permutations between the atom pairs within the N_2 molecules; but if we multiply X by these three numbers, we obtain $N!$ as the total number of permutations among all the atoms. Therefore:

$$X = N!/\{N_1!N_2!(2!)^{N_2}\} \qquad (6.102)$$

Write ϵ_{1j} for the energy levels of the free atoms and ω_{1j} for their degeneracy weights; $\epsilon_{2j} - W$ for the energy levels of the molecules and ω_{2j} for their degeneracies. Here W is the difference in energy between the lowest molecular state and the energy of two separated atoms at rest—it is the energy of dissociation. The Boltzmann number of complexions for the two sets of states corresponding to some particular distribution-in-energy specified by the numbers n_{1j} and n_{2j} is then

$$N_1! \prod_j \{(\omega_{1j})^{n_{1j}}/n_{1j}!\} N_2! \prod_j \{(\omega_{2j})^{n_{2j}}/n_{2j}!\} \qquad (6.103)$$

Multiplying this by X and dividing by $N!$ to correct for indistinguishability in the classical fashion, we obtain the total number of complexions for the given distribution-in-energy:

$$C = (2!)^{-N_2} \prod_j \{(\omega_{1j})^{n_{1j}}/n_{1j}!\} \prod_j \{(\omega_{2j})^{n_{2j}}/n_{2j}!\} \qquad (6.104)$$

To find the most probable distribution-in-energy we maximize this under the restriction (6.101) and that of constant total energy:

$$N = \sum_j n_{1j} + 2 \sum_j n_{2j} \tag{6.105}$$

$$E = \sum_j \epsilon_{1j} n_{1j} + \sum_j (\epsilon_{2j} - W) n_{2j} \tag{6.106}$$

We can write Eq. (6.104) in the form:

$$\ln C = \ln C_1 + \ln C_2 - N_2 \ln 2 \tag{6.107}$$

where C_1 and C_2 are the familiar expressions for ideal gases, containing respectively N_1 and N_2 particles. Eqs. (6.105) and (6.106) require that two undetermined multipliers α and β be introduced as before, and, adding the variations of Eqs. (6.105) and (6.106) and of the logarithm of C, we obtain, counting all the n's as independent variables:

$$(\partial/\partial n_{1j})\{\ln C_1 - \alpha \sum_j n_{1j} - \beta \sum_j \epsilon_{1j} n_{1j}\} = 0 \tag{6.108}$$

$$(\partial/\partial n_{2j})\{\ln C_2 - \ln 2 \sum_j n_{2j} - 2\alpha \sum_j n_{2j} - \beta \sum_j (\epsilon_{2j} - W) n_{2j}\} = 0 \tag{6.109}$$

Eq. (1.608) is the same as Eq. (2.305) and leads again to

$$\alpha = -\mu/kT \quad \text{and} \quad \beta = 1/kT$$

and the distribution-in-energy:

$$n_{1j} = \omega_{1j} \exp (\mu - \epsilon_{1j})/kT \tag{6.110}$$

just as in Eq. (3.513). Since we are discussing ideal gases, the energy levels and weights are the same as before, and we can write Eq. (6.111), after summing over all the levels, in the form:

$$N_1 = Q_1 e^{\mu/kT} \tag{6.111}$$

where

$$Q_1 = V(2\pi mkT/h^2)^{3/2} \tag{6.112}$$

is the classical partition function. To work out the solution of Eq. (6.109), we note that this equation can be obtained from Eq. (6.108) by substituting the constant $\ln 2 + 2\alpha$ for α and the energy $\epsilon_{2j} - W$ for ϵ_{1j}. Making this substitution in Eq. (6.110) leads then to

$$n_{2j} = \tfrac{1}{2}\omega_{2j} \exp (2\mu - \epsilon_{2j} + W)/kT \tag{6.113}$$

Summing over all levels gives

$$N_2 = \tfrac{1}{2}Q_2 \exp (2\mu + W)/kT \tag{6.114}$$

where Q_2 is the partition function for the molecule, which we have already evaluated in § 4.6:

$$Q_2 = V(2\pi 2mkT/h^2)^{3/2}Q_{int} \qquad (4.601) \quad (6.115)$$

Eliminating μ between Eqs. (6.112) and (6.114), we find

$$N_1^2/2N_2 = (Q_1^2/Q_2)e^{-W/kT} = K_N \qquad (6.116)$$

This is the chemical constant of the law of mass action expressed as a function of temperature in terms of the partition functions. An elementary algebraic transformation gives the relative concentrations of the two components in the mixture as a function of temperature.

6.2 Simple gas mixtures and the law of partial pressures. Consider an assembly containing N_t atoms of type $t = 1, 2, \cdots$, none of which has any chemical attraction for another. Let their energy spectra be ϵ_{tj} and degeneracy weights be ω_{tj}, $j = 1, 2, \cdots$. The classical number of complexions corresponding to any distribution-in-energy n_{tj} is the product of the number of complexions in each subassembly consisting of a single type of atom or molecule:

$$C = \prod_t \prod_j (\omega_{tj})^{n_{tj}}/n_{tj}! \qquad (6.201)$$

so that the logarithm of the total C is the sum of the logarithms of the subassembly numbers:

$$\ln C = \sum_t \ln C_t \qquad (6.202)$$

As there are no reactions between the types of particle, the total number of each type must remain constant:

$$N_t = \sum_j n_{tj} = \text{constant for each } t \qquad (6.203)$$

while we also impose the restriction to constant total energy

$$E = \sum_j \sum_t \epsilon_{tj}n_{tj} \qquad (6.204)$$

To maximize the number $\ln C$ by varying the numbers n_{tj}, we need an arbitrary multiplier for each value of t in Eq. (6.203), and one for Eq. (6.204); therefore we find that, for each value of t:

$$(\partial/\partial n_{tj})\{\ln C_t - \sum_j \alpha_t n_{tj} - \beta \sum_t \epsilon_{tj}n_{tj}\} = 0 \qquad (6.205)$$

Each of these equations is identical with that for a single assembly with just one type of particle, and we identify α_t with the chemical potential of the species t: $\alpha_t = -\mu_t/kT$ and $\beta = 1/kT$. Assuming ideal gas properties, energy spectra, and degeneracies we again derive the familiar equations, repeatedly for each species:

$$N_t = Q_t e^{\mu t/kT} \tag{6.206}$$

where

$$Q_t = \sum_j \omega_{tj} e^{-\epsilon_{tj}/kT} = V(2\pi m_t kT/h^2)^{3/2} \tag{6.207}$$

The definition of pressure exerted by the assembly, given in § 3.3, can be applied directly to the mixture of gases:

$$p = -(\partial E/\partial V)_S = -\sum_j \sum_t n_{tj}(\partial \epsilon_{tj}/\partial V) \tag{6.208}$$

or

$$p = \sum_t N_t kT(\partial \ln Q_t/\partial V)_T \tag{6.209}$$

or

$$p = \sum_t N_t kT/V \tag{6.210}$$

The first form here, Eq. (6.208), follows because keeping S constant is equivalent to keeping all the n's constant in Eq. (6.204); the second form, Eq. (6.209), follows in the same way as Eq. (4.111) followed from Eq. (4.113); and the last form follows at once from Eq. (6.207).

Now the expression $N_t kT(\partial \ln Q_t/\partial V)_T$ in Eq. (6.209) is exactly what we would get for the pressure exerted by species t alone in the enclosure and is called the partial pressure p_t of species t. Equation (6.210) is then written in the form:

$$p = \sum_t p_t \tag{6.211}$$

This is the law of partial pressures for ideal gas mixtures; the total pressure of the mixture is the sum of the pressures that each part would exert independently if alone in the same enclosure. The essential assumption made in the deduction is that the total energy of the assembly is simply the sum of the energies of the species in the mixture, and that there is no interaction energy between the species.

We have developed the law of partial pressures for a specially simple mixture in which no chemical or dissociative reactions occur. However, it is now easy to see that the same law applies even when reactions do occur, provided we define the parts of the assembly appropriately, i.e., to ensure that there is no interaction energy between the parts. Thus, in the first section on dissociative equilibrium, we can define two such parts, the unassociated atoms in one part and the molecules in the other. Atoms pass back and forth between these parts and maintain an equilibrium concentration; but we can neglect the internal energy of the molecule in calculating the pressure, since W is not a function of the volume. We can apply exactly the same reasoning, using Eq. (6.208) applied to Eq. (6.106), and find eventually

$$p = p_1 + p_2 \tag{6.212}$$

for the dissociative mixture, where

$$p_1 V = N_1 kT \quad \text{and} \quad p_2 V = N_2 kT \tag{6.213}$$

the two partial pressures p_1 and p_2 being derived from the ideal gas law holding for each subassembly separately.

6.3 Chemical equilibria in gaseous mixtures. Consider first a mixture of two species A and B between which only one reaction occurs:

$$A + B \rightleftharpoons AB \tag{6.301}$$

Let there be N_A atoms of species A and N_B of species B in the whole assembly. Suppose N_a atoms of species A remain uncombined, N_b atoms of species B remain uncombined, and that there are N_c molecules AB. Then there are two numerical restrictions in force:

$$N_A = N_a + N_c = \text{constant} \tag{6.302}$$

and

$$N_B = N_b + N_c = \text{constant} \tag{6.303}$$

The final objective of the calculation is to find the most probable or equilibrium values of the numbers N_a, N_b, and N_c subject to these restrictions and to that of constant total energy.

Let the energy spectrum of A species atoms be ϵ_{aj}, with degeneracies ω_{aj}, of the B-species, ϵ_{bj}, ω_{bj}, and of the molecules ϵ_{cj}, ω_{cj}. The energy ϵ_{cj} includes translational, rotational, and vibrational terms as in § 4.5, but we shall count it zero when the molecule is at rest in its lowest state, which is lower than that of two separate atoms at rest by the energy W of the reaction. The total energy of the assembly in a given distribution-in-energy is

$$E = \sum_j \{\epsilon_{aj} n_{aj} + \epsilon_{bj} n_{bj} + (\epsilon_{cj} - W) n_{cj}\} \tag{6.304}$$

The number of complexions with the distribution-in-energy defined by the numbers n_{aj}, n_{bj}, and n_{cj} is counted as follows. The number of ways N_a atoms can be chosen from among the total N_A, leaving N_c to be later combined into molecules, is $N_A!/N_a!N_c!$. The number of ways N_b can be chosen from N_B, also leaving N_c, is $N_B!/N_b!N_c!$. The number of ways N_c molecules can be formed from N_c atoms of species A and N_c of species B is just $N_c!$. Combining all these and dividing by $N_A!N_B!$ to correct for indistinguishability in the classical fashion yields

$$1/(N_a!N_b!N_c!) \tag{6.305}$$

Incidentally, if the student dislikes the fact that this number is likely to be a very small fraction of unity—and therefore an apparently meaningless result— he may postpone removing the factor $N_A!N_B!$ until later. The number of ways N_a atoms can be put into the specified distribution-in-energy is given by the Boltzmann count; similarly for the B type atoms and for the molecules; the total product is multiplied by Eq. (6.305) to give the classical expression for the number of complexions:

$$C = \prod_j \{(\omega_{aj})^{n_{ai}}/n_{aj}!\} \{(\omega_{bj})^{n_{bi}}/n_{bj}!\} \{(\omega_{cj})^{n_{ci}}/n_{cj}!\} \qquad (6.306)$$

We have to maximize the logarithm of this number by taking variations of all the n's under the restrictions (6.302)–(6.304), each of which requires its appropriate Lagrangian multiplier, and we obtain

$$(\partial/\partial n_{tj})\{\ln C - \alpha_a N_A - \alpha_b N_B - \beta E\} = 0 \qquad (6.307)$$

where the subscript t stands for any one of a, b, or c, and where we must write

$$\left.\begin{array}{l} N_A = \sum_j n_{aj} + \sum_j n_{cj} \\[2mm] N_B = \sum_j n_{bj} + \sum_j n_{cj} \end{array}\right\} \qquad (6.308)$$

C splits into factors C_a, C_b, and C_c, each of which is identical in form with the expression already familiar in the theory of homogeneous assemblies, so we find from Eq. (6.307), using Eqs. (6.304) and (6.308), that

$$(\partial/\partial n_{aj})\{\ln C_a - \alpha_a \sum_j n_{aj} - \beta \sum_j \epsilon_{aj} n_{aj}\} = 0 \qquad (6.311)$$

$$(\partial/\partial n_{bj})\{\ln C_b - \alpha_b \sum_j n_{bj} - \beta \sum_j \epsilon_{bj} n_{bj}\} = 0 \qquad (6.312)$$

$$(\partial/\partial n_{cj})\{\ln C_c - (\alpha_a + \alpha_b) \sum_j n_{cj} - \beta \sum_j (\epsilon_{cj} - W) n_{cj}\} = 0 \quad (6.313)$$

These three sets of equations are of the same form as for a single homogeneous assembly and lead to the same form of result in each case:

$$n_{aj} = \omega_{aj} \exp(-\alpha_a - \beta\epsilon_{aj}) \qquad (6.314)$$

$$n_{bj} = \omega_{bj} \exp(-\alpha_b - \beta\epsilon_{bj}) \qquad (6.315)$$

$$n_{cj} = \omega_{cj} \exp[-(\alpha_a + \alpha_b) - \beta(\epsilon_{cj} - W)] \qquad (6.316)$$

Since we are dealing with gases, we can immediately identify β with $1/kT$ and relate the two parameters α_a and α_b with the chemical potentials

$$\alpha_a = -\mu_a/kT \quad \text{and} \quad \alpha_b = -\mu_b/kT \qquad (6.317)$$

Summing over all energy levels, the three equations become

$$N_a = Q_a e^{\mu_a/kT}, \quad N_b = Q_b e^{\mu_b/kT} \qquad (6.318)$$

and

$$N_c = Q_c \exp(\mu_a + \mu_b + W)/kT \qquad (6.319)$$

where the Q's are the ordinary partition functions as already defined:

$$Q_t = \sum_j \omega_{tj} \exp\left(-\epsilon_{tj}/kT\right), \quad t = a, b, \text{ or } c \tag{6.320}$$

Equation (6.319) may be interpreted as proving that the chemical potential of the molecule is the sum of the chemical potentials of the constituents. The two chemical potentials can be eliminated between the three equations (6.318)–(6.319), leading to the law of mass action in the form:

$$N_c/N_a N_b = (Q_c/Q_a Q_b)e^{W/kT} \tag{6.321}$$

The right side of this equation is a function of temperature and volume that can be determined when we know the energy spectra required for the partition functions. If we use the partition functions for gas reactions, we have

$$Q_a = V(2\pi m_a kT/h^2)^{3/2}, \quad Q_b = V(2\pi m_b kT/h^2)^{3/2} \tag{6.322}$$

and

$$Q_c = V[2\pi(m_a + m_b)kT/h^2]^{3/2}Q_{\text{int}} \tag{6.323}$$

where the internal partition function is the one discussed in § 4.4. Because the volume-dependent parts of the energy of this assembly are simply additive in Eq. (6.304), the law of partial pressures again holds, and we find the total pressure of the mixture to be

$$p = p_a + p_b + p_c \tag{6.324}$$

where

$$p_t = N_t kT/V, \quad t = a, b, \text{ or } c \tag{6.325}$$

Writing these relations, together with the partition functions Eqs. (6.322) and (6.323), into Eq. (6.321), we obtain the law of mass action in terms of the partial pressures:

$$p_c/p_a p_b = (kT)^{-5/2}(2\pi M/h^2)^{-3/2}Q_{\text{int}}e^{W/kT} \tag{6.326}$$

where $M = m_a m_b/(m_a + m_b)$.

There is an important connection between the equilibrium constants of the law of mass action—i.e., the right-hand side of either Eq. (6.321) or of Eq. (6.326)—and the change in free energy of the reaction which may be looked upon as one of the fundamental theorems of physical chemistry. While a detailed discussion of the free energy of chemical reactions would take us too far afield, we shall derive this fundamental theorem and refer the student to treatises on physical chemistry or theoretical chemistry for the applications to practical chemical problems.

The free energy of the reaction may be defined by the following ideal experiment. We start out with equal numbers $N_A = N_B$ of the two constituents each at the same (arbitrary) standard pressure and temperature p and T, and end up with the whole assembly combined into diatomic molecules $N_c = N_A = N_B$, also at the same pressure and temperature that we started with. The difference in free energy between these two idealized situations is the desired quantity.

The free energy of a monatomic gas has already been found, Eq. (4.207), and we may therefore write for the free energy of the two constituents together:

$$F_1 = NkT\{2 \ln p - 5 \ln T - I_a - I_b\} \tag{6.330}$$

where I_a and I_b are the chemical constants of the two constituents; see Eq. (4.214). The free energy of a diatomic gas can easily be shown to have the same form:

$$F_2 = NkT\{\ln p - \tfrac{5}{2} \ln T - I_{ab} - W/kT\} \tag{6.331}$$

where

$$I_{ab} = \ln \{k^{5/2}[2\pi(m_a + m_b)/h^2]^{3/2}\} - \ln Q_{\text{int}} \tag{6.332}$$

The free energy of the reaction is

$$\Delta F = F_2 - F_1 \tag{6.333}$$

which, from the information contained in the previous three equations, we can prove easily reduces to the following:

$$\Delta F = -NkT\{\ln p + \ln K(p)\} \tag{6.334}$$

where $K(p)$ is the reaction constant in terms of the pressure form of mass action, i.e., the quantity on the right hand side of Eq. (6.326). If the standard pressure is taken as the unit of pressure, e.g., one atmosphere, the $\ln p$ term disappears and one has the familiar form of the basic theorem:

$$\Delta F^0 = -NkT \ln K(p) \tag{6.335}$$

The generalization of the foregoing discussions to cover all kinds of chemical reactions is chiefly a matter of setting up a notation sufficiently comprehensive to include all possible molecular species. There must be a Lagrangian multiplier for each chemical atomic species to take care of the restriction to constant total number of atoms of each species, and just one multiplier to take care of constant total energy, while being related to the uniform equilibrium temperature throughout the mixture. The chemical potential of each atomic species must be the same throughout the mixture, and the chemical potential of any molecular species is the sum of the chemical potentials of the constituent atomic species. The chemical potentials can be eliminated from such equations as (6.318) in the general case; there is always the right number of these equations to permit the elimination, and eventually we end up with the law of mass action, analogous to Eq. (6.321). The species on the right hand of the reaction equation appear in the numerator, and the species on the left, in the denominator; the same ratio of the partition functions as of the numbers is found, as is the exponential of the total energy of the reaction. More details concerning these questions are given in the references for wider reading.

6.4 Dissociative cluster theory of saturated vapor. In discussing the dissociative equilibrium represented by the chemical equation $H + H = H_2$ in § 6.1, no mention was made of the mechanism by means of which the processes of dissociation and association were effected. This mechanism is of no consequence for the equilibrium concentrations, and would be significant only in discussing the rate at which equilibrium is attained. Actually, the energy of binding between the H atoms in the molecule is due to an electron-sharing process; it is large compared with the energies of attraction due to van der Waals forces between two H atoms which are separated by ordinary interatomic distances such as exist in the gaseous or liquid phases.

In the present section, we shall discuss a theory of the saturated vapor based on the idea that in the vapor there always exist clusters of atoms bound together only by their van der Waals attractions. The distances between atoms in a cluster are comparable in magnitude with the interatomic distances in the liquid phase, and no chemical bonding is present. The mechanism of formation of such clusters is due simply to elastic collision processes. If three atoms collide, momentum and energy can be conserved even if one atom escapes from the collision with higher energy and leaves the other two trapped in each other's van der Waals potential fields. If two single atoms collide simultaneously with another cluster, one atom may emerge with increased energy, leaving the other trapped in the cluster, which thereby increases in size. Conversely, if one atom of sufficiently high energy collides with a cluster, two low-energy atoms may emerge, decreasing the size of the cluster. Two large clusters may collide, undergo fission, and emerge as two clusters of different sizes. A mechanism therefore exists whereby clusters may be formed and the size distribution be brought into thermal equilibrium, although the rate of such processes remains an open question, to be studied by the methods of kinetic theory, rather than statistical mechanics.

The foregoing remarks may serve to convince us that clusters, or liquid droplets, must in fact exist in the vapor. The mechanics of their formation play no part in the statistical calculations of the equilibrium concentrations of clusters of various sizes. For these calculations, we need only to know the partition functions of the various clusters. In this theory, the vapor is treated as a mixture of clusters of all sizes, and all forces of repulsion or attraction between clusters are neglected; in other words, the presence of clusters takes care of the van der Waals forces, and all potential energy is present inside the clusters rather than between them. To this approximation, the problem can be handled as if the assembly were composed of independent systems.

Let there be N atoms in the assembly, N_1 of them unclustered, N_2 pairs, N_3 triplets, $\cdots$ N_s clusters of size s, etc., so that

$$N = \sum_s sN_s \tag{6.401}$$

The objective of the work is to find the most probable values of the numbers N_s, $s = 1, 2, \cdots$, and then from these to find the equation of state of the vapor. Let us call the N_s clusters of size s a subassembly; there is one subassembly corresponding to every value of s. Each cluster in the s-subassembly has energy levels, $\epsilon_{sj} - W_s$, where j indicates the level and W_s is the energy of dissociation of the cluster from its lowest level into separate atoms at rest. Let ω_{sj} be the statistical weight of the jth level in the s-type cluster. Let there be n_{sj} clusters of size s in the jth level, the totality of numbers n_{sj} defining a distribution-in-energy of the assembly. The number of clusters of size s is evidently

$$N_s = \sum_j n_{sj} \qquad (6.402)$$

We now have to count the number of complexions corresponding to the given set of numbers n_{sj}, and then to maximize this number by making variations in the numbers n_{sj}. This problem is the same as that of the dissociative equilibrium of a diatomic gas, studied in § 6.1, except that here we have an indefinite number of subassemblies instead of just two.

First we arrange N_s groups each containing s atoms, $s = 1, 2, \cdots$, using up all the N atoms in accordance with Eq. (6.401). The number of ways this can be done is X, where

$$X \prod_s (s!)^{N_s} N_s! = N! \qquad (6.403)$$

because the number X does not include the permutations $s!$ within each group, nor the permutations $N_s!$ among the groups. Having formed these groups, we have to build up the clusters and assign them to their energy levels. Consider any one subassembly alone. The Boltzmann count of complexions for the subassembly is

$$N_s! \prod_j (\omega_{sj})^{n_{sj}}/n_{sj}! \qquad (6.404)$$

and the number for the whole set of subassemblies is the product of this expression over all s values. Finally we have to divide everything by $N!$ to correct for indistinguishability in the classical fashion. Combining X from Eq. (6.403) with the product of (6.404), we derive the total number of complexions for the given distribution-in-energy:

$$C = \prod_s C_s \qquad (6.405)$$

where

$$C_s = \prod_j (\omega_{sj}/s!)^{n_{sj}}/n_{sj}! \qquad (6.406)$$

We have to maximize $\ln C$ by variations of n_{sj}, subject to the restrictions: fixed total number N and fixed total energy E:

$$\delta N = \sum_s s \sum_j \delta n_{sj} = 0 \qquad (6.407)$$

$$\delta E = \sum_s \sum_j \delta n_{sj}(\epsilon_{sj} - W_s) = 0 \qquad (6.408)$$

The Lagrangian method at once leads to the equations

$$\sum_s \{\delta(\ln C_s) - s\alpha \sum_j \delta n_{sj} - \beta \sum_j \delta n_{sj}(\epsilon_{sj} - W_s)\} = 0 \qquad (6.409)$$

In this expression we can treat every δn_{sj} as an independent variable so we can also treat each value of s separately; in this way, we see that the expression for each s is identical in form with that for a single ideal gas, Eq. (2.305), except that here we have $s\alpha$ instead of α, $(\epsilon_{sj} - W_s)$ instead of ϵ_j, and $\omega_{sj}/s!$ instead of ω_j. Therefore, we shall find for the most probable distribution-in-energy the same result as before except for these substitutions, thus:

$$n_{sj} = (\omega_{sj}/s!) \exp \{ -s\alpha - (\epsilon_{sj} - W_s)/kT \} \tag{6.410}$$

Summing over all j-values yields the total number of s-clusters:

$$N_s = Q_s e^{-s\alpha} e^{W_s/kT} \tag{6.411}$$

where Q_s is the partition function for a cluster of size s, referred to the lowest energy of the cluster as zero:

$$Q_s = \sum_j (\omega_{sj}/s!) \exp (-\epsilon_{sj}/kT) \tag{6.412}$$

The energies ϵ_{sj} include the kinetic energy of the center of mass of the cluster, together with the internal rotational and vibrational energies of the cluster. The kinetic energy of the center of mass is the same as that in an ideal gas particle having mass sm, where m is the mass of one atom or molecule. Thus

$$Q_s = V(2\pi smkT/h^2)^{3/2} Q_{si} \tag{6.413}$$

where Q_{si} represents the partition function for the internal energies. Note that in writing this we have neglected the finite space occupied by each cluster, as we neglected the volume of the molecules in the theory of the ideal gas.

We can now write down the equation of state of the assembly from the law proved in § 6.2 that each subassembly exerts its own partial pressure, contributing the total pressure additively. The partial pressure of the s-subassembly is given by the analog of Eq. (6.209):

$$p_s = N_s kT \partial \ln Q_s/\partial V \tag{6.414}$$

The factor Q_{si} is independent of V, therefore, using Eq. (6.413), we have

$$p_s = N_s kT/V \tag{6.415}$$

and the total pressure is simply the sum of these:

$$p = \sum_s N_s kT/V \tag{6.416}$$

Because $\sum_s N_s$ is necessarily less than N—compare with Eq. (6.401). This means that the pressure of the vapor is less than that of an ideal gas at the same temperature and density. To make actual use of this equation, however, it is necessary to find the numbers N_s first.

Inspection of Eq. (6.411) shows that it is possible to eliminate the chemical potential α in many ways. Thus for each value of s, we have the law of mass action following at once from Eq. (6.411) with $s = 1$:

$$N_1{}^s/N_s = (Q_1{}^s/Q_s)e^{-W_s/kT} \tag{6.417}$$

where we have made use of the fact that the internal energy W_1 of a single un-clustered atom is necessarily zero. These equations together with Eq. (6.401) are sufficient in principle to solve for all the unknowns N_s, although in practice it may not be possible to solve in closed form. There are two extremes where the solutions can be found with relative ease. The one extreme is that where clustering is almost absent, and we can neglect all clusters except pairs; this leads to a theory of the van der Waals equation of an imperfect gas, to be discussed in the next section. The other extreme is that where the largest clusters become the most probable, and this leads to a theory of the saturated vapor.

Using Eq. (6.413) in Eq. (6.417), the latter may be written in the form:

$$N_s/N_1 = s^{3/2}Q_{si}e^{W_s/kT}[(N_1/V)(2\pi mkT/h^2)^{-3/2}]^{s-1} \tag{6.418}$$

Multiply this by s and sum over all values of s except $s = 1$:

$$(N - N_1)/N_1 = \sum_{s=2} s^{5/2}Q_{si}e^{W_s/kT}[(N_1/V)(2\pi mkT/h^2)^{-3/2}]^{s-1} \tag{6.419}$$

This equation contains only one unknown, namely N_1, and so could in principle be solved for this unknown. Then from Eq. (6.418), for each value of s from 2 up, we could find all the other unknowns, N_s. Equation (6.419) has a simple physical interpretation: on the left-hand side is the ratio of the total number of particles involved in clusters to the number of particles not involved in clusters. On the right-hand side, the series would rapidly converge and have a reasonably small sum if the expression in the square bracket were much less than unity—as would happen in case the density of the vapor were small enough. Thus at low densities we may expect the ratio of clustered to unclustered particles to be small. If now we follow through an isothermal compression of the assembly, keeping T constant but decreasing V on the right side of Eq. (6.419), we arrive eventually at a density so high that, on solving Eq. (6.419) for N_1, we would find an infinite series just reaching its limiting sum; i.e., such that if the expression in the square bracket were any greater the series would diverge to infinity. This evidently represents some kind of critical condition, and we must proceed to investigate the radius of convergence of the series.

The convergence of the series depends only on the asymptotic behavior of its terms at large values of s. At large values of s, the energy W_s may be written as the sum of two parts, one of which is proportional to s and the other proportional to the number of particles in the surface of the cluster:

$$W_s = sW - s^{2/3}\chi, \quad s \gg 1 \tag{6.420}$$

We can indeed accept this relation as generally valid, regarding it as a definition of the quantity χ, which, however, for small values of s is necessarily a function of s such that when $s = 1$,

$$W_1 = 0, \quad \chi = W \text{ at } s = 1 \tag{6.421}$$

So far as the convergence of the series is concerned, the important property of the term containing χ is that it increases with s less rapidly than s at large values of s. Using Eq. (6.420), we may now write Eq. (6.419) in the form:

$$(N - N_1)/N_1 = e^{W/kT} \sum_{s=2} A_s Z^{s-1} \tag{6.422}$$

where

$$A_s = s^{5/2} Q_{si} \exp\left(-s^{2/3}\chi/kT\right) \tag{6.423}$$

and

$$Z = (N_1/V)(2\pi mkT/h^2)^{-3/2} e^{W/kT} \tag{6.424}$$

We can show that

$$\lim_{s \to \infty} A_{s+1}/A_s = 1 \tag{6.425}$$

therefore, the convergence of the series (6.422) depends only on Z, and its radius of convergence occurs just at $Z = 1$. The critical condition thus occurs when $Z = 1$, or from Eq. (6.424):

$$(N_1/V)_c = (2\pi mkT/h^2)^{3/2} e^{-W/kT} \tag{6.426}$$

and also, putting $Z = 1$ in Eq. (6.422):

$$\{(N - N_1)/N_1\}_c = \sum_{s=2} A_s e^{W/kT} \tag{6.427}$$

Solving the last equation for N_1 and substituting the result into Eq. (6.426), we find

$$(N/V)_c = (2\pi mkT/h^2)^{3/2}[e^{-W/kT} + \sum_{s=2} A_s] \tag{6.428}$$

which expresses the critical density as a function of temperature.

If we now try to compress the assembly into a still smaller volume so that the density exceeds the critical value given by Eq. (6.428), we find it impossible to solve Eq. (6.422); this is because if Z were greater than unity the series would diverge to infinity—its sum is discontinuous at $Z = 1$. To circumvent this paradox, we note that although the series (6.422) has a very large number of terms, it is not strictly an infinite series because the cluster size cannot in fact be greater than N, the total number of particles in the assembly. What actually happens then is that Z does become very slightly greater than unity when the assembly is compressed beyond the critical density, and the series begins to diverge in the sense that the terms of largest s become the largest terms. Before the critical density is reached, the terms of smallest s dominate; after the critical density is passed, the dominant terms shift from small s to large s. Physically, we say that the assembly begins to condense into the liquid phase.

To put this picture into more exact mathematical terms, we split the series into two parts at some rather arbitrary term, say the Lth, such that before condensation, the first part of the series is much larger than the remainder. We can think of L as the size of a cluster—in order of magnitude at least—large enough to be free of Brownian movement and therefore qualified to be counted as a true drop of liquid rather than just a vapor cluster. While L is very large compared with unity, it is still very small compared with N. Write N^* for the number of particles not involved in clusters larger than L:

$$N^* = \sum_{s=1}^{L} sN_s \tag{6.429}$$

Summing Eq. (6.418) over all values of s up to L, we find, in place of Eq. (6.422),

$$(N^* - N_1)/N_1 = e^{W/kT} \sum_{s=2}^{L} A_s Z^{s-1} \tag{6.430}$$

and the remainder of the series is

$$(N - N^*)/N_1 = e^{W/kT} \sum_{s>L} A_s Z^{s-1} \tag{6.431}$$

When Z is less than unity, the remainder of the series is entirely negligible because L is a very large number. This means that N^* is practically equal to N, and so practically no particles are present in clusters greater than L. This situation persists right up to the critical value $Z = 1$ because the factors A_s become very small for large values of s. A further compression to smaller volume than V_c tends, through Eq. (6.426), to make Z greater than unity; now we can indeed put Z slightly greater than unity in Eqs. (6.430) and (6.431) because the series do have a finite number of terms. However, a very slight increase in Z beyond unity will give the remainder (6.431) a value enormously large compared with the first L terms in (6.430). There is therefore an almost discontinuous break in the behavior of the remainder (6.431); for Z less than unity, it stays practically zero, and at $Z = 1$, it suddenly begins to increase rapidly with further increase in Z. This can only happen if, with the slight increase in Z beyond unity, the number N_1 suddenly decreases rapidly, and with it N^*. A glance at Eq. (6.424) shows that, as long as N_1 and V decrease almost proportionally, Z does not have to increase very much, while the behavior of the remainder (6.431) ensures in fact that Z cannot increase very much while N_1 remains nonzero. Indeed, this last condition is so strong that in Eq. (6.424) we can take Z as just equal to unity for all further compression, any error being negligible in writing:

$$V \leq V_c: \qquad\qquad N_1/V = (2\pi mkT/h^2)^{3/2} e^{-W/kT} \tag{6.432}$$

The same approximation is also valid for summing the first L terms of the series, Eq. (6.430); writing $Z = 1$ therein, solving for N^*, and using Eq. (6.432) to eliminate N_1, we find:

$$V \le V_c: \qquad N^*/V = (2\pi mkT/h^2)^{3/2}\{e^{-W/kT} + \sum_{s=2}^{L} A_s\} \qquad (6.433)$$

These two equations state that during isothermal compression beyond the critical density given by Eq. (6.428), the density N^*/V of true vapor remains fixed, the number N^* reducing with V. A number $N - N^*$ go over into the larger clusters counted as true liquid phase, and this number fixes the exact value of Z through Eqs. (6.431) and (6.432), which yield

$$V \le V_c: \qquad N - N^* = V(2\pi mkT/h^2)^{3/2} \sum_{s=L}^{N} A_s Z^{s-1} \qquad (6.434)$$

As N^* decreases, following Eq. (6.433), this equation demands an increasing value of Z, but even when $N^* = 0$, the value of Z is still so very slightly greater than unity that no error is made in assuming $Z = 1$, as we did in deriving Eqs. (6.432) and (6.433). We may also write $Z = 1$ in Eq. (6.418) and find that the number of clusters of size s during the compression is given by

$$V \le V_c: \qquad N_s/V = Q_{si}(2\pi mskT/h^2)^{3/2} \exp(-\chi s^{2/3}/kT) \qquad (6.435)$$

The pressure exerted by the vapor during the compression is found from Eq. (6.416), summed only up to $s = L$:

$$V \le V_c: \quad p = kT(2\pi mkT/h^2)^{3/2}\{e^{-W/kT} + \sum_{s=2}^{L} s^{3/2}Q_{si} \exp(-\chi s^{2/3}/kT)\} \qquad (6.436)$$

This pressure remains constant during isothermal compression also.

Summarizing these results, we see that as V goes less than V_c that part of the assembly containing no clusters greater than L continues to exert a constant pressure and has a constant density, while decreasing in mass. The part of the assembly not included in clusters less than L continuously increases in mass but is assumed to contribute practically nothing to the pressure. It is left as an exercise to justify this last assumption. We are therefore reasonably justified in interpreting the process as condensation into the liquid phase. What we have called the critical volume is now to be regarded as the saturated volume, and the pressure, Eq. (6.436), is the saturated vapor pressure. Incidentally, Eq. (6.421) shows that the first term in the brackets of Eq. (6.436) is simply the missing term from the series in the same bracket, i.e., the term with $s = 1$. Thus:

$$p_{\text{sat}} = kT(2\pi mkT/h^2)^{3/2} \sum_{s=1}^{L} s^{3/2}Q_{si} \exp(-\chi s^{2/3}/kT) \qquad (6.437)$$

The density of the vapor at saturation can also be found, from Eqs. (6.435) and (6.429), the result being:

$$(N^*/V)_{\text{sat}} = (2\pi mkT/h^2)^{3/2} \sum_{s=1}^{L} s^{1/2}Q_{si} \exp(-\chi s^{2/3}/kT) \qquad (6.438)$$

In fact the upper limit L on the series can be dropped in these two results because the series are both rapidly converging.

If pushed to their logical conclusion, these formulae would allow V to go to zero, which apparently leaves no space for the liquid phase. This is essentially because we neglected the volumes of the clusters at the outset. However, Eqs. (6.437) and (6.438) are valid in the sense that we do not have to have more than a trace of the liquid present to ensure saturation, and we can arrange to remove the bulk liquid as soon as formed by condensation. One can modify the theory to account for the finite volume of the clusters to make it more precise in this respect, but this complicates the formulae rather seriously and the method loses its main advantage—that of simplicity and ease of application, over the more rigorous theory that will be discussed in the next chapter. The present theory has been applied to many vapor pressure curves and found to give fairly satisfactory agreement for temperatures well below the critical temperatures of the gases concerned.*

6.5   Dissociative cluster theory of the virial coefficients. It is assumed that the student is familiar with the van der Waals equation of state for a nonideal gas:

$$(p + a/V^2)(V - b) = NkT \tag{6.501}$$

which can be derived from a very simple kinetic theory model, viz., b is the volume occupied by the molecular repulsive force fields, and a/V^2 is the intrinsic pressure due to molecular attractions.

In modern experimental work in this field, the equation of state is usually expressed in the form:

$$pV/NkT = 1 + B_2/V + B_3/V^2 + \cdots \tag{6.502}$$

where B_n is called the nth virial coefficient, and can be theoretically evaluated in terms of the forces between the molecules. A more rigorous theory of this must await the next chapter, but here we can discuss the Eq. (6.502) in terms of the approximations of the previous section, i.e., the dissociative processes of clustering suffice to account for the nonideal behavior of the gas.

Using Eqs. (6.415) and (6.413) for the partial pressures, we can throw the law of mass action, Eq. (6.417), into the form:

$$p_s/p_1{}^s = K_s \tag{6.503}$$

where

$$K_s = s^{3/2} Q_{si} \{ kT(2\pi mkT/h^2)^{3/2} \}^{(1-s)} e^{W_s/kT}$$

The K's are functions of T only. From Eq. (6.416), the law of partial pressures, we have

$$p = \sum_s p_s = \sum_s K_s p_1{}^s$$

---

* Ch'eng, Tseng, Feng, and Band, *J. Chem. Phys.*, **9** (1941), p. 123; also **8** (1940), p. 20.

and so

$$dp/dp_1 = \sum_s sK_s p_1{}^{s-1}$$

while

$$NkT/V = (kT/V) \sum_s sN_s = \sum_s sp_s = \sum_s sK_s p_1{}^s$$

Combining these last two results yields

$$pV/NkT = (p/p_1)(dp_1/dp) \tag{6.504}$$

The series $p = \sum_s K_s p_1{}^s$ can be inverted to read

$$p_1 = p - K_2 p^2 + (2K_2{}^2 - K_3)p^3 - (5K_2{}^3 - 5K_2 K_3 + K_4)p^4 + \cdots$$

and Eq. (6.504) can then be expanded in the following form:

where

and

$$\left. \begin{aligned} pV/NkT &= 1 + A_2 p + A_3 p^2 + A_4 p^3 + \cdots \\ A_2 &= -K_2, \quad A_3 = 3K_2{}^2 - 2K_3, \\ A_4 &= -10K_2{}^3 + 12K_2 K_3 - 3K_4, \quad \text{etc.} \end{aligned} \right\} \tag{6.505}$$

The virial expansion Eq. (6.502) can also be expressed in a form directly comparable with Eq. (6.505):

$$pV/NkT = 1 + B_2(p/NkT) + (B_3 - B_2{}^2)(p/NkT)^2$$
$$+ (B_4 - 3B_2 B_3 + 2B_2{}^3)(p/NkT)^3 + \cdots \tag{6.506}$$

Comparison between these last two forms yields the following expressions for the virial coefficients in terms of the equilibrium constants for the clustering equilibrium:

$$\left. \begin{aligned} B_2 &= -NkTK_2, \quad B_3 = (4K_2{}^2 - 2K_3)(NkT)^2, \\ B_4 &= -(20K_2{}^3 - 18K_2 K_3 + 3K_4)(NkT)^3, \quad \text{etc.} \end{aligned} \right\} \tag{6.507}$$

In attempting to compare these results with observed equations of state, we have the parameters involved in the internal partition function of the clusters to adjust, and it might seem reasonable to expect to be able to fit the theory to almost any data. However, we must note that B_2 is necessarily negative according to the theory, whereas this is by no means the case experimentally. While B_2 is negative for the majority of gases at the lowest temperatures, it generally becomes positive for high enough temperatures; for helium, in fact, B_2 is positive at all temperatures. It turns out that the positive values of B_2 can be easily understood in terms of repulsive forces between particles, but the dissociative cluster model necessarily fails to take this effect into account properly.

One way to force the cluster picture to work in spite of this difficulty is to imagine the possibility of negative cluster numbers; in particular, we need N_2 to be negative when the second virial coefficient is positive. In fact the rigorous theory can be interpreted this way, because the mathematical quantities that replace the cluster numbers can be negative without violating common-sense notions. But there is a much simpler way of correcting the cluster picture for the effect of repulsive fields, essentially the same correction that appears in the van der Waals equation for the finite volume of the clusters. Writing $V - b$ for the empty space available to the particles in volume V, the partition function for a cluster of size s may be written

$$Q_s = (V - b)(2\pi smkT/h^2)^{3/2}Q_{si} \tag{6.508}$$

in place of Eq. (6.413), and corresponding to this, the equation of state (6.416) goes over into

$$p(V - b) = \sum_s N_s kT \tag{6.509}$$

The law of mass action is unaltered by this correction, and the expansion (6.505) becomes instead

$$p(V - b)/NkT = 1 + A_2 p + A_3 p^2 + A_4 p^3 + \cdots$$

which transcribes at once into

$$pV/NkT = 1 + (A_2 + b/NkT)p + A_3 p^2 + A_4 p^3 + \cdots \tag{6.510}$$

Comparing this with the virial form (6.506) gives the desired correction on the second virial coefficient:

$$B_2 = b - K_2 NkT \tag{6.511}$$

the other coefficients being unchanged by the correction.

In comparing this formula with observed second virial coefficients, we may assume that b is approximately equal to the volume per mole in the liquid phase —picturing the liquid as being almost "close-packed." Experimental data on B_2 then permit us to estimate K_2 and hence find the number of paired van der Waals clusters in the nonideal gas as a function of temperature. In fact from Eq. (6.505), we have $N_2/N_1{}^2 = kTK_2/V$ and so $N_2/N = (N_1/N)^2(b - B_2)/V$. But N_2/N is always very small so that N_1/N is nearly unity. If the volume is measured in Amagats, the volume per mole at NTP about 2.24×10^4 cm^3, then we have roughly

$$N_2/N = b - B_2 \text{ in Amagats} \tag{6.512}$$

Three examples will suffice to illustrate the surprisingly large numbers of cluster-pairs in actual gases according to this theory. Liquid helium at its normal boiling point (4 °K) has a mole volume about 12.8×10^{-4} Amagat, and a second virial coefficient that remains roughly constant near 5×10^{-4} Amagat from 70 °K up to 673 °K. Taking $b = 12.8 \times 10^{-4}$, the difference yields nearly one pair per thousand atoms. Neon, with a liquid mole volume about 7.5×10^{-4} Amagat, has a second virial coefficient that increases smoothly from -9.35×10^{-4} Amagat to 6.12×10^{-4} Amagat between the same limits of temperature, so the number of cluster-pairs increases with decreasing temperature from about one pair per thousand atoms at 673 °K to 17 pairs per thousand atoms at 65 °K. Argon has a liquid mole volume of 12.8×10^{-4} Amagat and a second virial coefficient -28.7×10^{-4} at 173 °K which increases to 6.83×10^{-4} Amagat at 673 °K, so there are 40 pairs per ten thousand atoms at the lower temperature but only 7 pairs per ten thousand at the higher temperature. (We shall return to a more detailed discussion in the next chapter.)

6.6 Chemical equilibrium in nonideal gases. In §6.3 we derived the law of mass action for chemical equilibrium in gaseous mixtures. The form of the law was strictly true only in gaseous reactions, because partition functions have a meaning only when the systems have independent energy spectra. In a nonideal gas the particles do not have independent energy spectra. However, the clustering approximation has permitted us to treat the nonideal gas as a mixture of noninteracting components, clusters of various sizes, and this picture leads to a very simple way of generalizing the law of mass action to include nonideal gas reactions.

We shall discuss in fact only slightly nonideal gases, and so include only cluster-pairs. There are, adopting the same notation as in § 6.3, N_a free A-type atoms, N_b free B-type atoms, and N_c molecules AB, and we now add N_{aa} pairs of A-type atoms and N_{bb} pairs of B-type atoms. We shall not count possible van der Waals pairs of unlike atoms A and B that fail to combine chemically, and we shall not count larger clusters, like a molecule AB plus an atom A or B, etc., although the method is easily generalized to include such larger clusters up to any order desired.

The numerical relations necessarily found are

$$\begin{aligned} N_A &= N_a + 2N_{aa} + N_c \\ N_B &= N_b + 2N_{bb} + N_c \end{aligned} \right\} \tag{6.601}$$

and it is an easy exercise to derive the most probable distributions by following the same kind of reasoning used in § 6.3:

$$n_{aj} = \omega_{aj} e^{-(\epsilon_{aj}-\mu_a)/kT} \tag{6.602}$$

$$n_{aaj} = \tfrac{1}{2}\omega_{aaj} e^{-(\epsilon_{aaj}-W_{aa}-2\mu_a)/kT} \tag{6.603}$$

$$n_{cj} = \omega_{cj} e^{-(\epsilon_{cj}-W_c-\mu_a-\mu_b)/kT} \tag{6.604}$$

with similar equations for n_{bj} and n_{bbj}. The energies W_{aa} and W_{bb} are energies of dissociation of van der Waals pairs, and W_c is the energy of dissociation of the molecule; W_c is much greater than the other two. Summing over all energy levels:

$$N_a = Q_a e^{\mu_a/kT}, \quad N_b = Q_b e^{\mu_b/kT} \tag{6.610}$$

$$\begin{aligned} N_{aa} &= Q_{aa} e^{(W_{aa}+2\mu_a)/kT} \\ N_{bb} &= Q_{bb} e^{(W_{bb}+2\mu_b)/kT} \end{aligned} \right\} \tag{6.611}$$

$$N_c = Q_c e^{(W_c+\mu_a+\mu_b)/kT} \tag{6.612}$$

The potentials can be eliminated in several ways, for example to yield

$$N_c/N_aN_b = (Q_c/Q_aQ_b)e^{W_c/kT} \tag{6.615}$$

and

$$N_c^2/N_{aa}N_{bb} = (Q_c^2/Q_{aa}Q_{bb})e^{(2W_c-W_{aa}-W_{bb})/kT} \tag{6.616}$$

Now neither of these is the ratio that one seeks for the law of mass action, which is $N_c/N_\alpha N_\beta$ where

$$N_\alpha = N_a + 2N_{aa} \quad \text{and} \quad N_\beta = N_b + 2N_{bb} \tag{6.617}$$

are the total numbers of atoms not associated in molecules. We have to construct the desired ratio less directly. We have

$$N_\alpha N_\beta = N_aN_b + 2(N_{aa}N_b + N_{bb}N_a) + N_{aa}N_{bb} \tag{6.620}$$

Dividing this by N_c will give the desired ratio. But the right side can be derived; thus from Eqs. (6.610)–(6.612) we can show that

$$N_{aa}N_b/N_c = N_a(Q_b/Q_a)(Q_{aa}/Q_c)e^{(W_{aa}-W_c)/kT} \tag{6.621}$$

$$N_{bb}N_a/N_c = N_b(Q_a/Q_b)(Q_{bb}/Q_c)e^{(W_{bb}-W_c)/kT} \tag{6.622}$$

We shall neglect $N_{aa}N_{bb}$ compared with the other terms, since the number of van der Waals clusters is small. Then we have

$$N_\alpha N_\beta/N_c = \theta(Q_aQ_b/Q_c)e^{-W_c/kT} \tag{6.623}$$

where

$$\theta = 1 + 2N_a(Q_{aa}/Q_a^2)e^{W_{aa}/kT} + 2N_b(Q_{bb}/Q_b^2)e^{W_{bb}/kT} \tag{6.624}$$

Then referring back to Eqs. (6.412), (6.503), and (6.507), we can show that

$$\theta = 1 - 2B_{2a}/V - 2B_{2b}/V \tag{6.625}$$

which expresses the deviation factor θ in terms of the virial coefficients of the two monatomic gases.

On the clustering approximation, the law of partial pressures holds in the sense that Eq. (6.416) and Eq. (6.415) hold. Applying this to the present question, we have

$$p = p_a + p_{aa} + p_b + p_{bb} + p_c \tag{6.626}$$

If we write

$$p_\alpha = p_a + p_{aa}, \quad p_\beta = p_b + p_{bb} \tag{6.627}$$

for the partial pressures of the monatomic constituents, the law of partial pressures becomes

$$p = p_\alpha + p_\beta + p_c \tag{6.628}$$

while

$$p_\alpha = (N_akT/V)(1 + B_{2a}/V), \quad p_\beta = (N_bkT/V)(1 + B_{2b}/V) \tag{6.629}$$

While proving Eq. (6.625), we can also show that

$$N_{aa}/N_a = -B_{2a}/V, \quad N_{bb}/N_b = -B_{2b}/V \tag{6.630}$$

Then from Eq. (6.617) we have

$$N_\alpha = N_a(1 - 2B_{2a}/V), \quad N_\beta = N_b(1 - 2B_{2b}/V) \tag{6.631}$$

Combining Eqs. (6.629) and (6.631) and neglecting squares of the virials, we have

$$N_\alpha = (p_\alpha V/kT)(1 - 3B_{2a}/V), \quad N_\beta = (p_\beta V/kT)(1 - 3B_{2b}/V) \tag{6.632}$$

Using these to rewrite the law of mass action in terms of partial pressures, Eq. (6.623) and Eq. (6.625) become

$$p_\alpha p_\beta/p_c = K_p(1 + B_{2a}/V + B_{2b}/V) \tag{6.633}$$

where K_p is the equilibrium constant determined in the same way as for ideal gases.

In the conventional calculation generally used by physical chemists, different "partial pressures" are employed than those suggested here. Thus a purely arbitrary definition is set up according to which

$$p^*_\alpha V/kT = N_\alpha \quad \text{and} \quad p^*_\beta V/kT = N_\beta \tag{6.634}$$

these partial pressures being simply proportional to the mole fractions of the uncombined constituents. The law of partial pressures does *not* hold for p^*'s, and the law of mass action (6.623) becomes

$$p^*_\alpha p^*_\beta/p_c = \theta K_p \tag{6.635}$$

where θ is given by Eq. (6.625). It would seem desirable to use the partial pressures p_α and p_β and the law of mass action (6.633), in terms of which the law of partial pressures *does* hold, to the same approximation as does the law of mass action itself.

EXERCISES AND PROBLEMS

1. Express the law of mass action, Eq. (6.116), in terms of the relative concentrations in the mixture.

2. What information is needed to compute the relative concentrations of H and H_2 in hydrogen gas? Use Eqs. (6.112) and (6.115) for the partition functions and develop Eq. (6.116) in full detail for hydrogen. How would the dissociative equilibrium theory proceed to take into account the stability of *ortho*- and *para*-hydrogen?

3. Find the rotational partition function for a diatomic molecule constrained to move in one plane. Consider the dissociative equilibrium between H_2 and H in an adsorbed film assuming that both atoms in the molecule are adsorbed with the same energy as the unassociated atom, and that motion is confined to the plane of the monolayer.

4. Set up an equilibrium that includes the dissociative equilibrium in a gas and dissociative equilibrium in an adsorbed film, using the Langmuir model for the adsorption process. Compare the concentrations of unassociated atoms in the film with that in the gas, assuming that the rotation of the molecule in the film is restricted to one plane. Does the adsorption process act as a catalyst?

5. Follow through the ideas of § 6.4 with atoms in a monolayer film and show that a condensed film could form from a monolayer vapor at a saturation pressure per centimeter given by

$$S_{sat} = kT(2\pi mkT/h^2) \sum_{s=1} sQ_{si} \exp(-\chi s^{1/2}/kT)$$

6. Justify the assumption made in the paragraph following Eq. (6.436) that the large clusters do not contribute significantly to the vapor pressure.

7. Prove Eqs. (6.331) and (6.332).

8. In the law of mass action of Eq. (6.321), assume that the total number of each constituent is equal, $N_A = N_B = N$, and then solve Eqs. (6.321), (6.302), and (6.303) for N_a, N_b, and N_{ab}.

[Ans. $N_a/K_n = (N_A/K_n + \frac{1}{4})^{1/2} - \frac{1}{2}$]

9. Derive Eq. (6.505) from Eq. (6.504), as outlined in the text.

10. Derive Eq. (6.506) from Eq. (6.507).

11. Show that Eq. (6.509) follows from Eq. (6.508).

12. Derive the distribution-in-energy given in Eqs. (6.602)–(6.604).

13. Prove Eq. (6.625) and (6.630).

14. Generalize the theory of § 5.6 for sublimation from a crystal to include the case where the gas phase undergoes molecular association in pairs, while the crystal is treated as monatomic in structure.

REFERENCES FOR FURTHER STUDY

Statistical Mechanics, J. E. Mayer and M. G. Mayer, Wiley, 1940; Chapters 7, 8, 9.
Mixtures, E. A. Guggenheim, Oxford, 1952.
A Treatise on Physical Chemistry, Taylor and Glasstone, Van Nostrand, 1942.

"Dissociation Treatment of Condensing Systems," W. Band, *J. Chem. Phys.*, **7** (1939), pp. 324 and 927.
"Statistical Mechanics of Condensation Phenomena in Mobile Monolayers," W. Band, *J. Chem. Phys.*, **8** (1940), p. 116.
"Adsorption Isotherms for Mobile Monolayers," W. Band, *J. Chem. Phys.*, **8** (1940), p. 178.
"Statistical Theory of Duplex Films," W. Band and S. K. Feng, *J. Chem. Phys.*, **8** (1940), p. 977.
"Imperfect Gas as an Association Problem," W. Weltner, Jr., *J. Chem. Phys.*, **22** (1954), p. 153.
"The Representation of Gas Properties in Terms of Molecular Clusters," H. W. Woolley, *J. Chem. Phys.*, **21** (1953), p. 236.
"Negative Cluster Concentrations," J. E. Kilpatrick, *J. Chem. Phys.*, **21** (1953), p. 1366.

Chapter VII

ASSEMBLIES OF DEPENDENT SYSTEMS

7.1 The assembly partition function. Up to this point we have either discussed assemblies of ideally independent systems, or else we have restricted ourselves to an approximate theory of interacting systems which is valid only insofar as the energy spectrum of any one system in the assembly is independent of the energy of any other system in the assembly. In general, the interactions between molecules in solids and liquids, even in many imperfect gases, are so important that one cannot solve the quantum mechanical problem in such a way as to obtain a unique energy spectrum for any one system; in fact, the whole spectrum of possible energies of any one system depends on what neighboring systems are doing. In this situation (as outlined in Chapter I), the quantum mechanical problem is solved by considering the assembly as a whole, and yields a spectrum of energy levels for the assembly as a whole. The stationary wave functions are functions of all the co-ordinates of all the systems in the assembly and cannot be separated into factors depending on only one system in the assembly. Nor can the eigenvalues of energy be regarded as sums over contributions from individual systems in the assembly; the energy cannot be localized on the systems but belongs to the assembly as a whole. To handle this problem statistically, we also have to accept the assembly as a unit, its Nf variables now being regarded as internal degrees of freedom. In place of finding the average condition of a system among a large number of similar systems in one assembly, we now have to look for the average condition of an assembly among a large number of similar assemblies. Instead of assuming each quantum state of a system to be a priori equally probable, we now assume that each quantum state of the assembly as a whole is a priori equally probable. Whereas in the earlier problem the large number of similar systems actually exists as the assembly of interest, here the large number of assemblies exists only in the imagination; the closest approach to such an "ensemble of Gibbs," as it is called, in reality is perhaps the totality of similar assemblies that happen to have been under observation in all the laboratories throughout the history of science. But actually we need a more specialized type of collection of assemblies than this accidental historical one, and we proceed to set up the following idealized ensemble of assemblies.

Let there be altogether **N** assemblies at rest relative to each other in a thermal bath at some definite temperature T. The assemblies are all copies of the assemblies of interest; they can exchange energy with each other via the thermal bath, but cannot influence each other's energy spectra. The assemblies are mutually distinct and distinguishable at all times, so that the statistics of Boltzmann type are exact in counting the complexions in any assigned distribution-in-energy. Let Ω_j be the number of assembly eigenfunctions associated with the energy E_j. Let a distribution-in-energy over the ensemble be specified by the numbers N_j of assemblies in the ensemble having the energy $E_j, j = 1, 2, \cdots$. The Boltzmann number of complexions corresponding to this distribution is

$$C = \mathbf{N}! \prod_j \Omega_j{}^{N_j}/N_j! \qquad (7.101)$$

We wish to maximize the logarithm of this number under the restrictions that the total number of assemblies **N** and their total energy in the ensemble **E** remain fixed. The variations in the numbers N_j satisfy the conditions:

$$\delta \mathbf{N} = \sum_j \delta N_j = 0 \qquad (7.102)$$

$$\delta \mathbf{E} = \sum_j \delta N_j E_j = 0 \qquad (7.103)$$

This problem is formally identical with that of an ideal gas, the assembly playing the same role as the atom. The most probable distribution is the exact analog of Eq. (2.314):

$$N_j = \mathbf{N}\Omega_j \exp\left(-\alpha - \beta E_j\right) \qquad (7.104)$$

where α is the Lagrangian multiplier for Eq. (7.102) and β that for Eq. (7.103). The physical interpretation of these parameters must await detailed discussion of the thermodynamic properties of the assembly.

The numbers N_j given by Eq. (7.104) are the most probable numbers in the ensemble of assemblies in the indicated energy levels. We then imagine an ensemble set up in this most probable distribution, take the average of all assemblies in this ensemble, and identify this average with the most probable behavior of the actual assembly under observation. The validity of this procedure depends on the ergodic hypothesis, in the sense that there must exist some mechanism whereby the one assembly under actual observation can spontaneously go through all the states that are consistent with the restrictions imposed on it—given **N** and **E**. A great deal of discussion exists in the literature regarding the truth of the ergodic hypothesis, but for the purpose of the present course, we shall simply assume that some logical justification will eventually be agreed upon by the philosophers, and for ourselves, adopt the somewhat crude but effective point of view that, as the procedure succeeds in getting the right results, it is acceptable until proved otherwise.

In line with the stated procedure we shall therefore accept $k \ln C$ as the entropy of the whole ensemble, divide this by **N** to get the average entropy of each assembly in the ensemble, and if the ensemble is in the distribution specified by Eq. (7.104), identify this average entropy with the actual entropy of the assembly under observation. This entropy is therefore

$$S = (1/\mathbf{N})k \ln (\mathbf{N}! \prod_j \Omega_j{}^{N_i}/N_j!) \tag{7.105}$$

Moreover, we shall define the temperature of the assembly by means of its thermodynamic relation with entropy

$$1/T = (\partial S/\partial E)_V \tag{7.106}$$

In this expression, E is the energy of the assembly, and this is the average energy of all assemblies in the ensemble in its most probable distribution; V is the volume of one assembly. The partial derivative is to be interpreted as a variation of the distribution-in-energy of the ensemble, causing a variation of the mean energy of the assemblies in the ensemble, without changing the energy spectrum E_j of possible assembly energies in the ensemble. Summing all equations like Eq. (7.104) over all j-values yields

$$\mathbf{N} = \mathbf{N}e^{-\alpha}\mathbf{Q} \tag{7.107}$$

where

$$\mathbf{Q} = \sum_j \Omega_j \exp (-\beta E_j) \tag{7.108}$$

The sum $\mathbf{Q}$ is called the assembly partition function from its exact analogy with the partition function of Eq. (4.102) of a system. Evidently from Eq. (7.107) we have

$$\alpha = \ln \mathbf{Q} \tag{7.109}$$

The average energy per assembly is given by dividing the total energy in the ensemble by $\mathbf{N}$:

$$E = (1/\mathbf{N}) \sum_j N_j E_j = (1/\mathbf{Q}) \sum_j \Omega_j E_j e^{-\beta E_i} \tag{7.110}$$

where we have made use of Eqs. (7.104) and (7.109). Clearly if we regard β as a variable while keeping the energy spectrum E_j constant, this result can be written in the form

$$E = -\partial \ln \mathbf{Q}/\partial\beta \tag{7.111}$$

Using the most probable distribution Eq. (7.104) in Eq. (7.105), the definition of entropy, and making use of the Stirling approximation on the logarithms of the factorials, it is easy to prove that

$$S = k(\ln \mathbf{Q} + \beta E) \tag{7.112}$$

Then the definition Eq. (7.106) of temperature yields

$$1/T = k\{(\partial \ln \mathbf{Q}/\partial\beta)(\partial\beta/\partial E) + E(\partial\beta/\partial E) + \beta\} \tag{7.113}$$

Because of Eq. (7.111), the first two terms in the bracket cancel, and we are left with the familiar relation again: $\beta = 1/kT$. The thermodynamic definition of the Helmholtz free energy of an assembly, $A = E - TS$, then yields, from Eq. (7.112):

$$A = -kT \ln \mathbf{Q} \tag{7.114}$$

Comparison with Eq. (7.109) thus identifies the parameter α:

$$\alpha = -A/kT \tag{7.115}$$

contrasting with Eq. (3.503) which gave α there as the Gibbs free energy. The two α's are of course different statistically as well as physically.

Having now found the Helmholtz free energy in terms of the assembly partition function, Eq. (7.114), we are in a position to find all the other thermodynamic variables in terms of the assembly partition function:

$$p = -(\partial A/\partial V)_T = kT(\partial \ln \mathbf{Q}/\partial V)_T \tag{7.116}$$

for the pressure of the most probable assembly, and

$$S = -(\partial A/\partial T)_V = k\{\ln \mathbf{Q} + (\partial \ln \mathbf{Q}/\partial \ln T)_V\} \tag{7.117}$$

for its entropy. From Eq. (7.111) it is easy to check that Eq. (7.117) is consistent with Eq. (7.112), and also to show that

$$E = kT^2(\partial \ln \mathbf{Q}/\partial T)_V = kT(\partial \ln \mathbf{Q}/\partial \ln T)_V \tag{7.118}$$

The whole problem therefore reduces itself to the evaluation of the partition function of the assembly in terms of T and V from the definition, Eq. (7.108), which reads

$$\mathbf{Q} = \sum_j \Omega_j \exp(-E_j/kT) \tag{7.119}$$

Before using this method to solve the problems for which it is designed, we shall first apply it to ideal gases and show that the assembly partition function formalism gives exactly the same results as the ordinary partition function method previously developed.

The wave function for an ideal gas separates into factors, each of which refers to a single particle; the energy of the gas is a sum over the individual energies of the particles. Each distribution-in-energy of the atoms in the gas determines the energy of the gas, so the energy levels of the gas as a whole are in one-to-one correspondence with the distribution-in-energy of the atoms:

$$E_j = \sum_r n_{rj}\epsilon_r \tag{7.120}$$

where n_{rj} means the number of particles in their rth level, ϵ_r, corresponding to their jth distribution-in-energy. The degeneracy weight Ω_j of the energy level E_j of the whole gas equals the number of complexions corresponding to the jth distribution-in-energy of the particles. This number was computed in our dis-

cussion of the Boltzmann statistics and corrected classically for indistinguishability of the particles [see Eq. (2.213)]:

$$\Omega_j = C_{\text{Boltz}}/N! = \sum_r \omega_r{}^{n_{ri}}/n_{rj}! \tag{7.121}$$

where ω_r is the degeneracy of the individual atomic states. Putting Eq. (7.120)
into Eq. (7.119) and using (7.121), we find for the assembly partition function,

$$\mathbf{Q} = \sum_j \prod_r (1/n_{rj}!)\{\omega_r \exp(-\epsilon_r/kT)\}^{n_{ri}} \tag{7.122}$$

To evaluate this, write

$$y_r = \omega_r \exp(-\epsilon_r/kT) \tag{7.123}$$

and expand $\sum_r y_r$ raised to the power N by the multinomial theorem:

$$\left\{\sum_r y_r\right\}^N = \sum_{\{n\}N} (N!/n_1!n_2!\cdots)y_1{}^{n_1}y_2{}^{n_2}\cdots \tag{7.124}$$

where the sum on the right is taken over all sets of numbers $\{n\}$ whose total
equals N: $\sum_r n_r = N$. If we now indicate each set of numbers by a subindex j,
the Eq. (7.124) can be written in the form:

$$\left\{\sum_r y_r\right\}^N = N! \sum_j \prod_r (1/n_{rj}!)y_r{}^{n_{ri}} \tag{7.125}$$

Comparing this with Eq. (7.122), we see at once that

$$\mathbf{Q} = (1/N!)\left\{\sum_r y_r\right\}^N \tag{7.126}$$

But the ordinary partition function of the particle is

$$Q = \sum_r \omega_r \exp(-\epsilon_r/kT) = \sum_r y_r \tag{7.127}$$

and therefore $\qquad\qquad \mathbf{Q} = Q^N/N! \tag{7.128}$

Taking the logarithm of this and applying Eq. (7.116) we find the pressure of
the assembly given by the assembly partition function formalism:

$$p = kT(\partial \ln \mathbf{Q}/\partial V)_T = NkT(\partial \ln Q/\partial V)_T$$

which is identical with the result of the ordinary partition function method in
Eq. (4.111). Also Eq. (7.114) with (7.128) gives $A = -NkT \ln Q + kT \ln N!$,
and because $F = A + pV = A + NkT$, this gives, after using Stirling's approximation, $F = NkT(\ln N - \ln Q)$, which is identical with the Gibbs free
energy given by the ordinary partition function method in Eq. (4.104). Because

all other thermodynamic variables can be derived from F, this completes the verification that the new method is consistent with the old where the latter is valid.

7.2 Debye's theory of the crystalline solid. In contrast to the Einstein theory of a crystal, developed in § 4.8, the Debye theory treats the entire crystal as a single member, or assembly, in an ensemble and forms the assembly partition function of the whole crystal. To do this, we first set up the classical Hamiltonian in the $3N$ co-ordinates and $3N$ momenta of the N atoms forming the crystal. This is theoretically possible if we know the lattice structure and interatomic forces. We may take as co-ordinates the (small) displacements of each atom from its equilibrium position or lattice point. In these co-ordinates the potential function has a minimum at the origin, and to a first approximation, its dependence on the displacements is purely quadratic:

$$H = \sum_{i=1}^{3N} \tfrac{1}{2}m\dot{x}_i{}^2 + \sum_{i=1}^{3N}\sum_{j=1}^{3N} \tfrac{1}{2}A_{ij}x_ix_j \qquad (7.201)$$

The nondiagonal terms in the matrix A_{ij} represent coupling terms, and the matrix itself represents a hyperellipsoid in $3N$ co-ordinate space. It is generally possible to find a linear transformation or rotation in this space such that in the new system of generalized co-ordinates, say q_i, the hyperellipsoid is referred to its principal axes and the matrix A is diagonalized. The corresponding rotation carried out in velocity space does not change the purely spherical form of the kinetic energy part of the Hamiltonian. If p_i are the generalized momenta corresponding to the new co-ordinates, the Hamiltonian reduces to the diagonal form:

$$H = \tfrac{1}{2} \sum_{i=1}^{3N} (p_i{}^2/m + 4\pi^2m\nu_i{}^2q_i{}^2) \qquad (7.202)$$

where the constants ν_i are the normal mode frequencies of the crystal. There are $3N$ such normal modes; they are not associated with individual atoms; each one involves motion of the entire crystal. Replacing p_i by the operator, $-i\hbar\partial/\partial q_i$, we obtain the Schrödinger equation for the whole crystal, $H\psi = E\psi$, in a form that is soluble by a function separable into factors, $\psi = \prod_i u_i(q_i)$. Each factor is a function of only one of the generalized variables and so refers to one of the normal modes of the crystal, and each is a solution of the Schrödinger equation for a linear oscillator with the corresponding normal mode frequency: $\{\hbar^2\partial^2/\partial q_i{}^2 + 2mE_i - (2\pi m\nu_iq_i)^2\}u_i(q_i) = 0$. The eigenvalues of the total energy are sums of the eigenvalues E_i of the normal modes, and these are, by Eq. (1.322), $E_i = (n_i + \tfrac{1}{2})h\nu_i$. The total energy is determined by the set of integers n_i:

$$E\{n\} = \sum_{i=1}^{3N} (n_i + \tfrac{1}{2})h\nu_i \qquad (7.203)$$

There is no degeneracy in the harmonic oscillator, so the partition function Eq. (7.119) is

$$Q = \sum_{\{n\}} \exp\left(-E\{n\}/kT\right) = \sum_{\{n\}} \prod_{i=1}^{3N} \exp\left\{-h\nu_i(n_i + \tfrac{1}{2})/kT\right\} \quad (7.204)$$

The fact that this summation extends over all conceivable sets of integers n_i, each set containing exactly $3N$ members, permits the product and sum operations to be interchanged, and in place of Eq. (7.204), we may write

$$Q = \prod_{i=1}^{3N} \sum_{n=0}^{\infty} \exp\left\{-h\nu_i(n + \tfrac{1}{2})/kT\right\} \quad (7.205)$$

This is the product of $3N$ infinite series, each of which is a simple geometric progression whose sum is well known:

$$Q = \prod_{i=1}^{3N} \left\{\exp\left(-\tfrac{1}{2}h\nu_i/kT\right)\right\}/\left\{1 - \exp\left(-h\nu_i/kT\right)\right\} \quad (7.206)$$

To make further progress, it is evidently necessary to know the entire spectrum of normal modes of the crystal, and as yet no feasible method has been devised to find this exactly.

To overcome this major difficulty, Debye suggested that the actual crystal be replaced by a simple model whose spectrum of normal modes could be easily calculated, and which imitates the actual crystal as closely as possible in its physical properties. Debye's model consists of a continuous elastic medium having the same density and the same elastic constants as the actual crystal. The normal modes of this model are well known, but one difficulty is that there is no upper limit to the frequency of vibrations in a continuous medium, the number of modes being infinite; whereas in the actual crystal of N atoms the number of modes is only $3N$. This number is of course extremely great, but it is not infinite and a definite upper limit must exist to their frequency. Debye suggested that we arbitrarily accept the $3N$ lowest frequencies in the spectrum of the continuous model, with the expectation that these will most closely imitate the true normal modes of the crystal. The success of this model in matching the observed thermodynamic behavior of actual crystals is its major justification.

To find the normal modes of the continuum we proceed as follows: Let the displacement of any element in the medium be expanded in a three-dimensional Fourier series:

$$\mathbf{u} = \sum_{k} A(\mathbf{k}) \sin\left(2\pi k_1 x\right) \sin\left(2\pi k_2 y\right) \sin\left(2\pi k_3 z\right)$$

where $\mathbf{u}$ is the displacement vector of the element originally located at (x,y,z), and where $A(\mathbf{k})$ is the vector amplitude of the mode characterized by the wavenumber vector $\mathbf{k} = (k_1, k_2, k_3)$. If the continuum is bounded by a cube of side

L, the boundary conditions applied to the Fourier series require that

$$k_j = n_j/2L, \quad j = 1, 2, 3. \tag{7.207}$$

where n_j are any three positive integers. The frequency of a mode is the velocity of propagation of the corresponding elastic wave multiplied by the wave number. In the actual crystal there are three modes of vibration to each wave number, two transverse and one longitudinal vibration. The continuum model must imitate the actual crystal in its elastic properties, so we must imagine it also to have the same three sets of modes, and the same velocities of propagation as in the actual crystal. Let c_l and c_t be the longitudinal and transverse wave velocities of propagation respectively, then the frequencies of vibration are

$$\left. \begin{aligned} \nu_l &= (c_l/2L)(n_1{}^2 + n_2{}^2 + n_3{}^2)^{\frac{1}{2}} \\ \nu_t &= (c_t/2L)(n_1{}^2 + n_2{}^2 + n_3{}^2)^{\frac{1}{2}} \end{aligned} \right\} \tag{7.208}$$

and there are two modes for each possible value of ν_t, one for each ν_l. The number of longitudinal modes having frequencies between ν and $\nu + d\nu$ is equal to the number of n-vectors satisfying the inequality:

$$2L\nu/c_l \leq (n_1{}^2 + n_2{}^2 + n_3{}^2)^{\frac{1}{2}} \leq 2L(\nu + d\nu)/c_l$$

This number is equal to the number of unit points, or to the volume in n-space, within an octant of the spherical shell lying between the radii, $R = 2L\nu/c_l$ and $R + dR = 2L(\nu + d\nu)/c_l$, which is

$$N_l(\nu)d\nu = \tfrac{1}{2}\pi R^2 dR = 4\pi(L/c_l)^3\nu^2 d\nu \tag{7.209}$$

The same form of result holds good for the transverse modes, with c_t replacing c_l, and there are twice as many. Thus altogether the number of modes whose frequencies lie between ν and $\nu + d\nu$ is

$$N(\nu)d\nu = 4\pi V(2/c_t{}^3 + 1/c_l{}^3)\nu^2 d\nu \tag{7.210}$$

where $V = L^3$ is the volume of the crystal. As already discussed, we arbitrarily select only the $3N$ lowest frequency modes to compute the partition function. The maximum frequency ν_m is given by

$$3N = \int_0^{\nu_m} N(\nu)d\nu = (4\pi/3)(2/c_t{}^3 + 1/c_l{}^3)\nu_m{}^3 V \tag{7.211}$$

This permits Eq. (7.210) to be written in terms of ν_m:

$$N(\nu)d\nu = 9N\nu^2 d\nu/\nu_m{}^3 \tag{7.212}$$

a result that will enable us to evaluate the logarithm of the partition function as an integral instead of a discrete sum.

From Eq. (7.206) we have

$$\ln Q = \sum_{i=1}^{3N} \{ -\tfrac{1}{2}h\nu_i/kT - \ln[1 - \exp(-h\nu_i/kT)] \}$$

and Eq. (7.118) then gives

$$E = \sum_{i=1}^{3N} \{\tfrac{1}{2}h\nu_i + h\nu_i/[\exp{(h\nu_i/kT)} - 1]\}$$

Replacing this sum by an integral, by using the density Eq. (7.212), we have

$$E = (9N/\nu_m{}^3) \int_0^{\nu_m} \{\tfrac{1}{2}h\nu + h\nu/[\exp{(h\nu/kT)} - 1]\}\nu^2 d\nu \qquad (7.213)$$

which may be written in the form

$$E = \tfrac{9}{8}Nh\nu_m + 3NkTD(\theta/T) \qquad (7.214)$$

$$\theta = h\nu_m/k \qquad (7.215)$$

$$D(\theta/T) = 3(T/\theta)^3 \int_0^{\theta/T} [x^3/(e^x - 1)]dx \qquad (7.216)$$

where θ is called the Debye characteristic temperature, and $D(\theta/T)$ is the Debye function. Values of this function have been tabulated, so that it is easy to read off the value of E as a function of the ratio T/θ. If instead we take the temperature derivative of E, we find the heat capacity:

$$C_v = 3Nk\{4D(\theta/T) - 3(\theta/T)/(e^{\theta/T} - 1)\} \qquad (7.217)$$

When $T \gg \theta$ this goes over into the classical limit $C_v = 3Nk$, while at very low temperatures it can be shown that Eq. (7.217) becomes

$$T \ll \theta: \qquad C_v = 3Nk\{(4\pi^4/5)(T/\theta)^3 + \text{smaller terms}\} \qquad (7.218)$$

This low-temperature result, that the heat capacity is proportional to T^3, is one of the major successes of the Debye theory, because it has been very well borne out by experiment.

According to Eq. (7.217) the heat capacity depends only on one physical parameter, the Debye characteristic temperature. All solids to which the Debye theory applies should therefore have heat capacity curves of the same shape when plotted on the appropriate temperature scale, T/θ. The value of θ for any particular solid can indeed be determined by making the best fit between the experimental heat capacity curve and the theoretical curve of Eq. (7.217). Alternatively the value of θ can be determined from the elastic constants of the material. Agreement between the two methods of determining θ is fairly good in those cases where a good fit with the heat capacity curve can be obtained, but there are many minor and some major exceptions that can be understood only in terms of deviations of the normal mode spectrum from that of the Debye continuum model. Most modern work on this subject is concerned with these deviations.

On the basis of the Debye model it is possible to proceed from the partition function to the free energy and the pressure. For this pressure to be identified with the exterior (atmospheric) pressure, the energy assessment made in the Debye model—that of the vibrational modes—must be supplemented to include the cohesive energy of the crystal. To the energy in Eq. (7.203), we must add a term $-NU$ to represent the energy when the atoms are all at rest, and to ln Q, we must add a term NU/kT. The cohesive energy of the crystal is highly sensitive to changes in density or volume, but under ordinary conditions it is a minimum at the natural density of the crystal. Thermal expansion changes the volume slightly, but the cohesive energy is assumed to make only negligible contributions to the heat capacity. Also it is not customary to think of the crystal as having different states of cohesion, so that no entropy is associated with it. The Debye model is, however, quite powerless to predict the equation of state —pressure, volume, temperature relation—because neither U nor its volume derivative is given by the Debye model.

7.3   The Born–von Karman theory of crystalline solid. Max Born and Theodore von Karman obtained a low temperature T^3 law for the heat capacity of a crystal almost simultaneously with the publication of the Debye theory. While the Debye model was admittedly idealistic, the Born–von Karman theory involved much more laborious computation; and since the two theories gave superficially the same results, Debye's naturally became the more popular as stimulus for further study. Improved experimental techniques have now produced so many data inconsistent with the Debye model that increased attention has lately been paid to the more realistic theory of Born and von Karman. We cannot spare space for a complete account of this theory but will give a brief outline designed to emphasize the main principles involved.

The statistical basis of the theory is exactly the same as that of the Debye theory, Eq. (7.206), for the crystal partition function. To find the approximate distribution-in-frequency of the normal modes of the crystal in as realistic a fashion as possible, it is assumed that any one atom in the lattice is acted on only by forces from its nearest neighbors and its next nearest neighbors. The calculations have to be tailored to the particular kind of lattice, e.g., body-centered cubic, face-centered cubic, etc. In the body-centered cubic lattice an atom at the (l,m,n) lattice point is acted on by Hooke's-law-type forces proportional to the relative displacements between the atom and its nearest neighbors, eight in number, $\alpha[r(l,m,n) - r(l\pm\frac{1}{2},m\pm\frac{1}{2},n\pm\frac{1}{2})]$, and also by forces proportional to the relative displacements between it and its six next nearest neighbors, $\gamma[r(l,m,n) - r(l\pm 1,m,n)]$, etc. The two parameters α and γ have to be adjusted to individual cases. The classical equations of motion can be written down for any lattice point (l,m,n). Since each atom has three degrees of freedom, there are three such equations for each atom, and we seek solutions of them in the form of three wave motions with wave numbers given by points in the reciprocal lattice space. Substitution of these solutions into the equations of motion for any choice of (l,m,n) yields a condition for the possible frequencies of the wave motion (independent of l, m, and n) in the form of a three-by-three determinant equated to zero—this is the secular equation of the problem. The three solutions of the secular equation represent the three types of wave motion ordinarily associated with longitudinal and two transverse polarized waves; in general, none of the three is completely polarized. In spite of this complication, one can derive the number of different frequencies possible in any given frequency range from the secular equations, either by direct numerical and graphical means, or analytically in the form of a series expansion:

$$N(\nu)d\nu = d\nu(K_0\nu^2 + K_1\nu^4 + \cdots) \tag{7.301}$$

where the K's are somewhat complicated expressions involving the two Hooke's law parameters α and γ. This is the Born–von Karman expression to replace the Debye expression (7.210); it is valid at low temperatures only, because the Hooke's law of interaction between nearest neighbors can be valid only for relatively small displacements. Anharmonic terms would undoubtedly perturb the problem at higher temperatures.

Using Eq. (7.301) and the method of § 7.2 for the heat capacity, one finds

$$C_v = Nk[K_0(kT/h)^3B(0) + K_1(kT/h)^5B(1) + \cdots] \tag{7.302}$$

where

$$B(n) = \int_0^\infty \frac{x^{2n+5}e^x dx}{(e^x - 1)^2}, \quad x = h\nu/kT \tag{7.303}$$

The integral is taken over the entire spectrum, and the upper limit is allowed to go to infinity because at low T there is practically no contribution to the integrand from large values of the variable. Comparing this result with the Debye form, Eq. (7.218), at low temperatures, it is possible to find an "effective Debye θ" as a function of temperature. Thus

$$1/\theta^3 = (5/12\pi^4)[(k/h)^3K_0B(0) + T^2(k/h)^5K_1B(1) + \cdots] \tag{7.304}$$

More complete numerical results can be obtained by a graphical examination of the spectral density function. Figures 7.31 and 7.32 show such results ob-

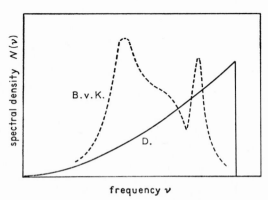

FIG. 7.31. Acoustical spectral density in body-centered cubic lattice, Born–von Karman and Debye models. Arbitrary units.

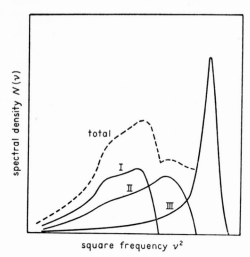

FIG. 7.32. Spectral distribution in a face-centered lattice. The units are arbitrary. Dotted curve shows the total number of modes, curves I and II, the transverse modes, and curve III, the longitudinal ones.

tained for a body-centered cubic crystal * and for face-centered cubic crystal.† Figure 7.33 shows the effective Debye θ curves appropriate to face-centered lattices with different values of γ. Figure 7.34 shows a comparison with the observed effective Debye θ in silver; it is clearly a great improvement over the straight Debye theory, although the hump below 10 °K remains unexplained by the theory.

The theory is completed by a detailed discussion of the observable elastic constants in terms of the Hooke's law parameters α and γ. Then from the data on the elastic constants obtained from the velocity of sound measurements, one can compute α and γ and so in principle predict the heat capacity curve, or, more conveniently, the effective Debye θ. In working on such a program, it is to be noted that there are three distinct elastic constants in the classical theory of elasticity, usually written c_{11}, c_{12}, c_{44}, so that the two Hooke's law constants α and γ result in elastic constants with one identity between them, viz., $c_{12} = c_{44}$, called the Cauchy relation. In actual metal crystals, the elastic constants do not satisfy this identity; the discrepancy involved may result in several per cent alteration in the effective Debye θ. This failure of the Cauchy relation has been

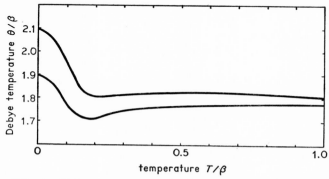

FIG. 7.33. Effective Debye temperature for face-centered cubic lattice. The unit of temperature is $\beta = (\hbar/k)\sqrt{2\alpha/m}$.

* P. C. Fine, *Phys. Rev.*, **56** (1939), p. 355.
† R. B. Leighton, *Revs. Modern Phys.*, **20** (1948), p. 165.

attributed to either of two causes: one is due to the effect of the conduction electrons on the elastic constants, and the other, to a volume dependence of the zero point energy of the Debye modes. Evidently both these effects must be taken

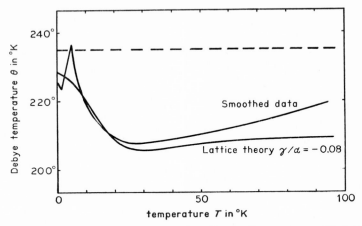

Fig. 7.34. Effective Debye temperature for silver. Comparison with lattice theory assuming $\gamma/\alpha = -0.08$.

fully into account before we can expect the Born–von Karman theory to give exact predictions.

7.4 Theory of imperfect gases. In this section we give the quasi-classical theory of imperfect gases, analogous to the classical theory of an ideal gas given in § 4.2. To this end we recall the general expression for the assembly partition function of Eq. (7.119):

$$Q = \sum_j \Omega_i \exp\left(-E_j/kT\right) \tag{7.401}$$

and proceed to write this sum in the form of an integral over the $6N$-dimensional phase space of the gas. A single element or cell in this phase space may be written as

$$d\tau = dq_1 dq_2 \cdots dq_{3N} dp_1 dp_2 \cdots dp_{3N} \tag{7.402}$$

The number of quantum states corresponding to this element is $h^{-3N} d\tau$. The energy of the whole gas is

$$E(\mathbf{p,q}) = \sum p_j^2/2m + U(\mathbf{q}) \tag{7.403}$$

where $U(\mathbf{q})$ is the whole potential energy of interaction, a function of all the q-variables, and the sum is over all the $3N$ degrees of freedom of the kinetic energy. Instead of the sum over discrete states, the partition function now becomes an integral over all the cells in phase space:

$$Q = (1/N!)h^{-3N} \int \cdots \int e^{-E(\mathbf{p},\mathbf{q})/kT} dq_1 \cdots dp_{3N} \qquad (7.404)$$

The integral includes all permutations among the particles of the gas and the factor $N!$ has to be removed to correct for this—like the classical correction for indistinguishability of the atoms. The momentum variables separate and the integrals over them can be carried out exactly as in Eq. (4.217), yielding

$$Q = (2\pi mkT/h^2)^{3N/2} Q(\mathbf{q})/N! \qquad (7.405)$$

where

$$Q(\mathbf{q}) = \int \cdots \int e^{-U(\mathbf{q})/kT} dq_1 \cdots dq_{3N} \qquad (7.406)$$

Evidently the evaluation of this integral is the crux of the problem.

We assume that the potential energy $U(\mathbf{q})$ is due only to central forces between pairs of atoms. Write $u(r_{ij})$ for the potential energy due to interaction between the ith and the jth particles, whose relative position vector is r_{ij}. The total potential energy is then expressible in the form:

$$U(\mathbf{q}) = \sum_{i>j}^{N-1} \sum_{j=1} u(r_{ij}) \qquad (7.407)$$

The summation takes i and j over all pairs just once, and so contains $\frac{1}{2}N(N-1)$ terms. Also we can write

$$e^{-U(\mathbf{q})/kT} = \prod_{N \geq i > j \geq 1} \prod e^{-u(r_{ij})/kT} \qquad (7.408)$$

A first approximation to the integral can be made by using a device due to Ursell. We write

$$f_{ij} = e^{-u(r_{ij})/kT} - 1 \qquad (7.409)$$

This function of r_{ij} vanishes if the interaction potential is zero and remains small so long as $u(r_{ij}) \ll kT$. In terms of f_{ij}, the right side of Eq. (7.408) becomes

$$\prod (1 + f_{ij}) = 1 + \sum_{N \geq i > j \geq 1} \sum f_{ij} + \sum_{i>j} \sum_{i'>j'} f_{ij} f_{i'j'} + \cdots \qquad (7.410)$$

and this replaces the integrand of Eq. (7.406):

$$Q(\mathbf{q}) = \int \cdots \int \{1 + \sum_{N \geq i > j \geq 1} \sum f_{ij} + \text{products of } f\text{'s}\} dq_1 \cdots dq_{3N} \qquad (7.411)$$

Integrating this over the whole of co-ordinate space, the co-ordinates of every particle are taken over the whole volume V, and for any particular pair of particles appearing in the subscripts of f_{ij}, there exists a region in space where the two particles are so close together that f_{ij} is large and positive due to mutual repulsion—and that is where the particles i and j are very close together. However, it is assumed in the Ursell approximation that these regions of phase space are so small in extent that they make a negligible contribution to the integral as a whole. The integrals of f_{ij} are then all small, and we may neglect the integrals over products of two or more f factors. Because every pair is equivalent in that they all have the same interaction potential, and because the integrations take them over the entire co-ordinate space, the integral (7.411) becomes

$$Q(\mathbf{q}) = \int \cdots \int \{1 + \tfrac{1}{2}N(N-1)f_{ij}\}dq_1 \cdots dq_{3N} \tag{7.412}$$

where the factor $\tfrac{1}{2}N(N-1)$ represents the number of pairs, and i, j are any arbitrarily chosen pair. Integration of the unity gives V for every particle, and there are $3(N-2)$ co-ordinates among the q's that have nothing to do with the pair i and j; hence the integration over these yields a factor V to the power $N-2$:

$$Q(\mathbf{q}) = V^N + \tfrac{1}{2}N(N-1)V^{N-2}\int \cdots \int f_{ij}dq_1 \cdots dq_6 \tag{7.413}$$

where $q_1 \cdots q_6$ represent the co-ordinates of the ith and jth particles. The function f_{ij} is a function only of the distance between the two particles; we may therefore write it here as $f(r)$, and the sixfold integral element can be expressed as a product of the volume element $4\pi r^2 dr$ and the volume element of co-ordinates referred to the position of one of the particles. We can think of the integration taking the pair as a whole over the whole volume while keeping r fixed, and later taking r over its whole range of possible values. The first part of this procedure integrates to give a factor V, because the integrand is not changed while r remains fixed; hence we can write

$$Q(\mathbf{q}) = V^N + \tfrac{1}{2}N(N-1)V^{N-1}\int_0^\infty 4\pi r^2 f(r)dr \tag{7.414}$$

Write for convenience,

$$b_2 = 2\pi \int_0^\infty r^2 f(r)dr \tag{7.415}$$

then because $N \gg 1$, we have

$$Q(\mathbf{q}) = V^N(1 + N^2 b_2/V) \tag{7.416}$$

Taking the logarithm and expanding this in series, and retaining only the first two terms, we find

$$\ln Q(\mathbf{q}) = N \ln V + N^2 b_2/V + \cdots \tag{7.417}$$

By using Eqs. (7.116) and (7.405) we obtain from this the equation of state, remembering that in the present approximation b_2 is independent of V:

$$pV = NkT(1 - Nb_2/V + \cdots) \tag{7.418}$$

If we neglect squares or higher powers of (Nb_2/V), and if b_2 were to depend on T through Eqs. (7.415) and (7.409) in such a way that

$$Nb_2 = -b + a/NkT \qquad (7.420)$$

where a and b are constants, then Eq. (7.418) would reduce to the familiar van der Waals form:

$$(p + a/V^2)(V - b) = NkT \qquad (7.421)$$

Empirically the equation of state of an imperfect gas is usually expressed in the form Eq. (6.502) as a power series in $1/V$, of which Eq. (7.418) contains only the first two terms, or the first two virial coefficients. The experimental data on the virial coefficients as functions of T are both extensive and highly precise and so provide a very sensitive method of checking theoretical values of b_2, and through Eq. (7.415), of theoretical force functions $f(r)$. The most successful form of interaction potential is that which was first suggested by Lennard-Jones:

$$u(r) = A/r^{12} - B/r^6 \qquad (7.422)$$

where A and B vary from one gas to another. To a very rough approximation, this potential does yield an integral like (7.420), but of course its usefulness extends to a far higher precision than the van der Waals equation.

A useful form of the Lennard-Jones potential is

$$u(r) = \epsilon_0\{(r_0/r)^{12} - 2(r_0/r)^6\} \qquad (7.423)$$

where r_0 is the radius at which the potential has its minimum ϵ_0. Lennard-Jones computed a universal curve, shown in Figure 7.41, applicable to all gases for which this potential form holds. The ordinate is $\ln(3B_2/2\pi D^3)$, where B_2

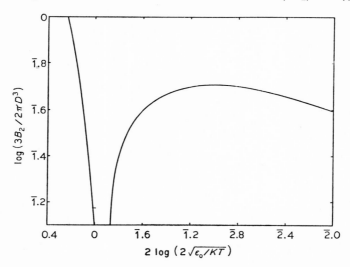

FIG. 7.41.   Universal curve of Lennard-Jones for second virial coefficient.

is the second virial coefficient, $B_2 = -Nb_2$ [see Eq. (6.502)], and $D = r_0/2^{1/6}$; the abscissa is $2 \ln (2\sqrt{\epsilon_0/kT})$. If one takes a sphere of radius $r_0/2^{1/2}$ as unit volume, and ϵ_0/k as unit temperature, all the curves of B_2 versus temperature should coincide. In practice, values of the parameters r_0 and ϵ_0 have to be adjusted to give the best fit between experiment and the Lennard-Jones curve. The general agreement is excellent for gases with spherically symmetrical mole-

LENNARD-JONES PARAMETERS

Gas	r_0 in Angstroms	ϵ_0/k in °K
Helium	2.87	10.22
Neon	3.08	35.7
Argon	3.85	120.0

cules—particularly, monatomic—and even for diatomic molecules at the higher temperatures, it is satisfactory. In the latter cases, where the force constants ought to be functions of relative orientation, the best fit presumably gives the average force constants over all directions. Other physical properties depend on the second virial coefficient, heat capacity, velocity of sound, Joule-Thomson coefficient, etc., and may be employed as independent checks. Insofar as the Lennard-Jones universal curve is applicable, all these properties ought to be the same for all gases when plotted against the appropriate temperature and volume scales; this is the "law of corresponding states" originally deduced from the van der Waals equation and expressed in terms of critical point values of p, V, and T.

In recent years the following interaction potential, called the "exp-six" law, has been preferred over the 12-6 law of Lennard-Jones, chiefly because it has some basis in quantum mechanical theory:

$$u(r) = \frac{\epsilon_0}{1 - 6/\alpha} \left\{ \frac{6}{\alpha} \exp\left[\alpha\left(1 - \frac{r}{r_0}\right)\right] - \left(\frac{r_0}{r}\right)^6 \right\} \qquad (7.424)$$

Here again r_0 is the radius at which the potential has its minimum ϵ_0, and is a parameter determining the steepness of the repulsive field. The curve has the form shown qualitatively in the accompanying Figure (7.42). The greater α, the steeper or "harder" the potential barrier.

PARAMETERS FOR THE EXP-SIX LAW

Gas	r_0 in Angstroms	ϵ_0/k in °K	α
Helium	3.135	9.16	12.4
Hydrogen	3.337	37.3	14.0

Figures 7.43 and 7.44 show a comparison between the data on second virial coefficient and on viscosity in helium gas, compared both with the Lennard-Jones

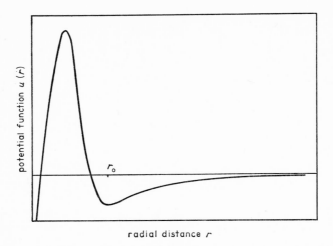

Fig. 7.42. Sketch of exp-six potential function. Arbitrary units.

and the exp-six law; * the exp-six law is clearly superior in correlating the several phenomena. It has another advantage: insofar as the values of α differ somewhat in different gases, we can understand small deviations from the law of corresponding states.

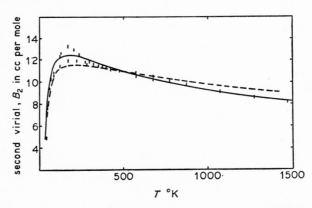

Fig. 7.43. Second virial coefficient of helium. Solid line: calculated from exp-six potential. Broken line; calculated from Lennard-Jones potential, 12-6. Dots: experimental values.

A detailed discussion of the kinetic properties and their relation to the second virial coefficient would take us too far afield; we discuss briefly the heat capacity of an imperfect gas. The energy is given by Eqs. (7.118) and (7.405) for the partition function; if the work is taken only as far as the second virial coefficient,

* E. A. Mason and W. E. Rice, *J. Chem. Phys.*, **22** (1954), p. 522.

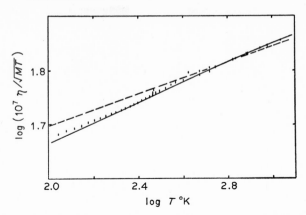

FIG. 7.44.   Viscosity of gaseous helium.   Solid line: calculated from exp-six potential. Broken line: calculated from Lennard-Jones potential, 12-6.   Dots: experimental values.

Eq. (7.416) can be used for $Q(\mathbf{q})$, B_2 being written for $-Nb_2$, the second virial coefficient, and we find

$$E = \tfrac{3}{2}NkT - NkT^2\partial \ln B_2/\partial T \qquad (7.425)$$

so the heat capacity at constant volume is

$$C_v = 3Nk/2 - 2NkTd \ln B_2/dT - NkT^2d^2 \ln B_2/dT^2 \qquad (7.426)$$

To find the heat capacity C_p at constant pressure, we first find the enthalpy, $H = E + pV$, and use Eq. (7.425) and Eq. (7.419):

$$H = \tfrac{5}{2}NkT - NkT^2d \ln B_2/dT + NkTB_2/V \qquad (7.427)$$

From the equation of state we have approximately

$$T(\partial V/\partial T)_p = V - B_2$$

and therefore from $C_p = (\partial H/\partial T)_p$, we find

$$C_p = C_v + Nk(1 + B_2{}^2/V^2) \qquad (7.428)$$

The ratio of the two specific heats enters the theoretical expression for the velocity of propagation of sound in the gas:

$$v = -(1/\rho)V(\partial p/\partial V)_T(C_p/C_v) \qquad (7.429)$$

The elasticity factor $(\partial p/\partial V)_T$ is obtained from the equation of state, and the ratio of the heat capacities from Eqs. (7.428) and (7.426); ρ is the density of the gas.   When this method is used with diatomic gases, sound waves of very high frequency sometimes deviate, the reason being that the period of the wave is too short to allow the dissociative equilibrium to adjust itself and follow the temperature variations in the wave.   This leads to dispersion and absorption of sound in the gas, and to an estimate of the relaxation time for dissociative equilibrium. It is interesting to speculate whether the dissociative cluster theory of the virial coefficients should not lead to a similar effect at high frequencies, specially in those gases where the second virial coefficient is somewhat sensitive to temperature. In view of the small concentrations of binary clusters calculated in § 6.5, it is rather doubtful whether the effect would be large enough to be readily observed.

7.5 Mayer's theory of the higher virial coefficients. A much more exact treatment of the integral of Eq. (7.411) over co-ordinate space is due to Joseph E. Mayer and leads to a proof that pair interaction can cause condensation of the gas into a denser state of aggregation. In this treatment we observe first that the product,

$$\prod_{N \geq i > j \geq 1} \prod (1 + f_{ij})$$

consists of $\frac{1}{2}N(N-1)$ factors, one factor for each conceivable pair of particles:

$$(1 + f_{21})(1 + f_{31})(1 + f_{32})(1 + f_{41}) \cdots (1 + f_{N, N-1}) \qquad (7.501)$$

In multiplying out this expression, we obtain a sum of products, each of which contains an arbitrary selection of f-terms; for example, one such product is

$$f_{31}f_{41}f_{52}f_{62}f_{65}f_{71}f_{73}f_{74}f_{9t}f_{98} \qquad (7.502)$$

This is a comparatively simple product containing only ten f-terms; the missing f-terms are absent because we multiplied by the unit terms instead in (7.501). Before integrating such a product as (7.502) over $3N$ co-ordinate space, as needed to evaluate $Q(\mathbf{q})$, we first group together those terms that are linked through their subscripts, $f_{31}f_{41}f_{74}f_{73}f_{71}$, $f_{52}f_{62}f_{65}$, and $f_{9t}f_{98}$, making sure that the groups are complete and mutually exclusive. Such a group is called a "cluster integrand." When the integration is carried out, the variables that do not appear in the group contribute a factor V for each absent subscript, while the integration over the particles that are present in the group contributes a result that depends only on the bonding pattern in the cluster, and not on the particular particles involved in the cluster. Let

$$I(\nu,\beta) = \int \cdots \int \prod_{(\nu,\beta)} f_{ij} \overset{3\nu}{\Pi} dq \qquad (7.503)$$

be the integral over a cluster integrand in which there are ν particles linked together in a specific bonding pattern indicated by β; the integration is carried out over only the 3ν co-ordinates of the ν particles in the cluster. In particular $I(1,\beta)$ means the cluster integral where only one particle is in the cluster; this can be thought of as a cluster in which only a unity (no f-term) is present in the integrand, and therefore we shall have

$$I(1,\beta) = V \qquad (7.504)$$

where of course the bonding pattern index β is superfluous. The integral $I(2,\beta)$

is just twice Vb_2 in Eq. (7.415), and again the bonding index is redundant. In general the expressions like Eq. (7.502) can be characterized by numbers $m_{\nu\beta}$ of clusters of ν particles with the β type bonding, a number $m_{\nu\beta}$ for each pair of values of ν and β present in the expression. The set of numbers $m_{\nu\beta}$ in the product is called the cluster pattern of the product, and m_1 is the number of unclustered particles not present in the expression. Integration of such a product yields

$$\prod_\beta \prod_\nu I(\nu,\beta)^{m_{\nu\beta}} \tag{7.505}$$

because the integral $I(\nu,\beta)$ depends only on ν and β, not on which particles are present.

The expression (7.501) includes $2^{\frac{1}{2}N(N-1)}$ products like (7.502). A definite number of them have the same cluster pattern, having the same set of numbers $m_{\nu\beta}$, but with different particles represented in the clusters. The number of such similar products equals the number of ways one can select from among N particles, $m_{\nu\beta}$ clusters of ν unspecified particles, multiplied by the number of ways a given bonding pattern β can be drawn in a cluster of ν specified particles. The number of ways we can form $m_{\nu\beta}$ clusters of ν particles is

$$N! \prod_\nu \prod_\beta \{(\nu!)^{m_{\nu\beta}} m_{\nu\beta}!\}^{-1} \tag{7.506}$$

The number of ways a given bonding pattern can occur among specified particles need not be calculated for the present; we may write it as $c(\nu,\beta)$. The contribution of the given bonding pattern to Eq. (7.501) occurs $\prod_\nu \prod_\beta \{c(\nu,\beta)\}^{m_{\nu\beta}}$ times. The complete integral of Eq. (7.501) now becomes

$$Q(\mathbf{q}) = N! \sum_{\{m\}N} \prod_\nu \prod_\beta \{c(\nu,\beta)\}^{m_{\nu\beta}} \{(\nu!)^{m_{\nu\beta}} m_{\nu\beta}!\}^{-1} \{I(\nu,\beta)\}^{m_{\nu\beta}} \tag{7.507}$$

where the sum is taken over all possible sets of numbers $m_{\nu\beta}$, such that all the particles in the assembly are included:

$$N = \sum_\nu \sum_\beta \nu m_{\nu\beta} \tag{7.508}$$

Here we have to understand by $m_{1\beta}$ again the number of particles not included in clusters. In order to rearrange the sums and products in Eq. (7.507), we write

$$I(\nu) = (1/\nu!) \sum_\beta c(\nu,\beta) I(\nu,\beta)$$

$$= (1/\nu!) \int \cdots \int \sum_\beta c(\nu,\beta) \left(\prod f_{ij}\right)^{3\nu} \prod dq \tag{7.509}$$

where the product over the f-terms is for one particular cluster pattern, ν,β. This expression sums $I(\nu,\beta)$ over all bonding patterns possible in the clusters of specified particles. If this equation is raised to the power m_ν, where

$$m_\nu = \sum_\beta m_{\nu\beta} \tag{7.510}$$

using the multinomial theorem, we find

$$\{I(\nu)\}^{m_\nu} = m_\nu! \sum_{\{m_{\nu\beta}\}} \prod_\beta (1/m_{\nu\beta}!) \{c(\nu,\beta) I(\nu,\beta)/\nu!\}^{m_{\nu\beta}} \tag{7.511}$$

where the sum is over all $m_{\nu\beta}$ satisfying Eq. (7.510) for a given m_ν. Therefore we can write Eq. (7.507) in the form:

$$Q(\mathbf{q}) = N! \sum_{\{m_\nu\}N} \prod_\nu (1/m_\nu!) \{I(\nu)\}^{m_\nu} \tag{7.512}$$

This follows because of the equivalence of the two operations

$$\sum_{\{m_{\nu\beta}\}N} = \sum_{\{m_\nu\}N} \sum_{\{m_{\nu\beta}\}m_\nu} \tag{7.513}$$

In the summation of Eq. (7.512) the numbers m_ν are restricted only by the relation

$$N = \sum_\nu \nu m_\nu \tag{7.514}$$

equivalent to Eqs. (7.508) and (7.510). The numbers m_ν are the numbers of clusters of size ν, and the summation in Eq. (7.512) is over all possible sets of numbers m_ν, each set containing all values of ν. Any one set of numbers m_ν characterizes a cluster pattern. Each possible cluster pattern contributes an additive term to $Q(\mathbf{q})$ in Eq. (7.512). It can be proved that when N is very large the logarithm of $Q(\mathbf{q})$ is practically equal to the logarithm of the maximum additive term in $Q(\mathbf{q})$. As the thermodynamic properties of the assembly are all derivable from $\ln Q(\mathbf{q})$ rather than $Q(\mathbf{q})$ itself, the cluster pattern that gives the maximum additive term contributed to $Q(\mathbf{q})$ is the physically significant one.

To find the most probable cluster pattern we evidently have to maximize the logarithm of the typical term in the sum of Eq. (7.512):

$$\ln \left[\prod_\nu \{I(\nu)\}^{m_\nu}/m_\nu! \right] = \sum_\nu \{m_\nu \ln I(\nu) - \ln m_\nu!\} \tag{7.515}$$

by varying the numbers m_ν under the restriction (7.514). Multiplying the variation of Eq. (7.514) by a Lagrangian multiplier γ, subtracting from the variation of (7.515), and equating the result to zero, we have

$$0 = \sum_\nu \{\ln I(\nu) - \ln m_\nu - \gamma\nu\} \delta m_\nu \tag{7.516}$$

Because the variations are now independent, this solves for every ν:

$$m_\nu = e^{-\gamma\nu} I(\nu) \tag{7.517}$$

Equating $Q(\mathbf{q})$ to its most probable term inside the logarithm, given by Eq. (7.517), we then have

$$\ln \{Q(\mathbf{q})/N!\} = \sum_\nu m_\nu \{\ln I(\nu) - \ln m_\nu + 1\}$$

$$= \sum_\nu m_\nu \{\ln I(\nu) + \gamma\nu - \ln I(\nu) + 1\}$$

and therefore

$$\ln \{Q(\mathbf{q})/N!\} = \gamma N + \sum_\nu I(\nu)e^{-\gamma\nu} \tag{7.518}$$

where in the last step we have again used Eq. (7.514). The parameter γ is determined by Eq. (7.514):

$$N = \sum_\nu \nu I(\nu)e^{-\gamma\nu} \tag{7.519}$$

Given the potential function, we can in principle solve this for γ, and then Eq. (7.518) gives the assembly partition function from which we can obtain the equation of state of the gas.

If the gas were ideal and the potential function zero, the integrals $I(\nu)$ would all vanish except $I(1)$, which remains equal to V. In this case Eq. (7.519) yields $e^{-\gamma} = N/V$ and the partition function becomes, from Eq. (7.518): $\ln Q(\mathbf{q})/N! = -N \ln (N/V) + N$, or $\ln Q(\mathbf{q}) = N \ln V$, and therefore $Q(\mathbf{q}) = V^N$. This is identical with the ideal gas expression obtained before and of course leads to the same equation of state from Eq. (7.405).

Successively better approximations for nonideal gases can be derived, but the computations of the integrals $I(\nu)$ become progressively more laborious. Formally, we can proceed as follows. Assume the range of interatomic forces to be small compared with the volume of the enclosure, then all the integrals $I(\nu)$ are proportional to V, and we can write

$$I(\nu) = Vb_\nu \tag{7.520}$$

and if for convenience

$$\theta = e^{-\gamma} \tag{7.521}$$

Eq. (7.519) becomes

$$N/V = \sum_\nu \nu\theta^\nu b_\nu \tag{7.522}$$

This indicates that we can express θ as a power series in N/V for the solution of Eq. (7.522). Indeed this can be done in closed form, but for the purposes of the present discussion we shall be satisfied with the computation of the first few terms in the series. To do this we assume the result to have the desired form, viz.:

$$\theta = (N/V)\{A_0 + A_1(N/V) + A_2(N/V)^2 + \cdots\} \tag{7.523}$$

Substitute this form into Eq. (7.522) and equate coefficients of powers of (N/V) in the standard fashion, obtaining

$$A_0 = 1/b_1 = 1, \quad A_1 = -2b_2, \quad A_2 = -3b_3 + 8b_2{}^2, \quad \text{etc.} \tag{7.524}$$

Eq. (7.518) can be written in the form

$$\ln \{Q(\mathbf{q})/N!\}^{1/N} = -\ln \theta + \sum_\nu (V/N)b_\nu \theta^\nu \qquad (7.525)$$

and if we use the above equation for θ in this, we find

$$(1/N)\ln \{Q(\mathbf{q})/N!\} = \ln (V/N) + 1 + b_2(N/V) + (b_3 - 2b_2{}^2)(N/V)^2 + \cdots$$

$$(7.526)$$

The equation of state is then given by this in the same way as we found Eq. (7.419): $p = kT\{\partial \ln Q(\mathbf{q})/\partial V\}_T$, and therefore

$$pV/NkT = 1 - Nb_2/V - N^2(2b_3 - 4b_2{}^2)/V^2 - \cdots \qquad (7.527)$$

The first term is the ideal gas approximation. The second term gives the second virial coefficient, $-Nb_2$, in agreement with the value given by the simple pair-collision approximation in Eqs. (7.419) and (7.415). The third term gives the third virial coefficient and involves the computation of the integral b_3. Successively higher coefficients can be found in this way.

Significant advances have recently been made in the theoretical calculation of the third virial coefficients by punched card computing machines. The same potential field parameters determined by the second virial coefficients are used to compute the third virial coefficients, and good agreement is obtained in many cases. But systematic errors have been pointed out, and it has been suggested * that different parameters may be appropriate for the different virial coefficients. The reason for this lies in the fact that the third virial coefficient is determined in part by the collisions or clustering of three molecules, while the second virial coefficient is determined by binary collisions or clusters alone. The formalism of the Mayer theory as outlined above was based on the assumption that the energy of three molecules is just equal to the sum of the energies of the three pairs among the three molecules, each pair interacting as if the third molecule were absent. If this were true, the same parameters ought to be used for the second and third virials. In the light of the quantum theory, however, the pair-interaction assumption is not exact. The interaction of any two molecules is due to the perturbation of the energy levels of each one by the proximity of the other, and it is clear that the proximity of a third molecule will perturb the levels of both the first ones and so alter their mutual pair interaction. In fact it is found that excellent agreement between theory and observation on the third virial coefficient can be obtained for a number of gases by a very slight modification of the Lennard-Jones parameters obtained from the second virial coefficient. For example, in argon it is found that $(r_{03}/r_{02})^6 = 1.0442$, and $\epsilon_{03}/\epsilon_{02} = 0.9904$, where r_{03} and r_{02} are the values of r_0 in Eq. (7.423) determined by the third and second virials respectively, and ϵ_{03}, ϵ_{02} are the energy parameters ϵ_0 needed for the third and second virials.

* H. W. Woolley, *J. Chem. Phys.*, **21** (1953), p. 236.

While the integrals become prohibitively laborious to compute for the higher virials, it is possible to find an asymptotic dependence of the integral b_ν on ν as ν approaches infinity. This leads to a study of the convergence characteristics of the series Eq. (7.519), and to a proof that the assembly goes over into a condensed phase with a typical first order transition like the clustering avalanche discussed in § 6.4. The details of this important theory will be discussed in § 13.1.

7.6 Approximate theory of the liquid phase. Provided the assembly remains fluid after the phase condensation has been carried through, Eq. (7.512), for the partition function of the potential energy, remains formally correct even in the condensed phase. If the assembly does not remain fluid, however, each particle becomes permanently attached to its own lattice point, and the assumptions on which the calculation of Eq. (7.512) were based become invalid. This is because in setting up the partition function (7.404) it was assumed that the co-ordinates of every particle could be varied throughout the whole volume of the enclosure occupied by the assembly, and that there was no way to distinguish permanently between the individual particles; in the crystalline phase these assumptions are not true. Up to the present time there is no known way to prove that interaction between pairs leads first to a condensation into a fluid phase and later into a third solid phase. The phase condensation derived from the Mayer theory could just as well be from the gas directly into a solid phase; the theory itself does not provide any criterion for deciding between these two alternatives. We therefore have to admit that the theory of the liquid phase is still in the quasi-empirical, or phenomenological, stage. We have in fact to assume that the assembly does remain fluid after condensation, so that we may still apply Eq. (7.404) to the condensed assembly. It is then possible to try various schemes for approximately evaluating the integral for the condensed phase. This in itself is an exceedingly troublesome problem because interactions are all strong, and none of the approximations used in the theory of imperfect gases is valid.

There exists an alternative line of approach starting from the theory of the solid phase. For this we observe the relatively slight difference in density between solid and liquid phases. We then picture the liquid as differing from the solid only in the circumstance that its atoms are not permanently attached to their lattice sites, but are instead confined more or less temporarily by their neighbors to small regions or cages, frequently leaking out from one such cage to a neighboring one. By making reasonable guesses at the average potential function within a cage due to the neighboring atoms, one can set up a partition function for the assembly somewhat in the same way as we did for the Einstein model of a crystal. It is further necessary to multiply the partition function by an arbitrary factor or to add entropy in order to account for the leakage mobility from cage to cage. Kirkwood has shown how this so-called communal entropy arises theoretically, although most discussions simply add it empirically to give the right results. For a clear discussion of this theory of liquids the student is referred to the text by J. Frenkel. Here we shall show how an approximate method of evaluating the partition function (7.404) leads directly to the same results as the cage model, thus uniting the two apparently different points of view.

Assuming fluidity, all particles are mobile throughout the enclosure, and their interaction potentials are independent of their velocities; therefore the momentum integrals can be evaluated independently, and we again obtain Eqs. (7.405) and (7.406). The mathematical problem is to evaluate the integral $Q(\mathbf{q})$. To this end we imagine the volume V divided into a large number X of equal fixed elements of volume v, X being much larger than the number of particles N, and v being so small that there is no possibility of more than one particle being in any such cell simultaneously. Let the cells v be indicated by a subscript running from 1 to X, and let n_α be the number of particles in the αth cell: n_α is either unity or zero. The set of numbers $\{n_\alpha\}$ determines to a good approximation the total potential energy of the assembly:

$$U(\mathbf{q}) = U\{n_\alpha\} = \sum_{\alpha > \beta} \sum n_\alpha n_\beta u(r_{\alpha\beta}) \tag{7.601}$$

where $r_{\alpha\beta}$ is the relative co-ordinate vector between the centers of the αth and βth cells, and $u(r_{\alpha\beta})$ is the pair-interaction potential between particles, if in the two cells. The approximation involved here is simply that if an atom has its center somewhere within the cell, we count it as at the center of the cell. We can omit the vector $r_{\alpha\beta}$ from the notation and write $u_{\alpha\beta}$ in place of $u(r_{\alpha\beta})$. If the cells α and β are close together, the potential may be large, while if they are not close neighbors, the potential is nearly zero. Consider the expression

$$U_\alpha = \tfrac{1}{2} \sum_{\beta \neq \alpha} n_\beta u_{\alpha\beta} \tag{7.602}$$

in terms of which the total potential energy is

$$U\{n\} = \sum_\alpha n_\alpha U_\alpha \tag{7.603}$$

Evidently U_α is the contribution to the total energy $U\{n\}$ from a particle in the αth cell; it is a function of the whole set of numbers n_β, but in practice depends only on the numbers belonging to closely neighboring cells, i.e., on the local order in the liquid. This local order is very like that in the solid phase, and this suggests that we substitute for the true interaction potential, a potential well whose floor undulates from place to place with the minima coinciding with the lattice points of a solid having the same local order as the liquid. This potential is not a function of the numbers n_α and assigns a definite potential to each cell, say $\bar{U}_\alpha$. In terms of this picture, the integration (7.406) becomes a sum over the small cells, the co-ordinates of every particle being taken successively over all the cells. The integrand is now a function only of the set of occupation numbers n_α, and every such arrangement of particles having the same set of numbers contributes additively the same sum to the integral. There are $N!/\prod_\alpha n_\alpha!$ different arrangements of particles corresponding to the same set of numbers n_α, so that

$$Q(\mathbf{q}) = \int \cdots \int \exp\{-U(\mathbf{q})/kT\}dq_1 \cdots dq_{3N}$$

$$= \sum_{\{n\}N} (N!/\Pi_\alpha n_\alpha!)v^N \exp\left(-\sum_\alpha n_\alpha \bar{U}_\alpha/kT\right) \qquad (7.604)$$

where the summation is over all sets of numbers n_α satisfying

$$\sum_{\alpha=1}^{X} n_\alpha = N \qquad (7.605)$$

Comparing the factorial coefficients in Eq. (7.604) with those of the multinomial theorem, we see at once that

$$Q(\mathbf{q}) = \left\{v \sum_{\alpha=1}^{X} \exp\left(-\bar{U}_\alpha/kT\right)\right\}^N \qquad (7.606)$$

and hence from Eq. (7.405), we have for the partition function of the whole liquid assembly:

$$\mathbf{Q} = (1/N!)Q^N \qquad (7.607)$$

where
$$Q = (2\pi mkT/h^2)^{3/2}v \sum_{\alpha=1}^{X} \exp\left(-\bar{U}_\alpha/kT\right) \qquad (7.608)$$

The relation (7.607) is exactly the same form as Eq. (7.127) where Q is the partition function of a single particle. In fact in the limit when the interaction potential between particles vanishes, the result goes directly over into the ideal gas Eq. (7.127); this is because when $U_\alpha = 0$ for all α, we have $v \sum_{\alpha=1}^{X} \exp\left(-\bar{U}_\alpha/kT\right)$ $= v \sum_{1}^{X}(1) = Xv = V$, and hence $Q = V(2\pi mkT/h^2)^{3/2}$, exactly the partition function per atom in the ideal gas.

To calculate the partition function for the liquid we should have to make a reasonable guess at $\bar{U}_\alpha$ as a function of α, and then we could approximate to the sum over α by means of an integral:

$$\lim_{X \to \infty} v \sum_{\alpha=1}^{X} \exp\left(-\bar{U}_\alpha/kT\right) \to \int \exp\left(-\bar{U}/kT\right)dV \qquad (7.609)$$

the integral being a simple volume integral over V. Essentially $\bar{U}_\alpha$ is a periodic function having N minima corresponding to the lattice sites, and we may actually go over to the cage model, regarding the integral of Eq. (7.609) as simply N times the integral over one cage:

$$\int \exp\left(-\bar{U}/kT\right)dV = N\int_{\text{cage}} \exp\left(-\bar{U}/kT\right)dV \qquad (7.610)$$

If we write

$$Q_c = (2\pi mkT/h^2)^{3/2} \int_{\text{cage}} \exp{(-\overline{U}/kT)}dV \qquad (7.611)$$

for the partition function of one particle as it usually appears in the cage model, we see that Eq. (7.607) becomes

$$\mathbf{Q} = (1/N!)(NQ_c)^N \qquad (7.612)$$

and therefore

$$\ln \mathbf{Q} = N + N \ln Q_c \qquad (7.613)$$

On the cage model itself $\ln \mathbf{Q} = N \ln Q_c$. The present theory includes an extra N and therefore automatically includes the communal entropy Nk.

If the assembly were to become solidified, the walls of the potential hollows would become so high that particles would be unable to wander between the cages. This has the effect of localizing the particles permanently on distinguishable sites. For this reason the factorial correction $1/N!$ in Eq. (7.607) for indistinguishability must be omitted from the partition function. At the same time, the partition function of a single particle is to be integrated only over one cage instead of all N cages, so the factor N is to be removed from Eq. (7.610); hence the particle partition function becomes Q_c instead of NQ_c. The assembly partition function for the solid phase is therefore

$$\mathbf{Q}_{\text{solid}} = Q_c{}^N \qquad (7.614)$$

so that

$$\ln \mathbf{Q}_{\text{solid}} = N \ln Q_c \qquad (7.615)$$

which differs from Eq. (7.613) for the liquid phase in the absence of the communal entropy term. Eq. (7.615) leads directly to the Einstein theory of the crystal if U is taken as a simple harmonic potential.

Several models closely related with the above formalism will be briefly discussed. The simple harmonic oscillator model is probably the most obvious. We let the potential $\overline{U}$ in a cage be represented by a simple harmonic restoring force directed towards the center of the cage:

$$\overline{U} = -U_0 + \tfrac{1}{2}mw^2r^2 \qquad (7.616)$$

where $-U_0$ is the potential minimum at the center, r is the distance of the particle from the center, and w is the angular frequency of the motion in the cage. The cage integral becomes

$$\int_{\text{cage}} \exp{(-\overline{U}/kT)}dV = (2\pi kT/mw^2)^{3/2} \exp{(U_0/kT)} \qquad (7.617)$$

The upper limit of r is taken infinite on the assumption that the cage is large enough to reduce the integrand to practically zero before reaching the physical boundaries of the cage. The partition function for the liquid is then given by

$$\ln Q_{liq} = N(1 + U_0/kT) + 3N \ln (kT/\hbar w) \tag{7.618}$$

There are two parameters in this model, U_0 and w, and both may depend on volume or density, but not on temperature. The equation of state derived from Eq. (7.116) is evidently

$$p = N\partial U_0/\partial V - 3NkT\partial \ln w/\partial V \tag{7.619}$$

Since the first term here represents the "intrinsic pressure," and since this is very much greater than one atmosphere, the relation (7.619) may be regarded as an approximate relation between the two parameters, taking p almost zero (one atmosphere!):

$$\partial U_0/\partial V = 3kT\partial \ln w/\partial V \tag{7.620}$$

The temperature derivative of Eq. (7.619) yields a result that can be made use of at once:

$$-3Nk\partial \ln w/\partial V = (\partial p/\partial T)_V = \alpha/\beta \tag{7.621}$$

where α is the coefficient of thermal expansion $(\partial V/\partial T)_p$ and β is the compressibility $-(\partial V/\partial p)_T$, both experimentally observable. For most monatomic liquids α is of the order 10^{-3} per degree Kelvin, and β about 10^{-4} per atmosphere, so that $-\partial \ln w/\partial V \sim 1/(24.7 \text{ cm}^3)$. It is generally assumed that the frequency w is inversely proportional to the linear dimensions of the cage, and therefore inversely proportional to the cube root of the molar volume:

$$w \propto V^{-\frac{1}{3}} \quad \text{and} \quad \partial \ln w/\partial V = -1/3V$$

Combining this with the previous numerical estimate yields $V \sim 8.23 \text{ cm}^3$ for the molar volume of any monatomic liquid. This is in fact the right order of magnitude, and by allowing a more general relation between the frequency and volume, and considering the detailed data on α and β, a more complete comparison between theory and experiment could be made. Actually such a comparison would not now be of much interest because the model has been superseded by a more realistic one due to Lennard-Jones and Devonshire, to be discussed in a moment.

The free volume model is apparently quite different, but is a natural outcome of the van der Waals picture of hard sphere molecules in a nonideal gas; only part of the gross molar volume V is considered accessible to the free motion of any one particle, viz., the term $V - b$ in the van der Waals equation. In imperfect gas theory b is much smaller than V so the Ursell power development was a legitimate process for evaluating the virial coefficients. In the liquid phase we find that $V - b$, the total accessible (free) volume, is considerably smaller than V, and there is no way of using the Ursell power development to derive an equation of state for the liquid, because b is itself comparable with V. Nevertheless the concept of a free volume $V_f = V - b$ has proved a very useful one in discussing the liquid phase, and we shall indicate its theoretical status and some of its applications here.

Let there be a flat negative potential $-U_f$ within the free volume V_f, then for any particle, Eq. (7.610) becomes

$$\int \exp\left(-\overline{U}/kT\right)dV = V_f \exp\left(U_f/kT\right) \qquad (7.623)$$

So far as the cage is concerned, there is essentially only one cage in which all the molecules are trapped—the whole free volume V_f. We can, however, write for convenience:

$$V_f = Nv_f \qquad (7.624)$$

to define v_f as the free volume per particle. Then if we write

$$Q_c = (2\pi mkT/h^2)^{3/2}v_f \exp\left(U_f/kT\right) \qquad (7.625)$$

in place of Eq. (7.611), Eq. (7.612) remains true, and we find

$$\ln \mathbf{Q}_{\text{liq}} = N(1 + U_f/kT) + N \ln v_f + N \ln (2\pi mkT/h^2)^{3/2} \qquad (7.626)$$

Again the two parameters U_f and v_f are functions of V, not T, and the analogs of Eqs. (7.620) and (7.621) are

$$\partial U_f/\partial V = -kT\partial \ln v_f/\partial V \qquad (7.627)$$

and

$$Nk\partial \ln v_f/\partial V = \alpha/\beta \qquad (7.628)$$

If the mean distance between centers of nearest neighbors is a and their diameters are d, a spherical free volume per molecule equals

$$v_f = (4\pi/3)(a - d)^3$$

The gross volume per molecule is a^3/γ, where γ depends on the local order: $\gamma = \sqrt{2}$ for face-centered cubic symmetry, for instance. The total free volume is then taken to be

$$V_f = (4\pi\gamma/3)(V^{1/3} - V_0^{1/3})^3 \qquad (7.629)$$

where $V_0 = Nd^3/\gamma$. Using this in Eq. (7.628) yields

$$V_f^{1/3}V^{2/3} = \gamma^{1/3}8.2 \text{ cm}^3 \qquad (7.630)$$

Liquid argon for example has a molar volume $V = 28.5$ cm^3, and if $\gamma = \sqrt{2}$, we find $V_f = 1.25$ cm^3.

We return now to the cage model, and consider briefly the refinement due to Lennard-Jones and Devonshire. The cage is again pictured as a sphere of radius a surrounding the molecule of interest; all its z nearest neighbors are wandering at random over the spherical surface, and the molecule within the sphere is subject to the Lennard-Jones forces from those on the surface. The cage integral (7.610) can be evaluated in terms of the parameters r_0 and ϵ_0, and from the resulting partition function an equation of state can be derived. From simple dimensional analysis it is not difficult to see that this equation of state may be expressed in the universal form:

$$pV/NkT = \phi(kT/\epsilon^*, V/V^*) \qquad (7.631)$$

where ϕ is a function, the same for all substances, of the temperature and volume expressed in suitable units: $V^* = r_0^3/\gamma$ and $\epsilon^* = z\epsilon_0$. The quantity pV/NkT plotted as a function of T and V is the same for all substances when the appropriate units are chosen. This is the law of corresponding states, already met with in § 7.4 in connection with the behavior of imperfect gases; here it is the equation of state of the liquid that is involved. The function ϕ is very complicated, and has to be obtained numerically. Isothermal curves are similar to the van der Waals curves for an imperfect gas, but of course valid now only in the liquid phase. They show a "wobble" through an unstable region into the gas phase. If $T = \epsilon^*/9k$ this wobble flattens out, and above this critical temperature the isotherms are monotonic and no phase separation occurs. Because the density at the critical point is quite high, the Lennard-Jones model is valid there, and ought to give a better picture than the van der Waals equation. In fact, assuming the same values of ϵ^* and r_0 as one derives from fitting the Lennard-Jones potential to the virial coefficients in the imperfect gas, one can calculate the critical temperature from $\epsilon^*/9k$, for the liquid model, and compare with the observed values. The results are quite impressive.

COMPARISON BETWEEN THEORETICAL AND EXPERIMENTAL CRITICAL TEMPERATURES

Liquid	r_0^3 Angs.	ϵ^* erg/mole	T_c theo.	T_c abs.
Ne	29.2	4.89×10^{-15}	47 °K	44 °K
N_2	72.5	13.25 "	128	126
A	56.2	16.5 "	160	150

Further tests of these models are possible only in connection with the phase equilibrium between solid and liquid, and between vapor and liquid. We discuss these briefly in the next section.

7.7   Phase equilibria. In §5.1 we proved statistically that two phases consisting of noninteracting particles may be in mutual equilibrium when their molecular chemical potentials are equal. The same theorem is true, as we know from elementary thermodynamics, even when the two phases consist of interacting particles. The statistical proof of this theorem will be given in Chapter XII, where the method of the Gibbs grand ensemble is introduced. For the moment we simply accept the theorem and apply it to the equilibrium between a liquid and either its solid or its vapor phase, using the various liquid models discussed in the last section.

In general [see Eqs. (7.114) and (7.116)] the appropriate free energy for phase equilibrium is $F = N\mu = A + pV$, or

$$F = -kT \ln Q + VkT(\partial \ln Q/\partial V)_T \qquad (7.701)$$

Using Eq. (7.618) for the oscillator model and neglecting the pV term completely, as we did in setting up Eq. (7.620), we find

$$F_{\text{liq}} = -NkT - NU_0 - 3NkT \ln (kT/\hbar w) \qquad (7.702)$$

From the free volume model on the other hand, Eq. (7.626) gives

$$F_{\text{liq}} = -NkT - NU_f - NkT \ln v_f - NkT \ln (2\pi mkT/h^2)^{3/2} \qquad (7.703)$$

Equilibrium between liquid and solid is established when $F_{\text{liq}} = F_{\text{sol}}$, and this occurs of course at the melting temperature $T = T_m$. We consider then, the melting of an Einstein model crystal whose partition function was found in § 4.8. This function, Eq. (4.803), was referred to an energy zero corresponding to a particle at rest in the crystal. To conform with the energy zero used in our liquid models, we rewrite Eq. (4.804) in the form:

$$\ln Q_{\text{sol}} = (U_s - \epsilon_0)/kT - 3 \ln (1 - e^{h\nu_s/kT}) \qquad (7.704)$$

where U_s is the energy of a particle at rest in the solid relative to a particle at rest in empty space. We have assumed all three modes to have the same frequency ν_s in the Einstein crystal. The melting temperature is generally higher than the Debye characteristic temperature, or than $h\nu_s/k$, and we may approximate to the partition function by expansion in powers:

$$\ln (1 - e^{h\nu_s/kT}) = \ln (h\nu_s/kT) + \ln (1 - h\nu_s/2kT)$$
$$= \ln (h\nu_s/kT) - h\nu_s/2kT$$

The last term of this approximation exactly cancels the zero-point energy term in Eq. (7.704), and the result is

$$\ln Q_{\text{sol}} = U_s/kT - 3 \ln (h\nu_s/kT) \qquad (7.705)$$

Again neglecting the pV term, we have

$$F_{\text{sol}} = -NU_s - 3NkT \ln (kT/h\nu_s) \qquad (7.706)$$

Comparison between this and Eq. (7.702) for the oscillator liquid model gives the melting temperature:

$$T_m = \frac{H_m/k}{1 + 3 \ln (2\pi \nu_s/w)} \qquad (7.707)$$

where

$$H_m = -U_0 + U_s \qquad (7.708)$$

is the molecular latent heat of melting. Considering that in most substances the local order in liquid and solid phases at the melting point is the same, and that only small changes in density occur, one would reasonably expect the frequencies $w/2\pi$ and ν_s to be almost equal. Equation (7.707) would then predict that H_m/kT_m would be about unity for all monatomic liquids. Actually a very large proportion of such substances do have values of H_m/kT_m between 0.85 and 1.25, in fair agreement with this simple theory.

The free volume model liquid is more convenient for a discussion of the liquid-vapor equilibrium. Treating the vapor as an ideal gas, we may write for its free energy [see Eq. (4.207)]:

$$F_{\text{vap}} = NkT \ln (p/kT) - NkT \ln (2\pi mkT/h^2)^{3/2} \qquad (7.709)$$

Comparing this with Eq. (7.703) for the liquid, the boiling point is given by $F_{\text{vap}} = F_{\text{liq}}$:

$$\ln (p/kT_b) = -1 - U_f/kT_b - \ln v_f$$

or

$$p_{\text{sat}} = (kT_b/v_f) \exp (-H_b/kT_b) \qquad (7.710)$$

where $H_b = kT_b + U_f$ is the latent heat of evaporation at the boiling point, neglecting the small term pV_{liq}. A relation of the form (7.710) is known to hold empirically over a considerable temperature range in many liquids:

$$p_{\text{sat}} = Ae^{-H/kT} \qquad (7.711)$$

where A has a value somewhere between 1.3 and 5×10^4 atmospheres, depending on the substance, and depending slightly on temperature. This would agree with Eq. (7.710) only if v_f were approximately proportional to T; numerically one finds only rough agreement. Returning to Eq. (7.710), we may substitute the observed values of H_b and T_b for argon, viz., $H_b = 1,500$ cal/mole, $T_b = 87.5$ °K, and $p_{\text{sat}} = 1$ atm., to find the free volume:

$$V_f = (NkT_b/p_{\text{sat}})e^{-H_b/kT_b} = 1.33 \text{ cm}^3/\text{mole} \qquad (7.712)$$

in satisfactory agreement with the figure of 1.25 cm³/mole derived from the expansion coefficients in the previous section.

EXERCISES AND PROBLEMS

1. Check the equivalence between the two expressions for entropy in Eqs. (7.117) and (7.112).

2. In the Debye theory we accepted the lowest $3N$ frequencies in the continuum spectrum regardless of how many of these were longitudinal and how many transverse. Revise the theory so that we take only the N lowest longitudinal and $2N$ lowest transverse modes. How does this affect the heat capacity formula?

3. Verify Eq. (7.218) for heat capacity at low temperatures.

4. Develop the theory of two-dimensional solid crystals analogous to the Debye theory, and prove that the heat capacity goes to zero like T^2 at very low temperatures.

5. Derive Eqs. (7.302) and (7.303) from Eq. (7.301).

6. Discuss the expression (7.425) for the energy of an imperfect gas as volume is allowed to go to infinity, and energy ought to approach the ideal limit $\frac{3}{2}NkT$.

7. Verify Eq. (7.524).

8. Derive Eqs. (7.627) and (7.628).

9. Verify Eq. (7.712) for the free volume of liquid argon.

10. From the method outlined in the paragraph following Eq. (7.104) for finding the averages over an ensemble, find the average number $\bar{n}_j$ of quanta in the mode of vibration having a frequency ν_j for the crystal having the energy spectrum of Eq. (7.203); prove that

$$\bar{n}_j + \tfrac{1}{2} = -(kT/h)\partial \ln \mathbf{Q}/\partial \nu_j$$

and hence that

$$\bar{n}_j = 1/(e^{h\nu_j/kT} - 1)$$

Compare with the distribution-in-energy of a Bose-Einstein gas.

REFERENCES FOR FURTHER STUDY

Statistical Mechanics, J. E. Mayer and M. G. Mayer, Wiley, 1940; Chapters 10–14.
Kinetic Theory of Liquids, J. Frenkel, Oxford, 1947.
Modern Theory of Solids, F. Seitz, McGraw-Hill, 1940; Chapter 3.
An Index of Mathematical Tables, Fletcher, Miller, and Rosenhead, McGraw-Hill, 1946.

"Frequency Spectrum and Specific Heat of a Face Centered Cubic Lattice," C. W. Garland and G. Jura, *J. Chem. Phys.*, **22** (1954), pp. 1108; 1114.
"Statistical Mechanics of Liquids and Gases of Hard Spheres," O. K. Rice, *J. Chem. Phys.*, **12** (1944), pp. 1; 521.
"Third Virial Coefficient of Non-Polar Gases," R. B. Bird, E. L. Spotz, and J. O. Hirschfelder, *J. Chem. Phys.*, **18** (1950), p. 1395.
"Third Virial Coefficients of Polar Gases and Critical Constants of Polar Gases," J. S. Rowlinson, *J. Chem. Phys.*, **19** (1951), pp. 827; 831.
"Statistical Mechanics of Imperfect Gases," E. W. Montroll and J. E. Mayer, *J. Chem. Phys.*, **9** (1941), p. 626.
"Note on Mayer's Theory of Cluster Integrals," Kodi Husimi, *J. Chem. Phys.*, **18** (1950), p. 682.
"Point of Condensation and the Volume Dependency of the Cluster Integrals," S. Katsura and H. Fujita, *J. Chem. Phys.*, **19** (1951), p. 795; *Progr. Theo. Phys.*, **6** (1951), p. 498.
"Cluster Integrals and the Thiele Semi-Invariants," Syu Ono, *J. Chem. Phys.*, **19** (1951), p. 504.
"Contribution to the Theory of Critical Phenomena," B. H. Zimm, *J. Chem. Phys.*, **19** (1951), p. 1019.
"Note on Theory of Critical Phenomena," J. E. Mayer, *J. Chem. Phys.*, **19** (1951), p. 1024.
"Application of Ursell and Mayer's Treatment for Imperfect Gases to Adsorption," Syu Ono, *J. Chem. Phys.*, **18** (1950), p. 397.
"The Third Virial Coefficient in Polymer Solutions," W. H. Stockmayer and E. F. Casassa, *J. Chem. Phys.*, **20** (1952), p. 1560.
"Low Temperature Second Virial Coefficients for a 6–9 Potential," G. M. Roe, L. F. Epstein, and M. D. Powers, *J. Chem. Phys.*, **20** (1952), p. 1665.
"A Statistical Theory of Liquids," G. Jaffe, *Phys. Rev.*, **62** (1942), p. 463; **63** (1943), p. 313.
"The Liquid State: The Guthrie Lecture," J. H. Hildebrand, *Proc. Phys. Soc.* (London), **56** (1944), p. 221.
"A Partition Function for Liquids from Harmonic Oscillator Model," F. A. Matsen and G. M. Watson, *J. Chem. Phys.*, **11** (1943), p. 343.
"Surface Tension and van der Waals' Equation," F. C. Auluck and R. N. Rai, *J. Chem. Phys.*, **12** (1944), p. 321.
"The Energy Levels of Holes in Liquids," F. C. Auluck and D. S. Kothari, *Proc. Cambridge Phil. Soc.*, **41** (1945), p. 180.
"On Lattice Theories of the Liquid State," H. M. Peek and T. L. Hill, *J. Chem. Phys.*, **18** (1950), p. 1252.

"Lennard-Jones and Devonshire Equation of State of Compressed Gases and Liquids," Wentorf, Buehler, Hirschfelder, and Curtiss, *J. Chem. Phys.*, **18** (1950), p. 1484.

"Discrete Energy Levels Associated with the Lennard-Jones Potential," J. E. Kilpatrick and M. F. Kilpatrick, *J. Chem. Phys.*, **19** (1951), p. 930.

"On the Latent Heat of Fusion and the Hole Theory," N. R. Mukherjee, *J. Chem. Phys.*, **19** (1951), p. 502.

"Structure of Liquids," C. E. Waring and P. Becher, *J. Chem. Phys.*, **15** (1947), p. 488.

"Surface Specific Heat," H. Koppe, *J. Chem. Phys.*, **18** (1950), p. 638.

"On the Distribution Function in Phase Space with Applications to the Theory of Liquids," E. Ikenberry, *J. Chem. Phys.*, **19** (1951), p. 467.

"Radial Distribution Functions and the Equation of State of Monatomic Fluids," Zwanzig, Kirkwood, Stripp, and Oppenheim, *J. Chem. Phys.*, **21** (1953), p. 1268.

"Equation of State for Liquids," F. Maslen and E. Aberth, *J. Chem. Phys.*, **19** (1951), p. 658.

"Critique of Free Volume Theory of Liquid State," J. G. Kirkwood, *J. Chem. Phys.*, **18** (1950), p. 380.

"Remarks on the Theory of Fusion and Condensation," A. J. F. Siegert, *Phys. Rev.*, **90** (1953), p. 97.

"Statistical Mechanics of Dilute Polymer Solutions," P. J. Flory and W. R. Krigbaum, *J. Chem. Phys.*, **17** (1949), p. 1374; **18** (1950), p. 1086.

"Equation of State Computations," J. E. Mayer and G. Careri, *J. Chem. Phys.*, **20** (1952), p. 1001.

"On the Theory of the Virial Development of the Equation of State of Monatomic Gases," R. J. Riddell, Jr., and G. E. Uhlenbeck, *J. Chem. Phys.*, **21** (1953), p. 2056.

"The Debye Function, Tables," J. A. Beattie, *J. of Math. and Phys.*, Massachusetts Inst. Tech., **6** (1926), p. 1.

Chapter VIII

INDEPENDENT SYSTEMS WITH QUANTUM DEGENERACY

8.1 Black-body radiation: photon gas. In Chapter II we developed the formulae for the most probable distribution-in-energy for the three kinds of statistics: Boltzmann for distinguishable systems; Fermi-Dirac and Bose-Einstein for indistinguishable ones. At high temperatures or low densities a corrected form of Boltzmann statistics was shown to suffice for all three. Now we turn to a study of examples where the classical correction to Boltzmann statistics is not sufficient to take care of the degeneracy due to indistinguishability of atoms. It was shown in § 3.6 that the condition for validity of the classical correction, viz.,

$$\exp\left(-\mu/kT\right) \gg 1 \tag{8.101}$$

is violated by assemblies of atoms whose masses are as small as those of H or He atoms at temperatures of a few degrees Kelvin, and of electrons at ordinary laboratory temperatures. The electron, being a single elementary particle, obeys the Pauli exclusion principle, and the wave functions of an assembly of electrons must be antisymmetrical in all electrons. Therefore the Fermi-Dirac statistics apply to an electron gas. We discuss this in § 8.4.

There is another interesting circumstance that can lead to violation of the condition (8.101). This comes about if the total number of systems in the assembly is not predetermined. This happens in black-body radiation treated as an assembly of photons. In finding the most probable distribution-in-energy of the photons, there is no specified total number of photons; there is therefore no Lagrangian parameter needed to take care of the numerical restriction, that is, there is no α. This is equivalent to setting $\alpha = 0$ in the formulae, or $\mu = 0$. If we put $\mu = 0$ in Eq. (8.101), it is obvious that the condition for classical statistics is violated.

Returning for the moment to examples where the total number of systems is known, and quoting the results of § 2.3 on the most probable distribution-in-energy, Eqs. (2.321) and (2.331), or Eqs. (3.511) and (3.512), we may summarize them all in one equation to determine the free energy μ:

$$N = \sum_j \omega_j \{\exp{(\epsilon_j - \mu)}/kT \mp 1\}^{-1} \tag{8.102}$$

where the upper sign refers to the Bose-Einstein, the lower to the Fermi-Dirac statistics. Both these expressions can be expanded in power series:

$$N = \sum_{j=0} \omega_j \sum_{r=1} (\pm 1)^{r-1} \exp{\{r(\mu - \epsilon_j)/kT\}} \tag{8.103}$$

From this it is obvious that we cannot write N as a product of a factor depending on the free energy, multiplied by a partition function, as was possible in classical statistics in § 4.1. The method of the particle partition function therefore breaks down with quantum degenerate assemblies. The reader should therefore take heed that none of the theorems developed in connection with the partition function method for indistinguishable systems is valid when quantum degeneracy is important. The method of the assembly partition function, however, remains valid, because the assemblies in an ensemble are mutually distinguishable, and the Boltzmann statistics are valid without correction. Quantum degeneracy enters the assembly partition function method only through the detailed computation of the assembly partition function itself. The theorems of the assembly partition function method remain valid. We discuss the partition function for quantum degenerate assemblies later in Chapter IX.

We turn now to a discussion of the photon gas. As was discussed briefly in Chapter I, energy is transmitted by electromagnetic radiation in the form of photons each having energy $h\nu$, where ν is the frequency of the electromagnetic waves. For many purposes photons can be treated as particles, and generally we can think of them as systems in a statistical assembly. Electromagnetic energy in equilibrium with matter at some definite temperature is found experimentally to have a unique spectral distribution-in-energy such that the energy density $U(\nu)$ per unit frequency spectral range is

$$U(\nu) = 8\pi h(\nu/c)^3(e^{h\nu/kT} - 1)^{-1} \tag{8.104}$$

where h is Planck's constant. This formula was discovered by Max Planck to fit the observed distribution exactly, even before any satisfactory theory of the distribution existed. We shall see immediately that it is actually the most probable distribution-in-energy of a gas of photons obeying the Bose-Einstein statistics.

Consider an enclosure of volume V whose walls are perfect reflectors of electromagnetic radiation. Let some arbitrary distribution of electromagnetic energy be present in the enclosure. Because the walls are perfectly reflecting and the interaction between photons themselves can be neglected, the distribution remains constant. Now we imagine a small piece of matter capable of absorbing and re-emitting radiation, introduced into the enclosure and keeping its thermal contact with the outside walls. This absorbs and re-emits radiation and in time produces a new distribution-in-energy in equilibrium with the temperature of the enclosure. We may then remove the piece of matter and consider the radiation alone, which of course maintains the equilibrium distribution indefinitely.

The energy levels of a photon are given by the possible frequencies of the radiation field, and these are the normal modes of the electromagnetic waves in the enclosure. Since we are supposing the walls to be perfect reflectors, these modes are easily found; indeed, they are identical with the Debye modes discussed in § 7.2. Translating the results of § 7.2 into the terms of the present problem, we find that the normal modes of the radiation field have frequencies:

$$\nu(n) = (c/2L)(n_1^2 + n_2^2 + n_3^2)^{\frac{1}{2}} \tag{8.105}$$

where (n_1,n_2,n_3) are any positive integers. Considering that electromagnetic waves are polarized, like the transverse Debye modes, the number of modes having frequencies between ν and $\nu + d\nu$ equals

$$\omega(\nu)d\nu = 8\pi(L/c)^3\nu^2 d\nu \tag{8.106}$$

Photons are freely absorbed and re-emitted during the processes required to establish this equilibrium, and the number of photons is not conserved during these processes. Therefore in finding the most probable or equilibrium distribution, the photons are not restricted to a constant total number, and, as just discussed above, we have to set $\mu = 0$. Moreover there is no limit to the number of photons in any one frequency, and therefore the Bose-Einstein statistics are appropriate. Putting $\mu = 0$, and taking the upper sign in Eq. (8.102), or using Eq. (3.511), we have

$$n_j = \omega_j\{\exp(h\nu_j/kT) - 1\}^{-1} \tag{8.107}$$

Combining this with Eq. (8.106), which gives ω_j as a continuous function, we find the most probable distribution of photons among their frequencies:

$$n(\nu)d\nu = 8\pi V(\nu^2/c^3)\{\exp(h\nu/kT) - 1\}^{-1}d\nu \tag{8.108}$$

Multiplying this by $h\nu$, the energy per photon, we at once obtain Eq. (8.104).

This agreement may be thought to constitute a very searching test of the particle picture of photon processes, but in fact this is not the case. We can get the same result if we regard the radiation field as a continuum having the modes of vibration given by Eq. (8.105) and evaluate the partition function for the whole enclosure, just as we did for the Debye crystal, instead of considering the photons individually. The final result is identical. The particle concept—as our discussion in the Introduction should have indicated—is not essential in any quantum mechanical problem. The essential point of the present problem is that electromagnetic energy be quantized, not that it should be localized in particles.

The total energy of the photon gas is

$$E = \sum_j n_j h\nu_j = \sum_j h\omega_j\nu_j\{e^{h\nu_j/kT} - 1\}^{-1},$$

and going over to the continuous approximation, this becomes

$$E = 8\pi h(L/c)^3 \int_0^\infty \frac{\nu^3 d\nu}{e^{h\nu/kT} - 1} = \frac{8\pi^5(kT)^4 V}{15(hc)^3} \qquad (8.109)$$

This is the familiar Stefan's law for black-body radiation. To find the entropy of the photon gas we use Eq. (2.243) and write

$$S = k \sum_j \{n_j \ln (\omega_j/n_j + 1) + \omega_j \ln (1 + n_j/\omega_j)\}$$

Then from Eq. (8.107), we have $\ln (\omega_j/n_j + 1) = h\nu_j/kT$ and $\ln (1 + n_j/\omega_j) = -\ln (1 - e^{-h\nu_j/kT})$, so that

$$S = k \sum_j n_j h\nu_j/kT - k \sum_j \omega_j \ln (1 - e^{-h\nu_j/kT}) \qquad (8.110)$$

The first term here is exactly E/T. Going over to the continuous approximation for the other sum, we get

$$S = E/T - 8\pi k(L/c)^3 \int_0^\infty \nu^2 \ln (1 - e^{-h\nu/kT}) d\nu = E/T + \frac{8\pi^5(kT)^3 Vk}{45(hc)^3} \qquad (8.111)$$

The Helmholtz free energy $A = E - TS$ follows immediately:

$$A = -(8\pi^5/45)(kT)^4 V/(hc)^3 \qquad (8.112)$$

From this the pressure of the photon gas, the radiation pressure, is found:

$$p = -(\partial A/\partial V)_T = E/3V = (8\pi^5/45)(kT)^4/(hc)^3 \qquad (8.113)$$

which, incidentally, is independent of volume.

At ordinary temperatures this pressure is negligible. On the surface of the hotter stars, $T = 3 \times 10^4$ °K, it is about 2,000 dynes/cm^2. The probable temperature generated in an atomic bomb explosion, 10^5 °K, would produce a radiation pressure of about one-fifth atmosphere, 2×10^5 dynes/cm^2. The temperature required to produce thermonuclear reactions is at least 10^7 °K, and this would generate a radiation pressure no less than ten million atmospheres, 10^{13} dynes/cm^2. An explosive nuclear reaction would of course not generate an equilibrium condition, but its radiation pressure must be of a similar order of magnitude; how much of such immense pressures would be effective in adding to the explosive force, would depend on how much of the radiation can be absorbed before it radiates away from the source. If any information of this nature has been secured from the Pacific H-bomb tests, it undoubtedly remains classified as "top secret."

8.2   The phonon gas. In § 7.2 we outlined the Debye theory of a crystal, and the student may have been aware of a close analogy between the formulae of that theory and some of those occurring in the theory of black-body radiation: in particular Eqs. (7.213) and (8.109). In the Debye model, a zero-point energy exists, which is neglected in the photon formulae, and in the Debye model a finite upper limit appears in the integral, but not in the photon formulae. Logically, a zero-point energy ought to appear in the photon formulae, which, because no upper limit exists to frequencies, would in fact be infinite. This infinite zero-point energy is ignored because it is constant and does not apparently alter any physically significant results.

It is instructive to follow up the analogy between the Debye crystal and the photon gas. The vibrational modes of the crystal can be thought of as an assembly of acoustical quanta—a gas of phonons. With each mode of vibration we associate quanta of energy, $h\nu$, called phonons; the amplitude of the acoustical wave determines the number of phonons associated with it. The phonons can be regarded as indistinguishable systems or "particles" with possible states determined by the spectrum of frequencies. The phonons are treated as a Bose-Einstein gas, and we find the energy and heat capacity of this gas coincide exactly with the results of the straight Debye theory as given in § 7.2. The crystal is to be treated as a box containing the phonon gas. The possible frequencies, or states of a phonon, are to be found exactly as in the Debye model—see Eqs. (7.209) and (8.106). There are here two spectra of frequencies, the one coming from the longitudinal modes, and the other from the transverse modes, the latter having double weight because of polarization. Except for these differences in detail, the argument given preceding Eq. (8.107) for the photon gas applies here with equal force, and we have in place of Eq. (8.108) for the number of phonons in any given frequency range:

$$n(\nu)d\nu = 4\pi V\nu^2(1/c_1{}^3 + 2/c_2{}^3)\{\exp(h\nu/kT) - 1\}^{-1} \qquad (8.201)$$

We multiply this by the energy $h\nu$ per phonon, integrate up to ν_m defined as in Eq. (7.211), and find for the total energy of the phonon gas:

$$E = (9N/\nu_m{}^3)\int_0^{\nu_m}\{\exp(h\nu/kT) - 1\}^{-1}h\nu^3 d\nu \qquad (8.202)$$

which is the same as Eq. (7.231) except for the zero-point energy.

The partition function corresponding to the present picture, the expression appearing in § 7.2, is not available now because we are not using Boltzmann statistics. To find the entropy of the phonon gas we resort to precisely the same method as used in the photon gas, Eq. (2.243), and find the analog of Eq. (8.111):

$$S = E/T - (9Nk/\nu_m{}^3)\int_0^{\nu_m}\nu^2 \ln(1 - e^{-h\nu/kT})d\nu \qquad (8.203)$$

It is convenient to introduce the Debye characteristic temperature $\theta = h\nu_m/k$, and to write Eq. (8.203) in the form:

$$S = E/T - 9Nk(T/\theta)^3\int_0^{\theta/T} x^2 \ln(1 - e^{-x})dx \qquad (8.204)$$

If this integral is subjected to partial integration and the result is compared with Eq. (8.202), we find

$$S = 4E/3T - 3Nk \ln (1 - e^{-\theta/T}) \tag{8.205}$$

where, incidentally, we may write

$$E = 3NkTD(\theta/T) \tag{8.206}$$

The free energy $A = E - TS$ is

$$A = -E/3 + 3NkT \ln (1 - e^{-\theta/kT}) \tag{8.207}$$

The radiation pressure of the phonon gas is now given by the volume derivative of this free energy:

$$p = -(\partial A/\partial V)_T = Nk\{D'(\theta/T) - 3(e^{\theta/T} - 1)^{-1}\}d\theta/dV$$

But $D'(\theta/T) = -3(T/\theta)D(\theta/T) + 3(e^{\theta/T} - 1)^{-1}$ and therefore

$$p = \gamma E/V \tag{8.208}$$

where

$$\gamma = -d \ln \theta/d \ln V \tag{8.209}$$

The free energy $F = A + pV$ is identically zero at all temperatures, for the following reason: in a material gas having a fixed number of particles, the free energy arises from the Lagrangian parameter restricting the variations so as to keep the total number of particles fixed. In the phonon gas (as also in the photon gas of the previous section) the number of systems is not conserved; the Lagrangian parameter is not needed and can be taken as zero. In the next section we shall find that the Bose-Einstein gas of material particles undergoes a *lambda*-type transition at the temperature where F approaches zero. This transition does not occur in the phonon gas, simply because the number of particles is not conserved and F is always zero. The mean number of phonons can of course be calculated from Eq. (8.201):

$$N_{\text{phon}} = 9N(T/\theta)^3 \int_0^{\theta/T} (e^x - 1)^{-1}x^2dx \tag{8.210}$$

This integral can be evaluated numerically; at sufficiently high temperatures, the asymptotic value is easily found:

$$T \gg \theta: \qquad\qquad N_{\text{phon}} = 9NT/\theta \tag{8.211}$$

At sufficiently low temperatures, the upper limit of the integral becomes practically infinite, and we can then expand the integrand and evaluate the integral term by term, the result being

$$T \ll \theta: \qquad\qquad N_{\text{phon}} \doteqdot 47N(T/\theta)^3 \tag{8.212}$$

where we have used 2.612 for the sum $\sum_j 1/j^3$.

To make use of Eq. (8.208) we need an estimate of the volume dependence of the Debye characteristic temperature. By means of quite plausible arguments it can be shown * that approximately

$$\gamma = \alpha V/\beta C_v \qquad (8.213)$$

where α is the coefficient of thermal expansion, β the compressibility, and C_v the heat capacity; compare Eq. (7.621). The same reasoning also suggests that this quantity is independent of temperature. Its value has been tabulated for a large number of elements by Mott and Jones (*op. cit.*, Appendix II). For gold $\gamma = 3.0$, $\theta = 170\ °\text{K}$, and we may calculate p at the melting point of gold, $T = 1336\ °\text{K}$. Here the total energy is practically its classical value $3NkT$, and a straightforward arithmetical calculation leads to the result:

Au at T_m: $\qquad\qquad p = 10^{11}$ dynes/cm^2, or 10^5 atm

Clearly this phonon radiation pressure is opposed by an intrinsic pressure exerted by the walls of the crystal, due essentially to cohesion, or binding energy U: $p_{\text{int}} = \partial U/\partial V$, and while the cohesive energy can be found experimentally at the natural volume of the crystal, its dependence on volume is less easily determined. At $0\ °\text{K}$ the extrapolated cohesive energy of gold is about 3.4×10^{11} ergs/cm^3 and so has the same order of magnitude as the phonon radiation pressure at the melting point. The difference, at any temperature, between the cohesive energy and the phonon pressure may be interpreted as the tensile strength, which, for gold, is about 1.4×10^{10} dynes/cm^2 at ordinary temperatures. As we shall see later, the electron gas in a metal also contributes appreciably to the internal pressure, so that no exact balance can be expected between the cohesion and the phonon pressure alone. The process of melting could be pictured as occurring when the phonon radiation pressure gets too big for the intrinsic pressure; in the liquid state, the phonon pressure is drastically reduced by removal of the transverse modes, and the intrinsic pressure is again sufficient to hold it.

8.3   Ideal Bose-Einstein gas of material particles. Assemblies of atoms having even mass numbers like D and He^4 are to be described by symmetrical eigenfunctions, and the Bose-Einstein statistics are appropriate. Although helium is no longer a gas under ordinary pressures at temperatures low enough to make quantum degeneracy effects large, it is nevertheless of great interest to study the theoretical properties of the Bose-Einstein gas because it is found that liquid helium exhibits many remarkable similarities in its behavior to a Bose-Einstein gas. It is widely believed that the anomalous properties of liquid helium at very low temperatures will eventually be understood in terms of the quantum degenerate anomalies of the Bose-Einstein statistics. We return to this practical question later.

The general expression for the most probable distribution-in-energy for the Bose-Einstein gas, Eq. (3.511), may be written

* Mott and Jones, *Properties of Metals and Alloys*, Oxford, 1936; p. 19.

$$n_r = \omega_r \{\exp (\epsilon_r - \mu)/kT - 1\}^{-1} \qquad (8.301)$$

where μ has to be found from the condition,

$$N = \sum_r n_r \qquad (8.302)$$

The weights ω_r were found in Eq. (3.204):

$$\omega_r = \omega(\epsilon)d\epsilon = 2\pi V(2m)^{3/2}h^{-3}\epsilon^{1/2}d\epsilon \qquad (8.303)$$

where the lowest energy level is taken as the zero. This expression is valid for an integral approximation to the sum in Eq. (8.302), which then becomes [see Eq. (8.103)]:

$$N = 2\pi V(2m/h^2)^{3/2} \int_0^\infty \epsilon^{1/2} \sum_{j=1}^\infty \exp \{j(\mu - \epsilon)/kT\}d\epsilon \qquad (8.304)$$

Writing $z = j\epsilon/kT$ and recalling that $\int_0^\infty z^{1/2}e^{-z}dz = \frac{1}{2}\sqrt{\pi}$ (Pierce's Tables #481), we find that

$$N = V(2\pi mkT/h^2)^{3/2} \sum_{j=1}^\infty (1/j)^{3/2}e^{j\mu/kT} \qquad (8.305)$$

This is the equation to be solved by inversion for μ as a function of T and N/V. At sufficiently high temperatures, it is clear by inspection that, for a given N/V, Eq. (8.305) requires that μ/kT be rather large and negative, and then the series reduces almost to its first (major) term. The equation then coincides with the corresponding equation (3.208) for the classical ideal gas, as of course it should. As T is decreased, N/V remaining fixed—or alternatively we may increase N/V keeping T fixed—it is clear that Eq. (8.305) requires that $-\mu/kT$ become smaller, and the series may no longer be equated to its first term. Let us lower T—or increase N/V—to the point where Eq. (8.305) requires μ/kT to be exactly zero. In this case the equation becomes

$$N = V(2\pi mkT/h^2)^{3/2} \sum_{j=1}^\infty 1/j^{3/2} \qquad (8.306)$$

We shall indicate this temperature by a subscript, and writing the numerical value of the series:

$$\sum_{j=1}^\infty 1/j^{3/2} = 2.612 \qquad (8.307)$$

we have

$$N/V = 2.612(2\pi mkT_0/h^2)^{3/2} \qquad (8.308)$$

Now let us try to evaluate μ for temperatures even lower than T_0, still using Eq. (8.305). Apparently it is necessary to find a value of μ that gives the series $\sum (1/j)^{3/2}e^{j\mu/kT}$ a somewhat greater value than 2.612; as we lower T continuously we need the series to have a continuously increasing sum. However, if we put a positive value of μ in the series, we find that the sum diverges immediately to infinity; there is no value of μ that gives the series a sum between 2.612 and infinity. It is therefore impossible to satisfy Eq. (8.305) for $T < T_0$. The trouble here is due to the integration approximation on which Eq. (8.305) is based. Let us inspect the discrete form, Eq. (8.302). The numbers of particles in the lowest states, remembering that the lowest one of all has zero energy, $\epsilon_0 = 0$, are

$$n_0 = \omega_0/(e^{-\mu/kT} - 1)$$

$$n_1 = \omega_1\{\exp(\epsilon_1 - \mu)/kT - 1\}^{-1}$$

etc.

If we put $\mu = 0$ in the formula for n_0, we would get $n_0 = \infty$, so that in fact we can never have μ exactly equal to zero no matter how low T may be. The integration approximation is therefore unreliable in the T_0 temperature region. As can be seen from Eq. (8.303), the integration approximation assigns zero weight to the lowest state, $\epsilon = 0$, so that ω_0 is effectively zero on this approximation, and the number $n_0 = 0/0$ is indeterminate.

Actually as T approaches T_0 from above, μ becomes almost zero, but not quite. It gets so close to zero that we can put it equal to zero in all but the lowest state, where an exact value is required; this exact value can make n_0 as large as necessary to make up the difference between N and the total in the other states.

The exact calculations are extremely involved, but a simple device exists that gives the same results to within about 0.2 per cent and is based on a sound physical picture. We accept the integration approximation as giving a good estimate of the number in all but the lowest state, and explicitly include the lowest state separately:

$$N = n_0 + V(2\pi mkT/h^2)^{3/2} \sum_{j=1} (1/j)^{3/2} e^{j\mu/kT} \qquad (8.309)$$

Above T_0 this is consistent with Eq. (8.305) because the integration approximation has ω_0 as zero and n_0 negligible. But Eq. (8.309) no longer fails below T_0 because we can now put $\mu = 0$ in the summed part and write

$T \leq T_0$: $\qquad\qquad N = n_0 + 2.612V(2\pi mkT/h^2)^{3/2} \qquad (8.310)$

Making use of Eq. (8.308), this can be written in the form

$T \leq T_0$: $\qquad\qquad n_0 = N\{1 - (T/T_0)^{3/2}\} \qquad (8.311)$

Equating this to $\omega_0/(e^{-\mu/kT} - 1)$, we find

$$-\mu/kT = \ln[1 + (\omega_0/N)\{1 - (T/T_0)^{3/2}\}^{-1}] \qquad (8.312)$$

In this result, ω_0 is a small number of order unity, so that, as soon as $T < T_0$, the term in ω_0/N becomes exceedingly small; hence we may write the logarithm equal to the small term itself:

$T < T_0$: $\qquad\qquad -\mu/kT = (\omega_0/N)\{1 - (T/T_0)^{3/2}\}^{-1} \qquad (8.313)$

Since N is of the order 10^{21}, we see that for all $T < T_0$ the value of μ is almost, but not exactly, zero.

Summarizing, it appears that μ increases with decreasing T from a negative value toward zero, which value it practically reaches at the temperature T_0, and below this temperature μ remains almost exactly zero. Above T_0 the population n_0 of the lowest state is practically zero, but as soon as T goes below T_0, the population n_0 starts to increase according to Eq. (8.311), in fact reaching a value comparable with the entire population of the gas as soon as T is appreciably lower than T_0. The number of particles remaining in the other (excited) states drops as T falls:

$$T < T_0: \qquad\qquad N_n = N - n_0 = N(T/T_0)^{3/2} \qquad\qquad (8.314)$$

As T approaches absolute zero, the entire gas condenses into the lowest state, leaving no atoms at all in the excited states.

The temperature T_0, at which the population of the lowest state suddenly begins to increase, depends on the density of the gas, through Eq. (8.308). If we imagine the gas to have the same density as liquid helium, T_0 turns out to be about 3.14 °K. Liquid helium in fact does have a transition temperature at 2.19 °K, below which it becomes a superfluid, and we shall see later why this is regarded as more than a coincidence.

The exact character of the transition in a Bose-Einstein gas at T_0 has been the subject of considerable discussion. The fact is that there is no mathematical discontinuity anywhere in the behavior of the free energy μ as a function of temperature, and doubt was originally felt as to whether any condensation really occurs. It has been proved, however, by Fowler and Jones,[*] that the sharpness of the break in the $\mu - T$ curve at T_0 increases with increasing N, and that in the limit $N \rightarrow \infty$, the gradient $d\mu/dT$ does indeed become discontinuous at T_0. As we shall see immediately, the heat capacity curve, $C_v - T$, suffers a similar break in gradient at T_0, and this too becomes mathematically discontinuous only in the limit $N \rightarrow \infty$.

This kind of discontinuity is really all we should ask for in statistical theory. Consider what it would mean to check by experiment whether or not dC_v/dT were discontinuous at T_0. In the first place, we have to measure a quantity of heat dH over a finite temperature interval dT below T_0 in order to find $C_v = dH/dT$; after this we have to repeat a similar measurement for another temperature range dT' and take the second difference. This whole process is to be repeated again with intervals dT_1 and dT_1' both above T_0. To examine the continuity at T_0 we must then allow all the temperature intervals to approach zero, converging on T_0 from either side. This last step is not only impracticable, it is in principle impossible. To measure a small temperature interval dT, one may for example use a sensitive thermocouple, which converts dT into an emf, and measure this with a sensitive potentiometer arrangement. This emf suffers

[*] R. H. Fowler and H. Jones, *Proc. Cambridge Phil. Soc.*, **34** (1938), p. 573.

from thermal noise—fluctuations about a mean value due to equilibrium fluctuations in the electron gas conducting the potential, and, if dT is made too small, the deflection gets swamped by the background noise. This kind of difficulty is inherent in the statistical nature of physical measurements; whatever macroscopic device one might use for measuring dT, it inevitably suffers from a blurring of the finest details. From this physical point of view, the question as to whether a mathematical discontinuity occurs or not is of no importance.

Let us calculate the energy of the Bose-Einstein gas:

$$E = \sum_r n_r \epsilon_r = \sum_r \omega_r \epsilon_r \{\exp\,(\epsilon_r - \mu)/kT - 1\}^{-1} \tag{8.315}$$

and again employ the integration approximation for all levels above the lowest. The lowest state may be included explicitly, but because its energy is zero, it will make no difference anyway. Thus:

$$E = 0n_0 + \int_0^\infty \frac{2\pi V(2m/h^2)^{3/2}\epsilon^{3/2}d\epsilon}{\exp\,(\epsilon - \mu)/kT - 1} \tag{8.316}$$

This integral is evaluated as in Eq. (8.304), using $\int_0^\infty z^{3/2}e^{-z}dz = \tfrac{3}{4}\sqrt{\pi}$ (Pierce's Tables #481), and the result is

$$E = (3kT/2)V(2\pi mkT/h^2)^{3/2} \sum_j (1/j)^{5/2} e^{j\mu/kT} \tag{8.317}$$

Making use of Eq. (8.305), this may be expressed in the form:

$$E = (3NkT/2) \left\{ \sum_j (1/j)^{5/2} e^{j\mu/kT} \right\} \div \left\{ \sum_j (1/j)^{3/2} e^{j\mu/kT} \right\} \tag{8.318}$$

although we must remember that, like Eq. (8.305), this equation is valid only above the temperature T_0.

The energy below T_0 is found by writing μ equal to zero in Eq. (8.317); the term in which we would need the more exact value of μ, the lowest state, is zero anyway. Thus:

$$T \leq T_0: \qquad E/V = \tfrac{3}{2}kT(2\pi mkT/h^2)^{3/2} \sum_j 1/j^{5/2} \tag{8.319}$$

Making use of Eq. (8.308) and the numerical value of the series,

$$\sum_{j=1} 1/j^{5/2} = 1.341 \tag{8.320}$$

we find

$$T \leq T_0: \qquad E/N = 0.7701kT(T/T_0)^{3/2} \tag{8.321}$$

The heat capacity below T_0 derived from this is evidently

$$T \leq T_0: \qquad C_v = 1.925Nk(T/T_0)^{3/2} \tag{8.322}$$

Turning next to the general solution of Eq. (8.305) for the dependence of μ on T and N/V at temperatures above T_0, it is convenient to introduce the following abbreviations:

$$Z = (2\pi m k T/h^2)^{3/2} e^{\mu/kT} = (N/V_0) e^{\mu/kT}/2.612 \qquad (8.323)$$

where V_0 is defined by

$$N/V_0 = (2\pi m k T/h^2)^{3/2} \sum_j 1/j^{3/2} \qquad (8.324)$$

Also

$$b_j = (2\pi m k T/h^2)^{3(1-j)/2}(1/j)^{5/2} = (1/j)^{5/2}(2.612 V_0/N)^{j-1} \qquad (8.325)$$

It is to be noted that V_0 is the volume which would make the assigned temperature T the transition temperature for the given N. In terms of these abbreviations, Eq. (8.305) may be written

$$N/V = \sum_{j=1} j b_j Z^j \qquad (8.326)$$

and the mathematical problem is to invert this series to express Z as a power series in (N/V):

$$Z = a_1(N/V) + a_2(N/V)^2 + \cdots \qquad (8.327)$$

The coefficients a_1, a_2, $\cdots$ are obtained by direct substitution of Eq. (8.327) into Eq. (8.326) and equating coefficients of equal powers of N/V. The result is eventually found to be

$$V \geq V_0: \quad Z = (N/V)\{1 - 0.9235(V_0/V) + 0.3926(V_0/V)^2 - 0.1027(V_0/V)^3$$
$$+ 0.0188(V_0/V)^4 - 0.0027(V_0/V)^5 \cdots\} \quad (8.328)$$

Putting this into Eq. (8.323), taking the logarithm, and expanding this logarithm as a series in (V_0/V), we find μ/kT as a function of V_0/V:

$$V \geq V_0: \quad \mu/kT = \ln(2.612 V_0/V) - 0.9235(V_0/V) - 0.034(V_0/V)^2$$
$$- 0.002(V_0/V)^3 \cdots \quad (8.329)$$

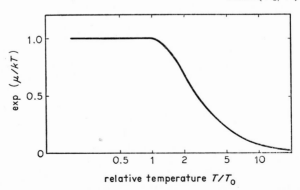

FIG. 8.31.   Free energy μ of B.E. gas.   Calculated from Eqs. (8.329) and (8.332).

Finally, we use these expressions to evaluate the sum appearing in Eq. (8.317) and the result is

$$V \geq V_0: \qquad E = \tfrac{3}{2}NkT\{1 - 0.462V_0/V - 0.0225(V_0/V)^2 - \cdots\} \qquad (8.330)$$

which is the desired expression for E as a function of T, through the temperature dependence of V_0 given by its definition in Eq. (8.324). Remembering this last point, and taking the temperature derivative of Eq. (8.330), we find the heat capacity:

$$V \geq V_0: \qquad C_v = \tfrac{3}{2}Nk\{1 + 0.231V_0/V + 0.045(V_0/V)^2 + \cdots\} \qquad (8.331)$$

To interpret these equations, we observe from Eq. (8.324) that the higher T, the smaller is V_0/V for a given N/V. In fact we may write Eq. (8.324), using Eq. (8.308), in the form:

$$V_0/V = (T_0/T)^{3/2} \qquad (8.332)$$

Thus for sufficiently high values of T/T_0, we may neglect the terms V_0/V in Eq. (8.331), and the heat capacity approaches the classical value $3Nk/2$ asymptotically. As T falls, the heat capacity rises above the classical value to a maximum at the transition temperature $T = T_0$, which can be shown to have exactly the same value (viz., $1.925Nk$) as that obtained from Eq. (8.322) as T approaches T_0 from below. There is no discontinuity of heat capacity, but there is a discontinuity in the slope of the heat capacity curve at T_0.

Finally we wish to find the equation of state of the Bose-Einstein gas, and to do this we first calculate the entropy and then make use of the elementary thermodynamic relations between entropy and pressure. The entropy is again defined as k times the logarithm of the number of complexions. From Eq. (2.243),

$$S = k \sum_r \{n_r \ln (\omega_r/n_r + 1) + \omega_r \ln (1 + n_r/\omega_r)\} \qquad (8.333)$$

From Eq. (8.301), we have $kT \ln (1 + \omega_r/n_r) = \epsilon_r - \mu$, and therefore $1 + n_r/\omega_r = \{1 - \exp (\mu - \epsilon_r)/kT\}^{-1}$; hence Eq. (8.333) becomes

$$S = \sum_r n_r(\epsilon_r - \mu)/kT - \sum_r k\omega_r \ln \{1 - \exp (\mu - \epsilon_r)/kT\} \qquad (8.334)$$

If we write $F = N\mu$ for the Gibbs free energy, the first sum in S is simply $E/T - F/T$. The second sum can be evaluated as an integral, using Eq. (8.303). Because μ is either negative or zero, the logarithm in the integrand can be expanded as a series, and we obtain

$$S = E/T - F/T + 2\pi kV(2m/h^2)^{3/2} \int_0^\infty \epsilon^{1/2} \sum_{j=1}^\infty (1/j)e^{j(\mu-\epsilon)/kT}d\epsilon \qquad (8.335)$$

This contains a sum of familiar definite integrals

$$\int_0^\infty \epsilon^{1/2}e^{-j\epsilon/kT}d\epsilon = (kT/j)^{3/2}(\tfrac{1}{2}\sqrt{\pi})$$

and we therefore have finally

$$S = (E - F)/T + kV(2\pi mkT/h^2)^{3/2} \sum_{j=1} (1/j)^{5/2} e^{j\mu/kT} \qquad (8.336)$$

Making use of the thermodynamic relation $pV = TS + F - E$, we have

$$pV = kTV(2\pi mkT/h^2)^{3/2} \sum_{j=1} (1/j)^{5/2} e^{j\mu/kT} \qquad (8.337)$$

Comparing this with Eq. (8.317), we see that

$$pV = 2E/3 \qquad (8.338)$$

—a relation that proves to be true also for Fermi-Dirac statistics. Moreover both Eqs. (8.337) and (8.317) are true below T_0 with $\mu = 0$, so that the Eq. (8.338) is also true below the transition.

Above the transition temperature, we use the development of Eq. (8.330) and find the equation of state in the form:

$$T > T_0: \qquad pV = NkT\{1 - 0.462V_0/V - 0.0225(V_0/V)^2 - \cdots\} \qquad (8.339)$$

and recalling Eq. (8.332):

$$T > T_0: \qquad pV = NkT\{1 - 0.462(T_0/T)^{3/2} - 0.0225(T_0/T)^3 - \cdots\} \qquad (8.340)$$

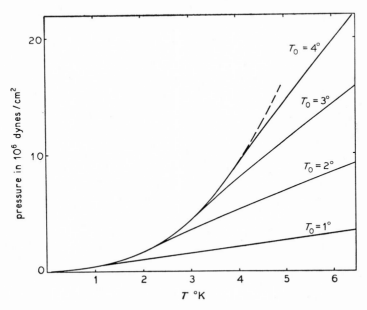

FIG. 8.32.   Pressure of B.E. gas.   Plotted for four different densities from Eqs. (8.340) and (8.342) with degeneracy temperatures T_0 1,2,3, and 4 °K; densities correspondingly $\rho = 0.027, 0.095, 0.139,$ and 0.214 g/cc.

At sufficiently high temperatures, this approaches the classical ideal gas equation. As T falls toward T_0 the pressure becomes appreciably less than the classical pressure for the given density. When T is lower than T_0 we may use Eqs. (8.338) and (8.319) to find

$$T \leq T_0: \qquad p = kT(2\pi mkT/h^2)^{3/2} \sum_{j=1} (1/j)^{5/2} \qquad (8.341)$$

The significant peculiarity about this result is that below T_0 the pressure of the Bose-Einstein gas ceases to depend on the density of the gas and depends only on the temperature. Making use of Eq. (8.308), we can put the last result in the form:

$$T \leq T_0: \qquad pV = 0.5134NkT(T/T_0)^{3/2} \qquad (8.342)$$

This shows that at $T = T_0$ the pressure for any given density has dropped to almost one-half the classical value. In one sense the equation may be misleading; its apparent dependence on density is fictitious because the factor $T_0^{3/2}$ is exactly proportional to N/V, so the terms cancel.

8.4   Ideal Fermi-Dirac gas—electrons.   As was remarked in § 3.6, the classical approximation is not valid for an assembly of electrons because of the small electronic mass. Indeed the classical statistics would be approximately valid only at temperatures above a million degrees Kelvin, and compared with such temperatures, one can regard ordinary laboratory temperatures as zero to a first approximation. It turns out therefore that the absolute zero temperature limit of the Fermi-Dirac statistics is of great interest, and it is sufficient to make first order corrections on this limit in order to describe the situation at ordinary temperatures.

The general expression for the most probable distribution-in-energy for the Fermi-Dirac gas, Eq. (3.512), is

$$n_r = \omega_r \{\exp (\epsilon_r - \mu)/kT + 1\}^{-1} \qquad (8.401)$$

where μ is to be found from the equation,

$$N = \sum_r n_r \qquad (8.402)$$

The degeneracy weights ω_r are just double those used before in Eq. (8.303), because there are two spin states of an electron to each wave function as counted in finding the weights; see § 1.5. Thus we shall take

$$\omega_r = \omega(\epsilon)d\epsilon = 4\pi V(2m/h^2)^{3/2}\epsilon^{1/2}d\epsilon \qquad (8.403)$$

This permits us to write Eq. (8.402) as an integral:

$$N = 4\pi V(2m/h^2)^{3/2} \int_0^\infty \{\exp (\epsilon - \mu)/kT + 1\}^{-1} \epsilon^{1/2}d\epsilon \qquad (8.404)$$

As remarked at the beginning of this section, we attempt to solve this for μ in the limit $T = 0$, calling the solution μ_0. For the Bose-Einstein gas, we found negative values of μ approaching zero at $T = 0$; however, it is clear that in the Fermi-Dirac gas if μ were negative as $T \to 0$, the term $e^{(\epsilon - \mu)/kT}$ would approach infinity, and the integral of Eq. (8.404) would be zero for all values of ϵ appearing in the integration. Evidently this could never satisfy Eq. (8.404), so we must look for positive solutions of the equation for μ near $T = 0$.

Since μ must be positive, we can consider those values of ϵ first that are less than μ. When T approaches zero, the term $e^{(\epsilon - \mu)/kT}$ becomes zero no matter how small $\epsilon - \mu$ may be, as long as it is negative. For this part of the energy range, the integrand of Eq. (8.404) is therefore equal to $\epsilon^{1/2}$ in the limit $T = 0$. Next consider those values of ϵ greater than μ. In this case the term $e^{(\epsilon - \mu)/kT}$ becomes infinite as $T \to 0$, and the integrand is therefore zero in this limit. Equation (8.404) thus may be written in the limit

$$\lim T \to 0: \qquad N = 4\pi V (2m/h^2)^{3/2} \int_0^{\mu_0} \epsilon^{1/2} d\epsilon \qquad (8.405)$$

which solves to give

$$\mu_0 = (h^2/8m)(3N/\pi V)^{2/3} \qquad (8.406)$$

Comparing Eqs. (8.405) and (8.403), we see that in the limit $T = 0$ every one of the states given by Eq. (8.403) is fully occupied up to the energy μ_0, while all of the states above this energy are empty. For free electrons in a metal the magnitude of μ_0 is several electron volts, comparable with the work function. It is also of the same order of magnitude as the kinetic energy of an atom in a classical gas at 10^5 °K, and therefore very great compared with the kinetic energy of atoms at ordinary laboratory temperatures.

The total energy of the electrons in the gas is obtained from the general formula

$$E = \sum_r \epsilon_r n_r$$

$$= 4\pi V (2m/h^2)^{3/2} \int_0^{\infty} \{\exp (\epsilon - \mu)/kT + 1\}^{-1} \epsilon^{3/2} d\epsilon \qquad (8.407)$$

Now let $T = 0$ and put μ_0 for μ in this; then we have

$$E = 4\pi V (2m/h^2)^{3/2} \int_0^{\mu_0} \epsilon^{3/2} d\epsilon = \tfrac{3}{5} N \mu_0 \qquad (8.408)$$

The mean energy per electron at the absolute zero—the zero-point energy—is therefore $3\mu_0/5$, and is very large compared with the gas kinetic energy per atom even at ordinary temperatures. This high zero-point energy is characteristic of the Fermi-Dirac statistics and is clearly due to the operation of the exclusion principle.

To find μ as a function of T and N/V, we have to evaluate the integral in Eq. (8.404), and we could proceed in precisely the same way as in the Bose-

Einstein problem by expanding the integrand in a series: $\{\exp{(\epsilon - \mu)/kT + 1}\}^{-1}$ $= \sum_j (-1)^{j-1} \exp{\{j(\mu - \epsilon)/kT\}}$. This series has a finite sum when $\mu < 0$, so we can integrate it term by term and obtain the following result:

$$N = 2V(2\pi mkT/h^2)^{3/2} \sum_j (-1)^{j-1}(1/j)^{3/2} e^{j\mu/kT} \qquad (8.409)$$

This is exactly analogous to Eq. (8.305) in the Bose-Einstein problem, and we define a degeneracy temperature T_0 at which $\mu = 0$:

$$N = 2V(2\pi mkT_0/h^2)^{3/2} \sum_j (-1)^{j-1}/j^{3/2} = 1.5286V(2\pi mkT_0/h^2)^{3/2} \quad (8.410)$$

When $T < T_0$, this fails to give a solution for μ, again because the series in Eq. (8.409) diverges if we try to put μ positive. In the Bose-Einstein case we were able to save the situation by noting that the population of the zeroth state became anomalously great as μ approached zero. Here we cannot say this, because $n_0 = \omega_0/(e^{-\mu/kT} + 1)$ remains of the same order of magnitude as μ passes through zero. In fact here μ does become positive as T drops through T_0; because the series expansion (8.409) becomes invalid, we proceed instead as follows, making use of the fact that the zero temperature limit makes a good first approximation.

Consider the function:

$$g(\epsilon) = \{\exp{(\epsilon - \mu)/kT + 1}\}^{-1} \qquad (8.411)$$

which appears in the integrand of Eq. (8.404). At $T = 0$, this is a step function, being unity in the energy range $0 < \epsilon < \mu$ and zero in the range $\mu < \epsilon < \infty$. At temperatures appreciably above zero, the function has its corners rounded off somewhat, and the step shifts a little because μ depends slightly on T. The object of the calculation is to find exactly how much μ shifts with increasing temperature. The function $g(\epsilon)$ has a gradient with respect to ϵ that is almost zero everywhere except in the immediate neighborhood of $\epsilon = \mu$. In order to include a discussion both of the integrand in (8.404) and that in (8.407), let us consider an integral of the form:

$$I = \int_0^\infty f(\epsilon)g(\epsilon)d\epsilon \qquad (8.412)$$

where $f(\epsilon)$ is a monatonic increasing function of ϵ starting from zero when ϵ is zero. Because of the special character of the function $g(\epsilon)$, we can integrate Eq. (8.412) by parts and obtain a new integrand that is different from zero only over a small range of ϵ–values, where $dg(\epsilon)/d\epsilon$ differs from zero appreciably. To carry this through, we write

$$F(\epsilon) = \int_0^\epsilon f(y)dy \qquad (8.413)$$

so that

$$dF(\epsilon)/d\epsilon = f(\epsilon)$$

Writing the last equation into Eq. (8.412), we see at once that

$$I = F(\epsilon)g(\epsilon)\Big|_0^\infty - \int_0^\infty F(\epsilon)\{dg(\epsilon)/d\epsilon\}d\epsilon \tag{8.414}$$

But from its definition Eq. (8.413), $F(\epsilon) = 0$ at $\epsilon = 0$, while $g(\epsilon)$ is zero at $\epsilon = \infty$, so the integrated part of Eq. (8.414) vanishes at both limits, leaving

$$I = -\int_0^\infty F(\epsilon)\{dg(\epsilon)/d\epsilon\}d\epsilon \tag{8.415}$$

Because $dg(\epsilon)/d\epsilon$ vanishes, except near $\epsilon = \mu$, we may usefully express $F(\epsilon)$ as a series in powers of $(\epsilon - \mu)$:

$$F(\epsilon) = F(\mu) + (\epsilon - \mu)F'(\mu) + \tfrac{1}{2}(\epsilon - \mu)^2 F''(\mu) + \cdots \tag{8.416}$$

from Taylor's theorem. Putting this series into Eq. (8.415), we get

$$I = -\sum_{r=0} (1/r!)F^r(\mu)\int_0^\infty (\epsilon - \mu)^r\{dg(\epsilon)/d\epsilon\}d\epsilon \tag{8.417}$$

Write $z = (\epsilon - \mu)/kT$, then from Eq. (8.411),

$$kT\{dg(\epsilon)/d\epsilon\} = -e^z/(1 + e^z)^2 \tag{8.418}$$

and Eq. (8.417) becomes

$$I = \sum_{r=0} (1/r!)F^r(\mu)(kT)^r \int_{-\mu/kT}^\infty z^r\{e^z/(1 + e^z)^2\}dz \tag{8.419}$$

The integrand here is practically zero, except in a small region around the value $z = 0$, so the lower limit can be changed to minus infinity without making any difference to the integral. We next observe that Eq. (8.418) is symmetrical with respect to sign changes in z: $e^z/(1 + e^z)^2 = e^{-z}/(1 + e^{-z})^2$. From this it follows that if r is odd, $\int_{-\infty}^\infty z^r\{e^z/(1 + e^z)^2\}dz = 0$, while if r is even, we can write the integral as twice that over half the range, viz., from zero to infinity, thus:

$$I = \sum_{n=0} \{2/(2n)!\}F^{2n}(\mu)(kT)^{2n}\int_0^\infty z^{2n}\{e^{-z}/(1 + e^{-z})^2\}dz \tag{8.420}$$

Expanding $1/(1 + e^{-z})^2$ by the binomial theorem, one obtains

$$\int_0^\infty z^{2n}\{e^{-z}/(1 + e^{-z})^2\}dz = \sum_{j=1} (-1)^{j-1}\int_0^\infty jz^{2n}e^{-jz}dz$$

(Pierce's Tables #493) $= (2n)! \sum_{j=1} (-1)^{j-1}/j^{2n}$ unless $n = 0$. In case $n = 0$ we can write down the $r = 0$ term in Eq. (8.419) at once, because the integral becomes simply $-\int_0^\infty \{dg(\epsilon)/d\epsilon\}d\epsilon = -g(\epsilon)\Big|_0^\infty = 1$. Finally therefore Eq. (8.420) becomes

$$I = F(\mu) + \sum_{n=1} 2F^{2n}(\mu)(kT)^{2n} \sum_{j=1} (-1)^{j-1}/j^{2n} \qquad (8.421)$$

To use this result to compute the integral in Eq. (8.404), we must set

$$F(\mu) = \int_0^\mu \epsilon^{1/2}d\epsilon = \tfrac{2}{3}\mu^{3/2}, \quad F'(\mu) = \mu^{1/2},$$

$$F''(\mu) = \tfrac{1}{2}\mu^{-1/2}, \quad F''''(\mu) = \tfrac{3}{8}\mu^{-5/2}, \quad \text{etc.}$$

and we find at once that

$$N = \tfrac{8}{3}\pi V(2m/h^2)^{3/2}\mu^{3/2}\{1 + \tfrac{3}{2}(kT/\mu)^2 \sum_{j=1} (-1)^{j-1}/j^2$$

$$+ \tfrac{9}{8}(kT/\mu)^4 \sum_{j=1} (-1)^{j-1}/j^4 + \cdots\} \qquad (8.422)$$

Making use of Eq. (8.406) on the left of this equation, and writing in the numerical values of the series on the right,[*] one obtains

$$\mu_0^{3/2} = \mu^{3/2}\{1 + (\pi^2/8)(kT/\mu)^2 + (7\pi^4/640)(kT/\mu)^4 + \cdots\} \qquad (8.423)$$

Because in fact μ is much greater than kT this series converges quite rapidly, and the above three terms are sufficient for an excellent approximation. However we need μ in terms of μ_0 and T, rather than the reverse that appears in Eq. (8.423); to invert the series, we write it in the form:

$$\mu_0^{3/2} = \mu^{3/2}(1 + Y) \quad \text{or} \quad \mu = \mu_0(1 + Y)^{-2/3}$$

where

$$Y = (\pi^2/8)(kT/\mu)^2 + (7\pi^4/640)(kT/\mu)^4 \qquad (8.424)$$

Expanding the right side by the binomial theorem, one gets

$$\mu = \mu_0(1 - 2Y/3 + 5Y^2/9 - \cdots)$$

and writing in the above value for Y, and evaluating it up to terms of the order $(kT/\mu)^4$, one obtains

$$\mu = \mu_0\{1 - (\pi^2/12)(kT/\mu)^2 + (\pi^4/720)(kT/\mu)^4 + \cdots\} \qquad (8.425)$$

The two smaller terms on the right may be evaluated in terms of μ_0 by successive approximation. Thus the first small term is found from the second approximation: $\mu = \mu_0\{1 - (\pi^2/12)(kT/\mu_0)^2\}$, while the term in $(kT/\mu)^4$ is so small we

---

[*] *Tables of Functions*, Jahnke and Emde, p. 269, defines the Riemann Zeta functions $\zeta(z) = \sum_{n=1} 1/n^z$ and $(1 - 2^{1-z})\zeta(z) = \sum_{n=1} (-1)^{n-1}(1/n)^z$ and gives tables of $\zeta(z)$ on p. 273.

may put $\mu = \mu_0$ without significant error.   Finally therefore

$$\mu = \mu_0\{1 - (\pi^2/12)(kT/\mu_0)^2 - (\pi^4/80)(kT/\mu_0)^4 + \cdots\} \qquad (8.426)$$

For most practical purposes the first two terms of this series are enough, but for precise estimates of temperature variations all three are needed.

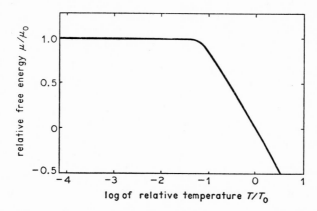

FIG. 8.41.   Free energy μ of a Fermi-Dirac gas. T_0 is the degeneracy temperature related to the Fermi energy $3.37\mu_0$ by Eqs. (8.406) and (9.210): kT_0.

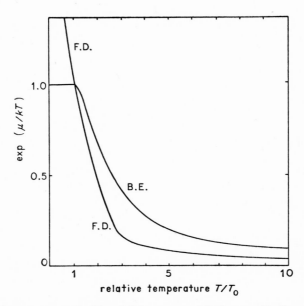

FIG. 8.42.   Free energy μ of a Fermi-Dirac gas and B.E. gas with the same degeneracy temperature T_0 calculated from Eqs. (8.329) and (8.426).   Note that the ratio of Fermi energy to the degeneracy temperature is a universal constant.

We are now ready to evaluate the energy of the gas from Eq. (8.407), using Eq. (8.421) with the following definitions:

$$F(\mu) = \int_0^{\mu} \epsilon^{3/2} d\epsilon = \tfrac{2}{5} \mu^{5/2}, \quad F''(\mu) = \tfrac{3}{2} \mu^{1/2},$$

$$F''''(\mu) = - \tfrac{3}{8} \mu^{-3/2}, \quad \text{etc.}$$

Using Eq. (8.406) to eliminate V from the expression, we find

$$E = \tfrac{3}{5} N (\mu/\mu_0)^{3/2} \mu \{ 1 + (5\pi^2/8)(kT/\mu)^2 - (7\pi^4/384)(kT/\mu)^4 + \cdots \}$$

Using Eq. (8.425) in each term on the right of this, retaining only terms up to $(kT/\mu_0)^4$, one finally derives

$$E = \tfrac{3}{5} N \mu_0 \{ 1 + (5\pi^2/12)(kT/\mu_0)^2 - (\pi^4/16)(kT/\mu_0)^4 + \cdots \} \quad (8.427)$$

With Eq. (8.406) this gives E as a function of T and N/V. Keeping V fixed, and therefore μ_0 constant, and taking temperature derivatives, we obtain the heat capacity at constant volume:

$$C_v = \tfrac{1}{2} \pi^2 N k (kT/\mu_0) \{ 1 - (3\pi^2/10)(kT/\mu_0)^2 + \cdots \} \quad (8.428)$$

To a first approximation this is linear in T.

It is of interest to derive formulae for the entropy of a Fermi-Dirac gas both in the low and higher temperature limits. We return to Eq. (2.244) and set

$$S_{\text{F.D.}} = k \sum_r \{ n_r \ln (\omega_r/n_r - 1) - \omega_r \ln (1 - n_r/\omega_r) \} \quad (8.429)$$

Using Eq. (8.401) in this we have

$$S_{\text{F.D.}} = k \sum_r n_r (\epsilon_r - \mu)/kT + \sum_r k \omega_r \ln \{ 1 + e^{(\mu - \epsilon_r)/kT} \}$$

Changing from sum to integral, expanding the logarithm, and performing the integration term by term, similar to the derivation of Eq. (8.409), we find

$$S_{\text{F.D.}} = (E - F)/T + 2kV(2\pi mkT/h^2)^{3/2} \sum_j (-1)^{j-1}(1/j)^{5/2} e^{j\mu/kT} \quad (8.430)$$

which is valid as long as μ is not positive, i.e., at higher temperatures. Of greater practical interest is the low temperature approximation, when μ becomes positive and approaches the value μ_0, or more precisely, the value given in Eq. (8.426). To evaluate the entropy in this case, we start from the form:

$$S_{\text{F.D.}} = (E - F)/T + 4\pi kV(2m/h^2)^{3/2} \int_0^{\infty} \epsilon^{1/2} \ln \{ 1 + e^{(\mu - \epsilon)/kT} \} d\epsilon \quad (8.431)$$

When T is very small we can approximate to the logarithm expression in the integrand (a) when $\epsilon < \mu$, and (b) when $\epsilon > \mu$:

Case (a): $\ln\{1 + e^{(\mu-\epsilon)/kT}\} = (\mu - \epsilon)/kT + e^{(\epsilon-\mu)/kT}$

Case (b): $\ln\{1 + e^{(\mu-\epsilon)/kT}\} = e^{(\mu-\epsilon)/kT}$

Therefore the integral breaks into two parts, and we have to evaluate

$$\int_0^\mu \{\epsilon^{1/2}(\mu - \epsilon)/kT + \epsilon^{1/2}e^{(\epsilon-\mu)/kT}\}d\epsilon + \int_\mu^\infty \epsilon^{1/2}e^{(\mu-\epsilon)/kT}d\epsilon$$

Integrating the logarithm by parts, and comparing the resulting expression with that for E in Eq. (8.407), we find that

$$S_{F.D.} = (E - F)/T + 2E/3T = 5E/3T - F/T$$

or, from the relations already derived for E and $F = N\mu$:

$$S_{F.D.} = (N\mu_0/T)\{(\tfrac{1}{2}\pi^2)(kT/\mu_0)^2 - (\pi^4/20)(kT/\mu_0)^4 \cdots\} \qquad (8.432)$$

The same result can also be derived from the thermodynamic formula:

$$S = \int_0^T (C_v/T)dT \qquad (8.433)$$

and from Eq. (8.428) for the heat capacity.

As mentioned earlier, it turns out that μ_0 is much greater than kT for all laboratory temperatures, so that Eq. (8.428) means that the heat capacity of an electron gas is exceedingly small, only about 1 per cent, compared with that of a classical gas. This is specially remarkable when we remember that the total energy of the electron gas is extremely large compared with that of a classical gas; the large energy remains almost constant as temperature is increased, until reaching exceedingly high temperatures of the order 10^5 °K, when the Fermi-Dirac gas begins to turn classical. One of the major troubles with the classical free-electron theory of conductivity of metals was the fact that the heat capacities of metals are very little different from those of nonconducting solids. If the metals contain free electrons in sufficient numbers to account for their high conductivity, these electrons ought, on the classical picture, to share in the equilibrium of kinetic energy, and so contribute a specific heat of the same order of magnitude as if they were ordinary atoms—which would roughly double the heat capacity of conductors compared with nonconductors. The fact that the Fermi-Dirac statistics of free electrons predicts an extremely small heat capacity contribution was one of the major factors leading to the general acceptance of the Fermi-Dirac statistics.

The lattice contributions to heat capacity vary roughly as T^3 at low temperatures; see § 7.2 on the Debye theory. Therefore if T can be made sufficiently small, the linear dependence of electronic heat capacity on T would permit it to become appreciable, compared with the lattice contributions; although, of course, both contributions are very small at such low temperatures, and accurate measurements are difficult. This method has actually been employed to make quantitative checks on Eq. (8.428), by fitting C_v, T curves to a formula of the type:

$$C_v = AT + BT^3 \qquad (8.434)$$

As an example we cite recent measurements by Estermann, Friedberg, and Goldman on the specific heats of several metals between 1.8° and 4.2 °K.[*] Plotting C_v/T versus T^2, we would expect a straight line, with slope proportional to $1/\theta^3$, and intercept giving the electronic term N/μ_0. Actually the Debye θ is not a constant over any extended temperature range, but may be taken constant over the liquid helium range used in this work. The results are tabulated below, giving the Debye characteristic temperature θ and the electronic term A. The values of A can be interpreted in the light of the energy band theory of metals, but for this, the student is referred to the original paper. The last column gives

Metal	θ °K	$A \times 10^4$ cal/mole °K²	m^*/m
Copper	315	1.80	1.47
Magnesium	342	3.25	1.33
Titanium	280	8.00	3.15
Zirconium	265	6.92	2.24
Chromium	418	3.80	2.93

the effective mass of the free electron compared with its true mass, as deduced from the linear term in the heat capacity.

Another interesting recent development concerns the pressure exerted by the electron gas in a metal. From $A = E - ST$ and $p = -(\partial A/\partial V)_T$, it is easy to prove that

$$p = 2E/3V = (2N\mu_0/5V)\{1 + (5\pi^2/12)(kT/\mu_0)^2 + \cdots\} \qquad (8.435)$$

Putting into this the numerical values ordinarily found for metals, e.g., $N/V \sim 10^{22}$, $\mu_0 \sim 5$ ev $= 8 \times 10^{-12}$ erg, we find $p \sim 10^{11}$ dynes/cm², or 10^5 atmospheres. This is the same order of magnitude as the phonon gas pressure and the cohesive energy in a metal. In our discussion, § 7.3, of the Born–von Karman theory of crystals, it was mentioned that the Cauchy relation between compressibility and rigidity, expected theoretically for an ideal crystal, is not satisfied in practice in metals. It is believed that this anomaly can in part be understood in terms of the electron gas pressure and its contribution to the bulk elasticity modulus of the metal.[†]

[*] *Phys. Rev.*, **87** (1952), p. 582.

[†] Jules de Launay, *N.R.L. Report* **4083** (Jan. 13, 1953); *J. Chem. Phys.*, **21** (1953) p. 1975.

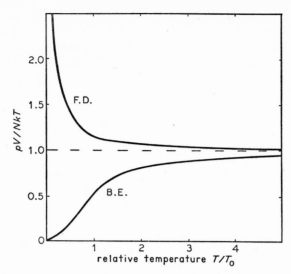

FIG. 8.43.   Equations of state of Fermi-Dirac and B.E. gas compared.

8.5   Quantum degenerate monolayers.   Recent experimental work on the adsorption of helium isotopes at very low temperatures makes it of interest to discuss both the Bose-Einstein and the Fermi-Dirac statistics of quantum degenerate monolayers. The results will be applied to the adsorption problem in the following chapter. The general formulae for the most probable distribution-in-energy are still valid here, except that we must now use the two-dimensional expressions for the weights (see Problem 9 of Chapter IV):

$$\omega(\epsilon)d\epsilon = A(2\pi m/h^2)d\epsilon \qquad (8.501)$$

where A is the area of the assembly. The free energy parameter is determined by integrating the distribution-in-energy in exact analogy with the three-dimensional problem in Eqs. (8.304) and (8.404):

$$N = A(2\pi m/h^2)\int_0^\infty \{\exp{(\epsilon - \mu)/kT \mp 1}\}^{-1}d\epsilon \qquad (8.502)$$

where the upper sign applies in Bose-Einstein statistics; the lower sign in Fermi-Dirac statistics. If the latter are applied to a monolayer of electrons, we have to double the weights; but at the moment we are interested in applying the formulae eventually to the isotopes of helium rather than electrons.

Confining our attention first to the Bose-Einstein case, the analogous expression to Eq. (8.305) is easily shown to be

$$N = A(2\pi mkT/h^2) \sum_{j=1} (1/j)e^{j\mu/kT} \qquad (8.503)$$

while the corresponding calculations of the energy of a Bose-Einstein gas start from

$$E = A(2\pi m/h^2)\int_0^\infty \{\exp(\epsilon - \mu)k/T - 1\}^{-1}\epsilon d\epsilon \tag{8.504}$$

and lead easily to

$$E = AkT(2\pi mkT/h^2)\sum_{j=1}(1/j)^2 e^{j\mu/kT} \tag{8.505}$$

Before solving Eq. (8.503) for μ as a function of T and N/V, we note first that it is significantly different from the result, Eq. (8.305), in the three-dimensional gas, in that, whereas the series in the latter had a finite sum at its radius of convergence, in the two-dimensional case, the series:

$$\sum_{j=1}(1/j)e^{j\mu/kT} = -\ln(1 - e^{\mu/kT}) \tag{8.506}$$

has an infinite sum when μ is put equal to zero. The sum can in fact have any desired value between zero and infinity by adjusting μ. This means that there is no transition temperature below which the integration approximation breaks down in the two-dimensional gas, and no sudden condensation into the lowest state.

To solve Eq. (8.503) generally, we may write Eq. (8.506) on the right and get

$$1 - e^{\mu/kT} = e^{-\theta} \tag{8.507}$$

where

$$\theta = N/(2\pi mkTA/h^2) \tag{8.508}$$

therefore

$$\mu/kT = \ln(1 - e^{-\theta}) \tag{8.509}$$

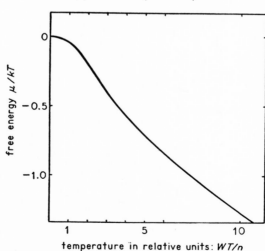

FIG. 8.51.   Free energy μ of a B.E. monolayer. The curve is plotted from Eq. (8.509) with the surface numerical density $N/A = n \times 10^{14}$; W is the atomic weight; T is in °K.

At sufficiently high temperatures $\theta < 1$, and we shall then be able to make the following development:

$$\mu/kT = \ln \theta + \ln (1 - \tfrac{1}{2}\theta + \theta^2/6 - \theta^3/24 + \cdots)$$
$$= \ln \theta - \tfrac{1}{2}\theta + \theta^2/24 - 0 + \cdots \qquad (8.510)$$

This series is valid when $\theta < 1$ and includes terms up to θ^3. At sufficiently low temperatures $\theta > 1$, and we can instead develop Eq. (8.509) in the following rapidly converging series:

$$\mu/kT = -e^{-\theta} - \tfrac{1}{2}e^{-2\theta} - \tfrac{1}{3}e^{-3\theta} - \cdots \qquad (8.511)$$

This series converges for all positive values of θ, but is useful only for low temperatures or large values of θ, where it converges rapidly.

These equations complete the specification of μ as a function of T if we include the definition Eq. (8.508).

Putting Eq. (8.510) into Eq. (8.505) gives E as a function of T, and after a straightforward algebraic calculation, the following result is derived:

$$\theta < 1: \qquad E = NkT(1 - \tfrac{1}{4}\theta + \theta^2/36 - \cdots) \qquad (8.512)$$

accurate to terms in θ^3. Remembering the temperature dependence of θ we can differentiate this to find the heat capacity at constant area:

$$\theta < 1: \qquad C_A = Nk(1 - \theta^2/36 + \cdots) \qquad (8.513)$$

also accurate to terms in θ^3.

On the other hand at low temperatures where $\theta > 1$, we shall use Eq. (8.509) directly in Eq. (8.505), use the binomial theorem on the jth power of $(1 - e^{-\theta})$, and find exactly:

$$E = NkT(1/\theta) \sum_{j=1} \left\{ 1/j^2 + \sum_{r=1}^{j} (-1)^r j! e^{-r\theta}/[j^2 r!(j-r)!] \right\} \qquad (8.514)$$

At sufficiently low temperatures, the second (double) sum can be neglected compared with the first sum. This is true even of the temperature derivative, so that the low temperature limit of the heat capacity is

$$\theta \gg 1: \qquad C_A = 2Nk(1/\theta) \sum_{j=1} 1/j^2 \qquad (8.515)$$

Comparing this result with that for the three-dimensional Bose-Einstein gas, we see that whereas the latter, Eq. (8.322), had a heat capacity proportional to $T^{3/2}$, here it is proportional to T. Moreover both the heat capacities, three- and two-dimensional, are independent of the number of atoms in the gas, because θ is proportional to N and so cancels it. Thus for the three-dimensional gas we may write Eq. (8.308) into Eq. (8.322) and get

$$T \leq T_0: \qquad C_v = 1.925 VkT^{3/2}(2\pi mk/h^2)^{3/2} \sum_{j=1} 1/j^{3/2} \qquad (8.516)$$

while in the two-dimensional gas, we get from Eqs. (8.508) and (8.515):

$$\theta \gg 1: \qquad\qquad C_A = 2AkT(2\pi mk/h^2) \sum_{j=1} 1/j^2 \qquad\qquad (8.517)$$

The smaller the number of atoms, the smaller the temperature range over which these peculiarities exist; in the three-dimensional gas they set in suddenly at T_0, while in the two-dimensional gas, they come on gradually as T is lowered below where $\theta = 1$. It is also worth noticing that, whereas in the three-dimensional gas C_v increases above the classical value as T goes down toward the transition temperature, in the two-dimensional gas C_A decreases continuously with decreasing T. These comparisons serve as an example, of which there are many in theoretical physics, of the dangers involved in extrapolating from the solution of a two-dimensional problem to possible solutions of an as-yet unsolved problem in three dimensions.

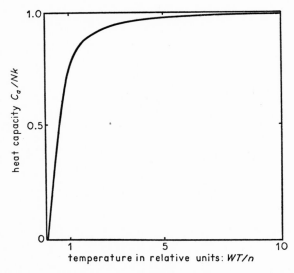

FIG. 8.52.   Heat capacity of B.E. monolayer at constant area.   The numerical density $N/A = n \times 10^{14}$; W is atomic weight; T is in °K.

Turning now to the equation of state of the monolayer, we proceed from the expression for entropy, in the same way as we did in the three-dimensional problem. Equation (8.334), being generally valid, can also be used here, but in going over from the discrete form to the integration approximation, we now use the weights of Eq. (8.501). In place of Eq. (8.335), therefore,

$$S = (E - F)/T + (2\pi mkA/h^2) \int_0^\infty \sum_{j=1} (1/j)e^{j(\mu-\epsilon)/kT} d\epsilon \qquad (8.518)$$

If we write Π for the "pressure" of the monolayer in dynes/cm, we have

$$\Pi A = TS + F - E$$

and so

$$\Pi = (2\pi mkT/h^2) \sum_{j=1} (1/j)e^{j\mu/kT} \int_0^\infty e^{-j\epsilon/kT} d\epsilon$$

$$= kT(2\pi mkT/h^2) \sum_{j=1} (1/j)^2 e^{j\mu/kT} \tag{8.519}$$

Comparing this with Eq. (8.505), we find

$$\Pi A = E \tag{8.520}$$

replacing the corresponding relation Eq. (8.338) in three-dimensional gas. Equations (8.512) and (8.514) at once lead to the equation of state in the two ranges of temperatures:

High T, $\theta < 1$:
$$\Pi A = NkT(1 - \tfrac{1}{4}\theta + \cdots) \tag{8.521}$$

Low T, $\theta \gg 1$:
$$\Pi = kT(2\pi mkT/h^2) \sum_{j=1} 1/j^2 \tag{8.522}$$

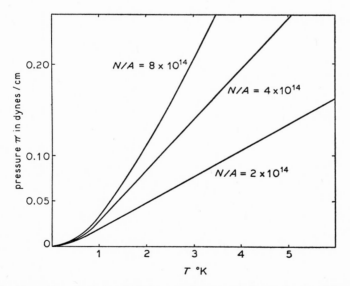

Fig. 8.53. Equation of state of B.E. monolayer of helium atoms. Note increased effect of quantum degeneracy with increased numerical density; note also the difference in form between these curves and those of Figure 8.32 for three-dimensional gas.

Like the three dimensional gas, the pressure of the monolayer becomes a function only of T at low enough temperatures, independent of density.

Returning now to the lower sign in Eq. (8.502), we have for the Fermi-Dirac case:

$$N = A(2\pi m/h^2)\int_0^\infty \{\exp{(\epsilon - \mu)/kT} + 1\}^{-1}d\epsilon \qquad (8.523)$$

As in the three dimensional case, the integrand again becomes a step function when $T = 0$. If μ_0 is the value of μ at $T = 0$, we have

$$N = A(2\pi m/h^2)\int_0^{\mu_0} d\epsilon = (2\pi m/h^2)A\mu_0$$

or

$$\mu_0 = Nh^2/2\pi mA \qquad (8.524)$$

The total energy of the monolayer at $T = 0$ is

$$E = A(2\pi m/h^2)\int_0^{\mu_0} \epsilon d\epsilon = A(\pi m/h^2)\mu_0{}^2 \qquad (8.525)$$

and using Eq. (8.524), this yields

$T = 0$:
$$E = \tfrac{1}{2}N\mu_0 \qquad (8.526)$$

The mean zero point energy per particle is one half the Fermi energy μ_0.

To find μ as a function of T, we first note that Eq. (8.523) can be expanded in the form:

$$N = A(2\pi mkT/h^2) \sum_{j=1} (-1)^{j-1}(1/j)e^{j\mu/kT} \qquad (8.527)$$

Writing θ from Eq. (8.508), this equation becomes

$$\theta = \ln{(1 + e^{\mu/kT})} \qquad (8.528)$$

or

$$\mu/kT = \theta + \ln{(1 - e^{-\theta})} \qquad (8.529)$$

At high temperatures this expands in the form:

$\theta < 1$:
$$\mu/kT = \ln\theta + \tfrac{1}{2}\theta + \theta^2/24 - 0 + \cdots \qquad (8.530)$$

while at sufficiently low temperatures,

$\theta \gg 1$:
$$\mu/kT = \theta - e^{-\theta} - \cdots \qquad (8.531)$$

The limiting value of this at $T = 0$ is clearly the same as that given by Eq. (8.524). Putting Eq. (8.530) for μ/kT at high temperatures into the expression for the energy as a function of T, yields

$$E = A(2\pi m/h^2)\int_0^\infty \{\exp{(\epsilon - \mu)/kT} + 1\}^{-1}\epsilon d\epsilon$$

$$= AkT(2\pi mkT/h^2) \sum_{j=1} (-1)^{j-1}(1/j)^2 e^{j\mu/kT} \qquad (8.532)$$

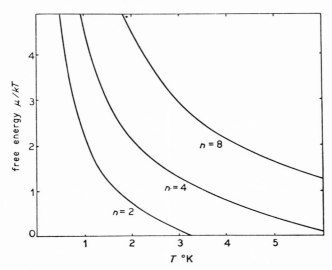

Fig. 8.54. Free energy μ of Fermi-Dirac monolayer of He^3 isotope atoms. The numerical density $N/A = n \times 10^{14}$. Any one of the three curves shown could be taken as a universal curve if the T axis is interpreted as atomic weight times T/n. Compare with Figure 8.51.

and writing Eq. (8.530) into this finally results in

$$\theta < 1: \qquad E = NkT(1 + \tfrac{1}{4}\theta + \theta^2/36 - \cdots) \qquad (8.533)$$

which is correct to terms in θ^3. Differentiating this gives

$$\theta < 1: \qquad C_A = Nk(1 - \theta^2/36 - \cdots) \qquad (8.534)$$

also correct to terms in θ^3. For very low temperatures, we use Eq. (8.529) directly in Eq. (8.532) to find

$$E = NkT(1/\theta) \sum_{j=1}^{\infty} (-1)^{j-1} \left\{ 1/j^2 + \sum_{r=1}^{j} (-1)^r j! e^{-r\theta}/[j^2 r!(j-r)!] \right\} e^{j\theta} \qquad (8.535)$$

Again at sufficiently low temperatures, the second (double) sum is negligible, and we are left with

$$\theta \gg 1: \qquad E = NkT(1/\theta) \sum_{j=1}^{\infty} (-1)^{j-1} e^{j\theta}/j^2 \qquad (8.536)$$

Because θ is very large, we shall have to change the form of this series to permit numerical evaluation. To do this we write $z = e^\theta$ and consider the series

$$f(z) = \sum_{j=1}^{\infty} (-1)^{j-1} z^j/j^2 \qquad (8.537)$$

and

$$zf'(z) = \sum_{j=1}^{\infty} (-1)^{j-1} z^j/j = \ln(1+z)$$

This is equivalent to

$$f'(z) = (1/z)\{\ln z + \ln (1 + 1/z)\}$$
$$= (1/z) \ln z + (1/z) \sum_{j=1} (-1)^{j-1}(1/z)^j/j$$

Integrating this series term by term yields

$$f(z) = \tfrac{1}{2}(\ln z)^2 - \sum_{j=1} (-1)^{j-1}(1/z)^j/j^2 + K \qquad (8.538)$$

where the arbitrary constant K is determined by comparing Eq. (8.537) with Eq. (8.538) at $z = 1$. The final result is

$$f(z) = \tfrac{1}{2}(\ln z)^2 + 2 \sum_{j=1} (-1)^{j-1}/j^2 - \sum_{j=1} (-1)^{j-1}(1/z)^j/j^2 \qquad (8.539)$$

When z is very large, we may neglect all the last sum in this expression, and so we find for Eq. (8.536) the following result:

$$\theta \gg 1: \qquad E = NkT\{\tfrac{1}{2}\theta + (2/\theta) \sum_{j=1} (-1)^{j-1}/j^2\} \qquad (8.540)$$

The first term is evidently independent of T, from Eq. (8.508) defining θ, and so does not contribute to the heat capacity, which is

$$\theta \gg 1: \qquad C_A = 4Nk(1/\theta) \sum_{j=1} (-1)^{j-1}/j^2 \qquad (8.541)$$

which, from Eqs. (8.508) and (8.524), may be written as

$$\theta \gg 1: \qquad C_A = 4Nk(kT/\mu_0) \sum_{j=1} (-1)^{j-1}/j^2 \qquad (8.542)$$

for comparison with Eq. (8.428) in the three-dimensional Fermi-Dirac gas. On the other hand, it may also be written in the form:

$$C_A = 4AkT(2\pi mk/h^2) \sum_{j=1} (-1)^{j-1}/j^2 \qquad (8.543)$$

showing that, like the Bose-Einstein gas, the limiting heat capacity at very low temperatures is independent of the number of atoms per unit area. The equation of state of the Fermi-Dirac monolayer is most easily found by first proving the theorem of Eq. (8.520), and this is easily done. Then we have directly:

$$\theta < 1, \text{High } T: \qquad \Pi A = NkT(1 + \tfrac{1}{4}\theta + \cdots) \qquad (8.544)$$

$$\theta \gg 1, \text{Low } T: \qquad \Pi A = NkT\{\tfrac{1}{2}\theta + (2/\theta) \sum_{j=1} (-1)^{j-1}/j^2\} \qquad (8.545)$$

The last equation may be written in the interesting form:

$$\Pi = (hN/A)^2/4\pi m + 4\pi m(kT/h)^2 \sum_{j=1} (-1)^{j-1}/j^2 \qquad (8.546)$$

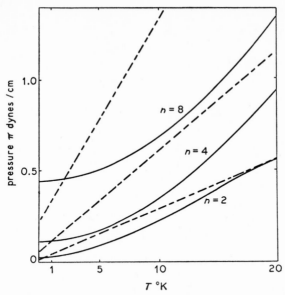

FIG. 8.55. Equation of state of Fermi-Dirac monolayer of He^3 isotope atoms. The numerical densities are $n \times 10^{14}$ per cm^2; the three dashed lines are the high temperature asymptotes for the densities $n = 2,4,8$.

which shows that the limiting pressure remaining at absolute zero of temperature is proportional to the square of the surface density.

8.6   A Bose-Einstein free volume liquid model. We saw in § 7.6 that it is possible to set up a phenomenological theory of the liquid phase, in which the atoms are free to wander throughout a potential well that occupies the free volume. A zeroth approximation consists in replacing the liquid by a gas trapped in a potential well of uniform depth. The atoms are then subject to the same statistics as the gas phase except that their energy spectrum is shifted down by an energy equal to the depth of the well. The depth of the well represents a smoothed out approximation to the van der Waals attractive forces between atoms, and therefore we expect to find that its depth must depend on the density of the liquid. We consider here the Bose-Einstein statistics of such a model. In finding the most probable distribution-in-energy, we take the variation of the logarithm of the Bose-Einstein number of complexions, and also the variations of total energy and total number of particles in the phase, combine these variations with Lagrangian multipliers, and equate the total to zero. The fact that the depth of the potential well depends on density makes our former results, viz., Eq. (8.301), inadequate here. Thus the expression for the total energy is

$$E = \sum_r n_r(\epsilon_r - W) \qquad (8.601)$$

where $\epsilon_0 = 0$ is the lowest energy level, and W represents the depth of the potential well. In making virtual variations of the system, we vary n_r and keep the energy spectrum unaltered; keeping the energy spectrum unaltered means keeping the free volume fixed, so that varying the numbers n_r means varying the density, which in turn varies W. Thus

$$\delta E = \sum_r \delta n_r \{ \epsilon_r - (W + N \partial W / \partial N) \} \tag{8.602}$$

Comparing this expression with that used in the Bose-Einstein gas, we see that ϵ_r is here replaced by $\epsilon_r - W^*$ where

$$W^* = W + N \partial W / \partial N \tag{8.603}$$

This correspondence carries through, as can easily be checked, and we find for the most probable distribution-in-energy:

$$n_r = \omega_r \{ \exp (\epsilon_r - W^* - \mu) / kT - 1 \}^{-1} \tag{8.604}$$

Going over to the integration approximation, yields the following equation for determining the free energy μ:

$$N = V_f (2\pi m k T / h^2)^{3/2} \sum_{j=1} (1/j)^{3/2} e^{j(\mu + W^*)/kT} \tag{8.605}$$

It is clear that we can now take over the results of § 8.3 on the Bose-Einstein gas, simply by substituting $\mu + W^*$ for μ everywhere. For example, to obtain the equation of state of the liquid at sufficiently high temperatures, we turn to Eq. (8.334), make the above substitution, and proceed as before to Eq. (8.337). Here we must remember that for E we now have Eq. (8.601), and then write in place of Eq. (8.336):

$$S = (E - F)/T - (N^2/T) \partial W / \partial N$$
$$+ k V_f (2\pi m k T / h^2)^{3/2} \sum_{j=1} (1/j)^{5/2} e^{j(\mu + W^*)/kT} \tag{8.606}$$

The pressure of the liquid is then found from the thermodynamic relation used to derive Eq. (8.337), giving

$$p = (V_f / V) kT (2\pi m k T / h^2)^{3/2} \sum_{j=1} (1/j)^{5/2} e^{j(\mu + W^*)/kT} - (N^2/V)(\partial W / \partial N) \tag{8.607}$$

The last part of this, depending on the potential well, corresponds to the intrinsic pressure of classical theory, and is clearly due to the fact that the depth of the potential well changes with density.

Inspection of Eq. (8.605) at once reveals that there is so close an analogy with the corresponding expression for the Bose-Einstein gas, that we expect a *lambda*-transition in this liquid model due to quantum degeneracy. Thus if T_0 is the temperature at which $\mu = -W^*$; then:

$$N/V_f = (2\pi m k T_0 / h^2)^{3/2} \sum_{j=1} 1/j^{3/2} \tag{8.608}$$

For all temperatures below T_0, the series in Eq. (8.605) diverges unless we keep μ at this critical value $-W^*$. The number given by (8.605) then represents only those not in the zeroth state. The number in the zeroth state is the difference $n_0 = N - V_f (2\pi mkT/h^2)^{3/2} \sum_{j=1} 1/j^{3/2}$, so that

$$T \leq T_0: \qquad\qquad n_0 = N\{1 - (T/T_0)^{3/2}\} \qquad\qquad (8.609)$$

exactly as in the Bose-Einstein gas. The pressure of the model liquid is

$$T \leq T_0: \quad p = (V_f/V)kT(2\pi mkT/h^2)^{3/2} \sum_{j=1} 1/j^{5/2} - (N^2/V)(\partial W/\partial N) \qquad (8.610)$$

Unlike the Bose-Einstein gas, the pressure of the liquid below the *lambda*-transition point is not independent of the density of the liquid, both because of the potential well term $\partial W/\partial N$ and because V_f depends on V and is not generally simply proportional to V.

The energy of the liquid model is

$$T \leq T_0: \qquad\qquad E = \tfrac{3}{2} V_f kT(2\pi mkT/h^2)^{3/2} \sum_{j=1} 1/j^{5/2} - NW \qquad (8.611)$$

and the heat capacity below the *lambda*-transition is

$$T \leq T_0: \qquad\qquad C_v = 1.925Nk(T/T_0)^{3/2} - N(\partial W/\partial T)_V \qquad (8.612)$$

In the ideal gas it was noted that the heat capacity had no discontinuity at the transition temperature, only a break in its temperature derivative. The extra term in C_v, here due to the potential well, may or may not contribute a discontinuity to the heat capacity. One would occur if the temperature derivative of W were discontinuous at the *lambda*-point:

$$T = T_0: \qquad\qquad \Delta C_v = -N\Delta(\partial W/\partial T)_V \qquad\qquad (8.613)$$

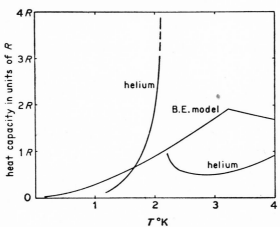

FIG. 8.61. Comparison between heat capacities of liquid helium and Bose-Einstein model liquid.

The dependence of the transition temperature on density is modified in the liquid model insofar as V_f is not proportional to V, as can be seen from comparing Eqs. (8.608) and (8.308). Differentiating Eq. (8.608) with respect to T_0, one finds

$$d \ln (N/V)/d \ln T_0 = \tfrac{3}{2} + d \ln (V_f/V)/d \ln T_0 \qquad (8.614)$$

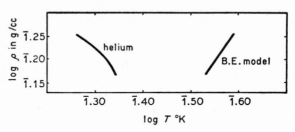

FIG. 8.62. Comparison between *lambda*-lines of liquid helium and Bose-Einstein model liquid.

If this model is used to discuss the properties of liquid helium at its *lambda*-transition, we substitute the observed numerical density N/V for the liquid and the mass of a helium atom for m in Eq. (8.608), and try to adjust V_f/V so that T_0 coincides with the observed transition temperature $T_\lambda = 2.19$ °K. Unfortunately the required ratio V_f/V turns out to be greater than unity, which violates the physical picture behind the free volume model.

A significant improvement in this model can be made as follows. In setting up Eq. (8.605) to determine μ, it was assumed that the same energy spectrum as in an ideal gas was appropriate for the liquid, except for the potential well. Obviously this is an oversimplification, and we may seek some relatively simple modification of this spectrum in an effort to make a more realistic model for liquid helium. An early suggestion due to F. London was very useful. This was that the spectrum remained essentially the same as that of an ideal gas but that the effective mass of each atom was increased. This hypothesis is a priori attractive for two reasons. First, it is a familiar result of hydrodynamics that any macroscopic body moving through a liquid has an increased effective mass because of the inertia of the liquid which its motion has to displace. Second, the motion of an atom among surrounding atoms may be compared with the motion of an electron in a lattice potential, and it is known that the lattice potential field results in a modified effective mass for the electron. Then if an effective mass m^* replaces m in Eq. (8.608) we can adjust m^* so that the transition temperature becomes identical with T_λ for liquid helium. Thus if $V_f = V$, $m^*/m = T_0/T_\lambda = 1.43$.

A further suggestion is also of great interest: that the lowest states have a finite energy gap between them and the other "excited states" in the spectrum. In working out the statistical formulae, these lowest states then have to be counted discretely, only the excited ones being amenable to the integration approximation. This leads to a considerable complication of the analysis, because the integrals are no longer between zero and infinity. The results are, however, encouraging: a finite jump in heat capacity occurs at the transition, and the heat capacity curve below the transition becomes sharper, and so fits the observed curve for liquid helium much better. A further advantage is that by virtue of the energy gap, transitions between the lowest states and the excited states are inhibited, and the particles in the lowest states are therefore unable to exchange momentum with the rest of the fluid: in other words the model "explains" the superfluidity of the lowest states. This model is of course nothing more than a phenomenological hypothesis, and before it can be taken very seriously, it will require justification in terms of a detailed molecular theory; not too much progress in this direction has yet been made. It is, however, a very fruitful hypothesis and forms the basis of the two-fluid model of liquid helium to be discussed in more detail in the next section.

8.7 Bose-Einstein gas with prescribed total momentum and the two-fluid model for liquid helium. In § 4.9 we developed the general expression for the most probable distribution-in-momentum, given a prescribed total momentum **P** for the whole assembly. For the Bose-Einstein gas, the result obtained was

$$n_\mathbf{p} = \omega_\mathbf{p}\{\exp{(\epsilon_\mathbf{p} - \mathbf{v}\cdot\mathbf{p} + \tfrac{1}{2}mv^2 - \mu)/kT} - 1\}^{-1} \qquad (8.701)$$

where **v** is the mean particle velocity (drift motion) due to the prescribed momentum $\mathbf{P} = Nm\mathbf{v}$. In the light of § 8.3, we may now look for a condensation in the momentum distribution at a low enough temperature. Summing over all the momentum states:

$$N = \sum_\mathbf{p} \omega_\mathbf{p} \sum_{j=1} \{\exp{[j(\mu - \epsilon_\mathbf{p} + \mathbf{v}\cdot\mathbf{p} - \tfrac{1}{2}mv^2)/kT]}\} \qquad (8.702)$$

Writing $\omega_\mathbf{p} = (V/h^3)dp_1dp_2dp_3$, $\epsilon_\mathbf{p} = (p_1{}^2 + p_2{}^2 + p_3{}^2)/2m$, and $\mathbf{v}\cdot\mathbf{p} = v_1p_1 + v_2p_2 + v_3p_3$, the sum over p can be treated as a triple integral, and after some elementary calculations, we find that Eq. (8.702) goes over precisely to the same result as for the distribution-in-energy, viz., Eq. (8.305). The condensation therefore occurs exactly as before, when $\mu \to 0$, and at the same degeneracy temperature as given by Eq. (8.306). Below this temperature we must exclude the lowest state from the integration approximation, and consider it separately, as in Eq. (8.310). The lowest state, however, is now given by the minimum (zero) value of the expression $\epsilon_\mathbf{p} - \mathbf{v}\cdot\mathbf{p} + \tfrac{1}{2}mv^2$, appearing in the exponent of Eq. (8.701). This expression is just $(\mathbf{p} - m\mathbf{v})^2/2m$, since $\epsilon_\mathbf{p} = p^2/2m$, and therefore the momentum state into which the condensation occurs is exactly that for which

$$\mathbf{p} = m\mathbf{v} = \mathbf{p}_0 \qquad (8.703)$$

The number in this state is the same as given in Eq. (8.311):

$$n_{\mathbf{p}0} = N\{1 - (T/T_0)^{3/2}\} \qquad (8.704)$$

We notice particularly that the condensation is not into the lowest energy state, but into the one momentum state that happens to coincide with the mean atomic velocity vector due to the prescribed total momentum. All the n_{p0} atoms have exactly the same momentum. The remaining atoms, the normal fraction of the liquid, are still distributed over the whole spectrum in the normal fashion, their average making a contribution to the total prescribed momentum.

These results are of great interest in connection with the two-fluid model of liquid helium already mentioned in the last section. Here we consider a model with a special energy level spectrum designed to lead to a two-fluid effect in a Bose-Einstein gas. The particles condensed into the momentum state $\mathbf{p}_0$ will be called the low-energy semiphase, the remainder the normal semiphase. The reason the two semiphases can be considered separately will be evident shortly. We suppose that the energy of any atom depends in a completely normal fashion on its momentum, whatever that momentum may be:

$$\epsilon_{\mathrm{p}} = p^2/2m \qquad (8.705)$$

but that a critical momentum exists, $\mathbf{p}_c$, relative to a co-ordinate system at rest with the center of mass of the normal semiphase, such that the density of states ω_{p} is anomalously small for all momenta less than $\mathbf{p}_c$. In Eq. (8.705) the mass m may be an effective mass rather than the true mass. To match the properties of liquid helium, it is found that the critical momentum $\mathbf{p}_c$ must be roughly equal to the momentum of a helium atom moving with the speed 30 cm/sec. The number of states in a normal spectrum having momenta less than this is of the order 10^{13}, so it is possible for the postulated anomaly to reduce the number of states by many orders of magnitude, and still leave a very large number of states available for the low-energy semiphase: so many indeed that in summing over these states, an integration approximation can still be used. Except for the one state into which the condensation occurs, the population of the other states is proportional to the degeneracy of the state, and hence the population of the low-energy states can be made very small compared with the states just above the critical momentum $\mathbf{p}_c$—except of course for the one state containing the condensed semiphase. If the assembly has zero prescribed momentum, condensation occurs into the lowest energy, and $p = 0$; there is effectively a gap in energy, $p_c^2/2m$, between the condensate and the next state, just above $\mathbf{p}_c$, with any appreciable population. The quantum theory of transition probabilities shows that these probabilities are proportional to the density of states into which the transition occurs, while they decrease rapidly with increasing energy difference between the two sets of states involved. Therefore there will be much fewer than the normal number of transitions between the low-energy semiphase and the normal semiphase states. Also, because almost all the atoms in the low energy states have exactly the same momentum, there can be practically no viscosity in the low-energy semiphase, and no friction between it and the normal semiphase. Therefore we can regard the low-energy semiphase as a separate superfluid that can be given a mass momentum different from and independent of the motion of the normal semiphase. Indeed, this internal relative motion between the two semiphases is a new constant of the motion, characteristic of this model, that can be prescribed in advance. Alternatively, we may prescribe individual total momenta for each of the two semiphases, using parameters like γ of Eq. (4.902) for each one. To see exactly how this goes, we have to start again from the beginning. The restrictions replacing Eq. (4.901) are now:

$$N = \sum_p n_p, \quad E = \sum_p \epsilon_p n_p \tag{8.706}$$

$$\mathbf{P}_n = \sum_{p>p_c} \mathbf{p} n_p, \quad \mathbf{P}_s = \sum_{p<p_c} \mathbf{p} n_{ps} \tag{8.707}$$

The argument proceeds exactly as before, and we arrive at the following distribution-in-momentum:

$$|\mathbf{p} - \mathbf{p}_n| < \mathbf{p}_c: \quad n_{ps} = \omega_{ps}\{\exp(\alpha + \beta\epsilon_{ps} + \gamma_s \cdot \mathbf{p}_s) - 1\}^{-1} \tag{8.708}$$

$$|\mathbf{p} - \mathbf{p}_n| > \mathbf{p}_c: \quad n_p = \omega_p\{\exp(\alpha + \beta\epsilon_p + \gamma_n \cdot \mathbf{p}) - 1\}^{-1} \tag{8.709}$$

where $\mathbf{p}_n$ is the mean drift momentum $\mathbf{P}_n/N_n$ of the normal semiphase.

It can be shown that in approximating to the sum $N_n = \sum_{p>p_c} n_p$ by means of an integral, it makes very little difference to leave out the states below the small critical momentum $\mathbf{p}_c$, and the integral can be taken from zero up, to a good enough approximation. Therefore the parameters α and γ_n turn out to have the same interpretation as before, in terms now of the normal fluid alone:

$$\left.\begin{aligned} \gamma_n &= -\mathbf{v}_n/kT \\ \alpha &= -\mu/kT + \tfrac{1}{2}m v_n{}^2/kT \end{aligned}\right\} \tag{8.710}$$

where $\mathbf{v}_n = \mathbf{p}_n/m$ is the velocity of the center of mass of the normal fluid. Recalling that γ_n is determined from the prescribed momentum of the normal fluid, we know also that γ_s is determined from the prescribed momentum of the superfluid upon condensation. Condensation occurs when the series obtained by summing Eq. (8.709) begins to diverge, at $\mu = 0$; and we require this condensation to occur into the state having the prescribed momentum $\mathbf{p}_s = \mathbf{P}_s/N_s$. This can be secured only by adjusting the parameter γ_s so that this state $\mathbf{p}_s$ does indeed make the exponent in Eq. (8.708) go to zero when $\mu = 0$. Using Eq. (8.710) for α, we therefore need

$$\tfrac{1}{2}m(v_n{}^2 + v_s{}^2)/kT + m\gamma_s \cdot \mathbf{v}_s = 0 \tag{8.711}$$

The interpretation of γ_s is evidently not as simple as that of γ_n. If the motion of the normal fluid is prescribed to be zero,

$$\mathbf{v}_n = 0: \qquad \gamma_s = -\tfrac{1}{2}\mathbf{v}_s/kT \tag{8.712}$$

If on the other hand $\mathbf{v}_n$ and $\mathbf{v}_s$ are prescribed in such a way that the center of mass of the whole mixture remains at rest, $N_n\mathbf{v}_n + N_s\mathbf{v}_s = 0$, we find instead, after some elementary algebra:

$$\gamma_s = -\tfrac{1}{2}\mathbf{v}_s\{1 + (N_s/N_n)^2\}/kT \tag{8.713}$$

If the momentum of the superfluid were prescribed to be greater than $\mathbf{p}_c$, nothing in the foregoing algebra would break down, but the condensation would send the system into one of the states having normal degeneracy and interacting strongly with the normal fluid; this would destroy the superfluid character of the condensed part and forbid our having prescribed its momentum as an independent constant. The velocity corresponding to $\mathbf{p}_c$ is therefore a critical velocity above which the superfluid can no longer exist as a separate semiphase without viscosity. This result corresponds to the observed phenomenon in liquid helium, that a critical velocity exists, roughly 25 or 30 cm/sec, above which the relative motion ceases to be free of viscosity.

One of the most important characteristics of the superfluid liquid helium is its apparent zero entropy. We shall show how the present model takes care of this anomaly. The vast majority of the superfluid atoms are condensed into one state, $\omega_s = 1$, and therefore make no contribution to the entropy; this can be seen from the basic definition of entropy, Eq. (3.401), where $S = k \ln C$, and C is given by Eq. (2.223), a product of contributions from all states:

$$(n_k + \omega_k - 1)!/n_k!(\omega_k - 1)!$$

In fact any state for which $\omega_k = 1$ can make no entropy contribution, because $C = 1$ for such a state. Even if the lowest state is degenerate, ω_s being a few units but $\omega_s \ll n_s$, its contribution to the entropy is still completely negligible. Thus when $n_s \gg \omega_s$ we have $\ln[(n_s + \omega_s - 1)!/(\omega_s - 1)!n_s!] = (\omega_s - 1)\ln n_s - \ln(\omega_s - 1)!$. The entropy per particle is therefore not greater than

$$k(\omega_s/n_s)\ln n_s$$

and as soon as an appreciable number of atoms enter the lowest state, $n_s \sim 10^{19}$, so that even if we allow ω_s to be as large as 10^{10} for example, the entropy per atom would still be no greater than $10^{-7}k$.

Finally consider the other low-energy states, between zero and the critical momentum $\mathbf{p}_c$. All the energies involved in these states are much less than kT, even for $T \sim 10^{-3}$ °K. Therefore in the expression for the entropy we may approximately set $e^{-\epsilon_p/kT} = 1 - \epsilon_p/kT$. Thus in Eq. (8.334) for the entropy of a Bose-Einstein gas, we put $\mu = 0$, because we are below T_0, and approximate to Eq. (8.301) with $n_p = \omega_p(kT/\epsilon_p - 1)$, so deriving

$$S = k \sum_{p<p_c} \omega_p - k \sum_{p<p_c} \omega_p \ln(\epsilon_p/kT) \tag{8.714}$$

In the normal part of the spectrum, above $\mathbf{p}_c$, the weights ω_p are equivalent to $\omega\epsilon^{1/2}d\epsilon$ on the continuous approximation, where $\omega = 2\pi V(2m/h^2)^{3/2}$; see Eq. (3.204). In the superfluid states we now assume the spectrum to have the same general form, but leave open the magnitude of ω. The sums again go over into integrations that can be evaluated immediately, yielding the result:

$$S = \tfrac{2}{3}\omega k\epsilon_0{}^{3\!/_2}\{\tfrac{5}{3} - \ln\,(\epsilon_0/kT)\} \tag{8.715}$$

where ϵ_0 is the energy corresponding to $\mathbf{p}_c$: $\epsilon_0 = p_c{}^2/2m$. If the spectrum were normal, $\omega \sim 10^{46}$ per cm^3, and $S \sim 10^{14}k$. If there are 10^{19} atoms in the low-energy states, this entropy would be 10^{-5} k per atom, and this is to be considered a norm against which the superfluid entropy is to be compared. If in the model we now reduce ω a millionfold to 10^{40}, we would reduce the entropy by the same factor compared with the normal spectrum. In the normal spectrum there would be a total of about 10^{13} states with momentum less than $\mathbf{p}_c$ (30 cm/sec), and in the anomalous spectrum of this model only about 10^7 states. This number still leaves plenty of freedom for the superfluid, without any measurable entropy. We shall return to a more detailed discussion of this two-fluid model in the last chapter.

8.8 Entropy and the Heisenberg uncertainty principle. The foregoing discussion of the entropy of helium superfluid raises an interesting question regarding both Fermi-Dirac and Bose-Einstein statistics. Very frequently the individual energy levels are strictly nondegenerate, $\omega_r = 1$, so that in Eq. (2.223) and Eq. (2.231) the numbers of complexions $C_{\mathrm{F.D.}}$ and $C_{\mathrm{B.E.}}$ are both exactly unity, and the entropy $S = k \ln C$ is identically zero. Experimentally this is wrong. Ordinarily we forget this point, go over to the form given in Eqs. (2.243) and (2.244), having employed the Stirling approximation on the assumption that all the numbers involved are very large; and this gives the experimentally confirmed results. To put the theory into a form where the numbers and weights are actually large, we have to lump together a large number of energy levels $\omega(\epsilon)d\epsilon$ in a small energy range $d\epsilon$, and consider the number of particles in each energy range as determining the distribution-in-energy. Then if $n(\epsilon)d\epsilon$ is substituted for n_j, and $\omega(\epsilon)d\epsilon$ for ω_j in Eqs. (2.223) and (2.231), we are justified in using the Stirling approximation and proceeding to the usual results.

The question is: since the energy levels are really nondegenerate, ought we not strictly to stay with the discrete analysis and find $C = 1$, $S = 0$? There is clearly an inconsistency here: the experimentally confirmed results are obviously wrong mathematically. There appears to be only one logical escape from this dilemma, through the Heisenberg uncertainty relation. The life-time of any one particle in any one of the nondegenerate energy states is finite, say Δt. For most assemblies of interest Δt is of the order of a few microseconds or less. This means there is an uncertainty in the energy given by $\Delta\epsilon\Delta t \sim 10^{-27}$ erg/sec. If the discrete nondegenerate energy spectrum has many levels within an energy range given by this relation, we are completely justified in using the continuous approximation and arriving at the usual results. If on the other hand the energy interval $\Delta\epsilon$ is comparable with or less than the spacing between the nondegenerate energy levels of the spectrum, we are not justified in using the continuous approximation, and the entropy must be regarded as absolutely zero.

To see how this works in practice, consider a gas of photons whose life-times are equal to n wave periods: $\Delta t = n/\nu$. Since $E = h\nu$, the uncertainty principle gives $\Delta\nu/\nu = 1/n$. Equation (8.106) for the density of states allows us to find the number of states in this frequency range: for visible light in a box of 1 cm side we find for example with $\nu = 10^{15}$ per sec, $\omega_j \sim 10^{15}/n$. Ordinarily the number of waves in a single coherent train is certainly less by many orders than 10^{15}; hence $\omega_j \gg 1$, and the uncertainty relation saves us from the dilemma. However, one could easily imagine a situation where this was not the case. For instance, if we made the box very small, perhaps 10^{-2} cm on a side, with perfectly reflecting walls, and if we imagined the coherent waves to number 10^9 in length, visible light would then have a $\Delta\epsilon$ roughly equal to the spacing between the levels, and Eq. (8.106) would lead to $\omega(\epsilon)d\epsilon \sim 1$. Therefore we should in this case stay with the discrete picture and write $C = 1$, and $S = 0$. The usual black-body radiation at a temperature of 1000 °K has entropy in such a small box of about $10^8 k$; this entropy must be considered a direct consequence of the uncertainty principle, because the life-time of coherent waves is much shorter than 10^9 wave periods and their energies are less sharply determined.

Consider next an electron gas with Fermi-Dirac statistics in a normal conductor. The mean free path is of the order 10^{-7} cm, the mean speed corresponding for example to a Fermi energy of 1 ev giving a mean life-time of the order 10^{-5} sec between collisions. The uncertainty in energy induced by this short life-time is of the order 10^{-12} erg. The number of states in this energy interval, given by Eq. (8.403) at energies near 1 ev, turns out to be no less than 10^{34} per cm^3. So the continuous approximation is very secure here. But in a superconductor where currents can persist for days, one might guess a life-time greater than 1,000 sec, an energy of 0.01 ev, and take a volume as small as 10^{-5} cm thick and come out with only one energy state within the uncertainty range. Here the entropy would be absolutely zero, contrary to the results of the continuous approximation.

Finally consider the superfluid film of liquid helium. It is found in practice that this film carries no entropy; in fact, a capillary that is narrow enough will pass superfluid only, and filter out entropy at the entrance. The critical diameter is of the order 10^{-5} cm; any wider capillary allows entropy and normal fluid to pass. For a Bose-Einstein model of this, in terms of § 8.7, we may consider the energy intervals between different states given by Eq. (1.303): $\Delta\epsilon = h^2/8\pi mL^2 \sim 10^{-23}$ erg. Therefore a time uncertainty not less than $\Delta t \sim 10^{-4}$ sec would narrow down the energy uncertainty to less than the above interval. In fact evidence from the high thermal conductivity in liquid helium indicates that the relaxation time for transitions between states is not less than 10^{-3} sec, so that we should regard $C = 1$, and $S = 0$. This picture also explains why wider capillaries cannot filter out the entropy; for the wider capillaries, L is larger and the energy intervals narrower, so it becomes possible for the uncertainty principle to blur the energy levels and so create entropy in the normal fashion inside the capillary.

EXERCISES AND PROBLEMS

1. Prove the last steps in Eqs. (8.109) and (8.111).

2. Derive Eq. (8.107) without assuming Eq. (3.511).

3. Derive Eq. (8.205) from Eq. (8.204).

4. Verify Eqs. (8.212) and (8.211).

5. Check the developments quoted in Eqs. (8.328), (8.329), (8.330), and (8.331).

6. Find the density-in-energy of a nondegenerate spectrum defined by

$$E_n = \gamma \sum_{j=1,2,3} (n_j \lambda_j / L_j)^{1/c_j}$$

where n_j are positive integers, L_j the linear dimensions of the enclosure, λ_j standard lengths, and γ, c_j arbitrary constants not necessarily integers. (*Hint:* find the volume in n-space enclosed between an energy surface and the three planes $n_j = 0$.)

[*Answer:* $\omega(E) = (L_1 L_2 L_3 / \lambda_1 \lambda_2 \lambda_3)\Gamma(1 + c_1)\Gamma(1 + c_2)\Gamma(1 + c_3)E^{c-1}/\Gamma(c)\gamma^c$,   where $c = c_1 + c_2 + c_3$.]

7. Given a Bose-Einstein gas of N systems having an energy spectrum like that described in the previous problem, show that the *lambda*-transition temperature T_0 is given by

$$N = (L_1 L_2 L_3 / \lambda_1 \lambda_2 \lambda_3)\Gamma(1 + c_1)\Gamma(1 + c_2)\Gamma(1 + c_3)(kT_0/\gamma)^c \sum_j 1/j^c$$

8. Show that the heat capacity of the gas in the previous two problems, for $T \leq T_0$ is:

$$C_v = Nkc(1 + c)(T/T_0)^c \sum_j (1/j^{c+1})/\sum_j (1/j^c)$$

Show that a discontinuity in heat capacity occurs as T rises through T_0:

$$\Delta C_v = -Nkc^2 \sum_j (1/j^c)/\sum_j (1/j^{c-1})$$

(*Hint:* Find $d(\mu/kT)/dT$ by differentiating the N,μ equation and then let $\mu = 0$.) Discuss then the nature of the discontinuity for the special cases $c = \frac{3}{2}, 3, 6$.

9. Reduce the number of dimensions in Problems 6, 7, and 8 to two, and find a spectrum that will produce a *lambda*-transition and heat capacity discontinuity in the monolayer; compare with the ideal gas spectrum.

10. Check the developments given in Eqs. (8.425), (8.426), and (8.427).

11. Derive Eqs. (8.430) and (8.432) as outlined in the text. Also use Eq. (8.433) to derive Eq. (8.432).

12. Prove Eq. (8.434) for the pressure of an electron gas.

13. From Eqs. (8.406) and (8.410) prove that $\mu_0 = 1.019kT_0$.

14. Consider the possible effect of the zero-point energy of the Debye modes on the elastic moduli of the crystal.

15. Use the energy spectrum of Eq. (8.403) with the mixed statistics discussed in Problem 7 of Chapter II, and show that no abrupt transition can occur for any finite value of the parameter p.

16. Verify Eqs. (8.503) and (8.505).

17. Check the developments given in Eqs. (8.510), (8.511), (8.512), and (8.514).

18. Check the developments given in Eqs. (8.530), (8.531), (8.535), and (8.539).

19. Sketch isotherms of an ideal Bose-Einstein gas on a p,V diagram. Show that a phase boundary is present corresponding to the *lambda*-transition, given by the equation $pV_0^{5/3} = $ constant. Find this constant.

20. Prove that Eq. (8.520), $E = \text{II}A$, is true also in the Fermi-Dirac monolayer.

21. Write down the details in the proof of Eq. (8.604).

22. Show that Eq. (8.305) can be derived from Eq. (8.702) as described in the text.
23. Derive Eqs. (8.708) and (8.709).
24. Derive Eq. (8.713).
25. Derive Eq. (8.715).

REFERENCES FOR FURTHER STUDY

Statistical Mechanics, J. E. Mayer and M. G. Mayer, Wiley, 1940; Chapter 16.
Helium, W. H. Keesom, Elsevier, 1942.
Low Temperature Physics, Four Lectures, Simon, Kurti, Allen, and Mendelssohn, Academic Press, 1952.

"Specific Heats of Several Metals between 1.8 °K and 4.2 °K," I. Estermann, S. A. Friedberg, and J. E. Goldman, *Phys. Rev.*, **87** (1952), p. 582.
"The Electronic and Lattice Specific Heats in W, Mo, and Re," M. Horowitz and J. G. Daunt, *Phys. Rev.*, **91** (1953), p. 1099.
"On Some Properties of Bose-Einstein Gases," L. Goldstein, *J. Chem. Phys.*, **9** (1941), p. 472.
"Distance Correlations and Bose-Einstein Condensation," F. London, *J. Chem. Phys.*, **11** (1943), p. 203.
"Note on the Bose-Einstein Integral Functions," J. E. Robinson, *Phys. Rev.*, **83** (1951), p. 678.
"The State of Liquid Helium near Absolute Zero," F. London, *J. Phys. Chem.*, **43** (1939), p. 49.
"Theory of Liquid Helium II," H. Y. Hsu and W. Band, *Phys. Rev.*, **59** (1941), p. 1013.
"On Phase Changes of B. E. Fluid Models," L. Goldstein, *J. Chem. Phys.*, **14** (1946), p. 276.
"Zero Point Energy of Helium," C. L. Pekeris, *Phys. Rev.*, **79** (1950), p. 884.
' On the *Lambda* Point of He⁴-He³ Mixtures," Akira Harashima, *J. Phys. Soc.* (Japan), **6** (1951), p. 271.

Chapter IX

PHASE EQUILIBRIA AMONG QUANTUM DEGENERATE SYSTEMS

9.1 Adsorption isotherm for mobile monolayer: Bose-Einstein gas. Physical adsorption of a quantum degenerate gas is a particularly simple example in terms of which one may discuss the general problem of phase equilibria, and it is in itself of interest in the study of the properties of helium at very low temperatures. Before following the analysis of this section, the student is advised to review § 5.1, where the same problem was solved in classical statistics.

The Bose-Einstein analog of Eq. (5.102) gives the total number of complexions in the distribution-in-energy specified by the numbers n_{gr} in the rth level of the parent gas, and n_{fj} in the jth level of the mobile two-dimensional film:

$$C_{\text{B.E.}} = \prod_r \frac{(n_{gr} + \omega_{gr})!}{n_{gr}!\omega_{gr}!} \prod_j \frac{(n_{fj} + \omega_{fj})!}{n_{fj}!\omega_{fj}!} \qquad (9.101)$$

There are no other factors multiplying this, because the number of different ways in which the total number N of indistinguishable atoms can be divided into two parts N_g and N_f is exactly unity.

The logarithm of C has to be maximized by varying the numbers n_{gr} and n_{fj}, under the two restrictions that N and E are conserved:

$$N = \sum_r n_{gr} + \sum_j n_{fj} \qquad (9.102)$$

$$E = \sum_r n_{gr}\epsilon_{gr} + \sum_j n_{fj}\epsilon_{fj} \qquad (9.103)$$

The variation equations are therefore once again [compare Eq. (5.114)]:

$$\left.\begin{array}{l} (\partial/\partial n_{gr})(\ln C - \alpha N - \beta E) = 0 \\ (\partial/\partial n_{fj})(\ln C - \alpha N - \beta E) = 0 \end{array}\right\} \qquad (9.104)$$

Every term in the operand here breaks into two parts, one depending only on the n_g's and the other only in the n_f's, so the results follow in the same way as before [compare Eq. (5.117)]:

$$n_{gr} = \omega_{gr}\{\exp (\epsilon_{gr} - \mu)/kT - 1\}^{-1}$$
$$n_{fj} = \omega_{fj}\{\exp (\epsilon_{fj} - \mu)/kT - 1\}^{-1}$$
(9.105)

where as before we have written $\alpha = -\mu/kT$ and $\beta = 1/kT$. The value of μ is to be determined by summing both Eqs. (9.105) and equating the total number to N in accord with Eq. (9.102). These equations are identical with those obtained for separate assemblies, but with the same μ in both as a result of the mutual equilibrium between the two. We again adopt the integration approximation, using the degeneracy weight factors Eq. (8.303) in the gas and Eq. (8.501) in the film:

$$\omega_{gr} \rightarrow \omega_g(\epsilon)d\epsilon = 2\pi V(2m/h^2)^{3/2}\epsilon^{1/2}d\epsilon$$
$$\omega_{fj} \rightarrow \omega_f(\epsilon)d\epsilon = 2\pi A(m/h^2)d\epsilon$$
(9.106)

Let W be the energy of adsorption; then we picture the film as a two-dimensional gas trapped in a potential well of depth W. The lowest energy of an atom in the film is $-W$, and the highest energy is zero, if we take the lowest energy in the gas as zero. The integration approximations are then:

$$N_g = \int_0^\infty \omega_g(\epsilon)\{\exp (\epsilon - \mu)/kT - 1\}^{-1}d\epsilon$$
(9.107)

$$N_f = \int_0^W \omega_f(\epsilon)\{\exp (\epsilon - \mu - W)/kT - 1\}^{-1}d\epsilon$$
(9.108)

As long as μ is negative and large compared with kT, as it is at low enough temperatures, we may substitute infinity for the upper limit W on the integral in Eq. (9.108). The integrals are then identical with those already studied in the separate phases, Eqs. (8.304) and (8.502):

$$N_g = V(2\pi mkT/h^2)^{3/2} \sum_{j=1} (1/j^{3/2})e^{j\mu/kT}$$
(9.109)

$$N_f = A(2\pi mkT/h^2)^{3/2} \sum_{j=1} (1/j)e^{j(\mu+W)/kT}$$
(9.110)

If the temperature is not too low, $\mu + W$ must be negative, and the series in Eq. (9.110) converges; hence the same results as obtained in § 8.3 and § 8.5 for the pressure remain valid here, and thus from Eq. (8.337),

$$p = kT(2\pi mkT/h^2)^{3/2} \sum_{j=1} (1/j^{5/2})e^{j\mu/kT}$$
(9.111)

and from Eq. (8.519),

$$\Pi = kT(2\pi mkT/h^2) \sum_{j=1} (1/j^2)e^{j(\mu+W)/kT}$$
(9.112)

while the parameter μ is found from Eqs. (9.109) and (9.110).

For all interesting examples, like helium near 4 °K, the quantity $(2\pi mkT/h^2)$ is of the order 10^{14} per cm^2, so that as long as the series in Eq. (9.110) converges, the value of N_f/A is only some 10^{-7} times that of N_g/V; the number N_f is then entirely negligible compared with N_g in the equation determining μ, viz., $N = N_g + N_f$. Indeed, we can write the equation simply as Eq. (9.109) with N replacing N_g. This coincides with the equation determining μ in the absence of the film: Eq. (8.305). The result will then be the same as in § 8.3, viz., Eq. (8.329). If we use this expression for μ/kT in Eq. (9.110) we find N_f as a function of T, and it is convenient to express this in the following form, making use of the definition of V_0 in Eq. (8.324):

$$N_f V/N_g A = (2\pi mkT/h^2)^{3/2} e^{W/kT}\{1 + a(V_0/V) + b(V_0/V)^2 + \cdots\} \qquad (9.113)$$

where

$$\left. \begin{aligned} a &= 1.306 e^{W/kT} - 0.924 \\ b &= 2.270 e^{2W/kT} - 2.412 e^{W/kT} - 0.393 \end{aligned} \right\} \qquad (9.114)$$

In Eq. (9.113), N is essentially equal to N_g, the assumption being that N_f is much less than N_g. This gives the ratio of the number adsorbed to the density of the parent gas. If we wish instead to find the number adsorbed as a function of the pressure of the parent gas, or vice versa, this can be done if we use Eq. (8.340) for the pressure of the gas, and eliminate (V_0/V) between this and Eq. (9.113) by reversing the series. This is left as an exercise.

Inspection shows, from Eq. (8.329), that at sufficiently large volumes the quantity μ/kT is negative and even lower than $-W/kT$, so that the series in Eq. (9.110) does converge. But certainly, for any given T, there exists a volume V_1 at which μ/kT appears to equal $-W/kT$, at least if it is found from Eq. (8.329). If, however, we put $\mu = -W$ in Eq. (9.110), the series diverges, and we can no longer neglect N_f in finding μ, as we did in using Eq. (8.329). This situation is mathematically identical with that appearing at the condensation of the Bose-Einstein gas into its lowest state, with the film now taking the role of the lowest state. Following the same line as in Eq. (8.309), we may now write

$$N = N_f + V(2\pi mkT/h^2)^{3/2} \sum_{j=1} (1/j^{3/2}) e^{j\mu/kT} \qquad (9.115)$$

as the equation determining μ. At volumes $V > V_1$, we may still neglect N_f as before, but if V approaches V_1 very closely, then N_f becomes appreciable; V_1 is defined by

$$N = V_1(2\pi mkT/h^2)^{3/2} \sum_{j=1} (1/j^{3/2}) e^{-jW/kT} \qquad (9.116)$$

However, when V is less than V_1, μ must approach $-W$ more and more closely, and can be written exactly equal to $-W$ in the series of Eq. (9.115):

$$V \leq V_1: \qquad N = N_f + V(2\pi mkT/h^2)^{3/2} \sum_{j=1} (1/j^{3/2}) e^{-jW/kT} \qquad (9.117)$$

This will result in demanding N_f to be of the same order of magnitude as N, and can then, through Eq. (9.110), tell us just how close to $-W$ we have to make μ. Of course the film cannot hold an indefinite number of atoms, and the condensation into the film must stop when the film is filled up. This can be taken care of in the theory by allowing W to drop to zero when the population fills the film. This may be expected to happen when the density of atoms in the film per square centimeter reaches the order of magnitude of the surface density of atoms in the liquid phase.

The pressure of the parent gas, at which the density in the adsorbed film suddenly begins to increase anomalously, is to be found from Eq. (9.111), with $\mu = -W$:

$$V \leq V_1: \qquad p = kT(2\pi mkT/h^2)^{3/2} \sum_{j=1}^{\infty} (1/j^{5/2})e^{-jW/kT} \qquad (9.118)$$

a formula which remains true as the condensation continues, because μ remains almost equal to $-W$ below the transition point. For isothermal compression, this pressure remains constant, in close analogy with the first order phase change from vapor to liquid.

The results of this section will be used later in the theory of multilayer adsorption, and in the discussion of adsorption isotherms of helium at very low temperatures. The remarkable thing about these results is that the Bose-Einstein statistics' predictions are very different from the classical statistics, even at temperatures that are actually much too high for quantum degeneracy to have any effect on a single phase assembly—the latter can occur only when μ approaches zero; the present effects occur when μ approaches $-W$, and this happens at considerably higher temperatures.

9.2 Adsorption isotherm for mobile monolayer: Fermi-Dirac gas. In studying the equilibrium between a Fermi-Dirac gas and a two-dimensional Fermi-Dirac film, we may proceed exactly as in the last section, writing out the Fermi-Dirac analog to Eq. (9.101), following through Eq. (9.102) to Eq. (9.104), and arriving finally at the Fermi-Dirac analog of Eq. (9.105), which reads:

$$\left.\begin{aligned} n_{gr} &= \omega_{gr}\{\exp{(\epsilon_{gr} - \mu)}/kT + 1\}^{-1}\\ n_{fj} &= \omega_{fj}\{\exp{(\epsilon_{fj} - \mu)}/kT + 1\}^{-1} \end{aligned}\right\} \qquad (9.201)$$

the value of μ being determined by summing these equations and equating their total to N. Again these equations are identical with those for separate phases, but with the same free energy μ in both. Formally this equation determining μ may be found by using Eqs. (8.409) and (8.527):

$$N = V(2\pi mkT/h^2)^{3/2} \sum_{j=1}^{\infty} (-1)^{j-1}(1/j^{3/2})e^{j\mu/kT}$$

$$+ A(2\pi mkT/h^2) \sum_{j=1}^{\infty} (-1)^{j-1}(1/j)e^{j(\mu+W)/kT} \qquad (9.202)$$

if we take the zero of energy at the lowest state of the atom in the parent gas, and the energy of adsorption as equal to W. If applied to electrons, a degeneracy spin factor of 2 appears in both sums. There are two difficulties with this equation. In the first place, as mentioned in connection with Eq. (8.409), the series for N_g is generally of no use for successive approximations because the terms get progressively larger. In the second place, the series for N_f, derived from Eq. (8.527), includes all energies up to positive infinity in the film, whereas in the present problem, any atom with energy greater than zero would automatically be counted out of the film—it would be evaporated into the gas. This led to no trouble in the Bose-Einstein case, because μ was there always negative and below $-W$. Here this is not so. The film is essentially inside a potential well of depth W and contains no stable states of energy higher than the walls of the well. We must therefore follow through the determination of μ from the beginning, starting from the following equation, which is rigorous as far as the integration approximation is valid:

$$N = 4\pi V(2m/h^2)^{3/2} \int_0^\infty \{\exp\,(\epsilon - \mu)/kT + 1\}^{-1}\epsilon^{1/2}d\epsilon$$
$$+ 2A(2\pi m/h^2) \int_{-W}^\infty \{\exp\,(\epsilon - \mu)/kT + 1\}^{-1}d\epsilon \quad (9.203)$$

including electron spin weight 2.

If we were interested in electrons, we would find that the absolute zero of temperature is a good approximation to ordinary temperatures, and we therefore solve Eq. (9.203) in the limit of zero T. Later we wish to discuss the adsorption isotherms of helium isotope of mass 3, and the discussion of Eq. (9.203) at all temperatures will be undertaken.

At the absolute zero, both integrands in Eq. (9.203) become step functions, the factor $\{\exp\,(\epsilon - \mu)/kT + 1\}^{-1}$ being unity when $\mu > \epsilon$ and zero when $\epsilon > \mu$. However because the upper limit of the integral over the film states is set at zero, and because μ is generally positive, the integrand here is unity for the whole range of the integration, and we find:

$$T \to 0: \qquad N = 2A(2\pi m/h^2)W + (\pi/3)V(8m/h^2)^{3/2}\mu_0^{3/2} \qquad (9.204)$$

In this situation the film is filled to capacity, and the atoms in the gas are all sitting in all the lowest states in accordance with the Pauli exclusion principle. The numerical value of the film term in Eq. (9.204) is exceedingly small, equivalent in order of magnitude only to the superficial density of atoms in the gas, and so this term makes no essential difference to the value of μ_0, which turns out to be given therefore by practically the same equation as if the gas were isolated and the film absent; see Eq. (8.406). Any finite temperature above zero has the effect of evaporating atoms out of the film slightly, increasing the number in the gas compared with that in the film, and raising the upper limit of the occupied levels in the gas. The neglect of N_f in calculating μ_0 is therefore a fortiori justified in calculating μ at higher temperatures. The value of μ is therefore determined by Eq. (8.426) from the gas phase alone, and this value of μ has to be put into the expression for the film to find N_f:

$$N_f = 2A(2\pi m/h^2) \int_{-W}^{0} \{\exp(\epsilon - \mu)/kT + 1\}^{-1} d\epsilon \qquad (9.205)$$

with Eq. (8.426) for μ. Because ϵ is always negative in this integral, and μ is positive, we can expand the integrand by the binomial theorem and integrate term by term. The result is easily found:

$$N_f = 2A(2\pi mkT/h^2)\{W/kT + \sum_{j=1} (-1)^j (1/j) e^{-j\mu/kT}[1 - e^{-jW/kT}]\} \qquad (9.206)$$

The pressure of the parent gas in equilibrium with the film having this population is given by the general relation (8.338), $pV = 2E/3$, and Eq. (8.427) for the energy, thus:

$$p = \tfrac{2}{5}(N/V)\mu_0\{1 + (5\pi^2/12)(kT/\mu_0)^2 - (\pi^4/16)(kT/\mu_0)^4 + \cdots\} \qquad (9.207)$$

where, from Eq. (9.204) neglecting N_f we may use

$$\mu_0 = (h^2/8m)(3N/\pi V)^{2/3} \qquad (9.208)$$

These expansions are valid so long as μ_0 is greater than kT, and are good for electron theory. For helium isotopes, it turns out that even in the range of temperatures between 1° and 4.2 °K, μ is negative and the above results are of no use; the temperature has to be small compared with 1 °K before the absolute zero approximation method can be used.

Proceeding next with the discussion of the situation of interest in applications to helium isotopes, we know from the general theory of Chapter III that at sufficiently high temperatures the Fermi-Dirac and Bose-Einstein statistics give the same results. We have just seen that the Bose-Einstein problem gave negative values of μ at high temperatures, while here in the Fermi-Dirac case μ is positive at sufficiently low temperatures. Therefore there must exist a temperature, T_1, at which μ goes through zero in the Fermi-Dirac case. At sufficiently high temperatures, $T > T_1$, the series in Eq. (9.202) becomes valid again; we can still neglect N_f, and so use Eq. (9.209) to find:

$$N = V(2\pi mkT/h^2)^{3/2} \sum_{j=1} (-1)^{j-1}(1/j^{3/2})e^{j\mu/kT} \qquad (9.209)$$

The temperature below which this becomes invalid is that at which it gives $\mu = 0$:

$$N = V(2\pi mkT_1/h^2)^{3/2} \sum_{j=1} (-1)^{j-1}(1/j^{3/2}) \qquad (9.210)$$

Reversing the series (9.209) to find μ as a function of N/V, we proceed in the same way as in the Bose-Einstein gas, following Eq. (8.323), to Eq. (8.329). We define V_1 by the relation:

$$N/V_1 = 0.7643(2\pi mkT/h^2)^{3/2} \tag{9.211}$$

and write

$$Z = (N/V_1)e^{\mu/kT}/(0.7643) \tag{9.212}$$

and then find the following expansions:

$$Z = (N/V)\{1 + 0.2703(V_1/V) + 0.03359(V_1/V)^2$$
$$+ 0.002635(V_1/V)^3 + \cdots\} \tag{9.213}$$

$$\mu/kT = \ln(0.7643V_1/V) + 0.2703V_1/V$$
$$- 0.00295(V_1/V)^2 - 0.00546(V_1/V)^3 - \cdots \tag{9.214}$$

valid for $V \geq V_1$ or $T \geq T_1$. The high-temperature expression for the energy of the parent gas is the Fermi-Dirac analog of Eq. (8.317):

$$E = (3kT/2)V(2\pi mkT/h^2)^{3/2} \sum_{j=1} (-1)^{j-1}(1/j^{5/2})e^{j\mu/kT} \tag{9.215}$$

and pV is two-thirds of this. Writing Eq. (9.213) or (9.214) in here for $e^{\mu/kT}$, we find the equation of state for the Fermi-Dirac gas at high temperatures:

$$pV = NkT\{1 + 0.1352V_1/V - 0.00199(V_1/V)^2 + 0.00344(V_1/V)^3 \cdots\} \tag{9.216}$$

To find the number of atoms in the film corresponding to this pressure in the parent gas, we have to use Eq. (9.214) in Eq. (9.205). Because μ is now negative and the expansion (9.206) invalid, we have instead to split the integral in Eq. (9.205) into two parts, from $-W$ to μ, and from μ to 0. In the lower part we may expand the integrand as a power series in $e^{(\epsilon-\mu)/kT}$, and the upper part, as a power series in $e^{(\mu-\epsilon)/kT}$. The two series can then be integrated term by term over the appropriate ranges, and we find

$$N_f = A(2\pi mkT/h^2)\left\{(\mu + W)/kT + \sum_{j=1}(-1)^j(1/j)[e^{j\mu/kT} - e^{-j(\mu+W)/kT}]\right\} \tag{9.217}$$

We can now use Eq. (9.213) or (9.214) in this to obtain a series that converges rapidly enough as long as $-W < \mu < 0$:

$$N_f/A = (2\pi mkT/h^2)\left\{\ln(0.7643V_1/V) + a(V/V_1)^3 + b(V/V_1)^2 + c(V/V_1)\right.$$
$$\left. + d + c'(V_1/V) + b'(V_1/V)^2 + a'(V_1/V)^3 + W/kT\right\} \tag{9.218}$$

where

$$a = 0.7460e^{-3W/kT} + \cdots$$
$$b = (-0.8560 - 0.6050e^{-W/kT} + \cdots)e^{-2W/kT}$$
$$c = (1.308 + 0.4625e^{-W/kT} + 0.2520e^{-2W/kT} + \cdots)e^{-W/kT}$$
$$d = (-0.3536 - 0.1301e^{-W/kT} - 0.0719e^{-2W/kT} + \cdots)e^{-W/kT}$$
$$c' = -0.4940 + 0.0516e^{-W/kT} + 0.0255e^{-2W/kT}$$
$$b' = 0.0825 - 0.0054e^{-W/kT} + \cdots$$
$$a' = -0.0222 \tag{9.219}$$

This expansion is valid for $V_1 < V < V_2$, where V_2 means the volume at which Eq. (9.215) would make $\mu = -W$. If $V > V_2$, the integrand of Eq. (9.205) can be expanded entirely in a power series in $e^{(\mu-\epsilon)/kT}$, and we find

$$N_f = A(2\pi mkT/h^2) \sum_{j=1}(-1)^j(1/j)e^{j\mu/kT}[1 - e^{jW/kT}] \tag{9.220}$$

Equations (9.213) and (9.214) are still valid, and we can use them to obtain an expansion like Eq. (9.218). However, it turns out that the condition of validity of this expansion is outside the range of interest in practical applications, so the development will not be given here.

To emphasize the magnitude of the quantum degeneracy effect, and illustrate the use of Eq. (9.218) we may calculate the film density in equilibrium with saturated vapor of the helium isotopes of mass 3 and 4, using published data on the density of the vapor and heat of adsorption of He^4 on charcoal. The latter naturally can give only an order of magnitude for He^3, but the results are nevertheless of considerable interest. The table gives the calculations at two temperatures assuming $N = 6.02 \times 10^{23}$ and $m = 5.01 \times 10^{-24}$ g. The last column gives the values of N_f/A that one would expect on classical statistics, Eq. (5.206), computed from the formula:

$$N_f/A = (N/V)(2\pi mkT/h^2)^{-\frac{1}{2}}e^{W/kT} \tag{9.221}$$

and it is apparent that Fermi-Dirac statistics would be responsible for a reduction of film densities by a factor of from fivefold to eightfold.

ADSORPTION OF FERMI-DIRAC MONOLAYER, He^3

$T\ °K$	$V_1\ cm^3$	$V\ cm^3$	μ/kT	W/kT	N_f/A q.m.	N_f/A class
2.91	161.1	189.7	−0.2083	3.594	81.2×10^{13}	675×10^{13}
2.69	181.2	271.8	−0.4968	3.075	57.94×10^{13}	294×10^{13}

Adsorption measurements on He^3 have not yet been published, so no comparison with experiment can be presented here.

9.3 Adsorption isotherms for isotope mixtures. The effects of quantum degeneracy are even more evident theoretically in the adsorption of isotopic mixtures, one component of which is Fermi-Dirac and the other Bose-Einstein. Let the subscript s denote the Bose-Einstein, and a the Fermi-Dirac, component.

The equilibrium numbers of Bose-Einstein particles in the gas and film phases respectively are

$$N_{sg} = V(2\pi m_s kT/h^2)^{3/2} \sum_{j=1} (1/j^{3/2})e^{j\mu_s/kT} \tag{9.301}$$

$$N_{sf} = A(2\pi m_s kT/h^2) \sum_{j=1} (1/j)e^{j(\mu_s+W_s)/kT} \tag{9.302}$$

where μ_s is the free energy of this component, m_s is the mass of the isotope and W_s is the energy of adsorption. These equations are valid so long as V is greater than the value V_{0s} at which $\mu_s = -W_s$. At smaller volumes than this, the number N_{sf} as given by Eq. (9.302) diverges and adsorption becomes multi-layer, according to the picture to be developed later; see § 9.5. In general we may solve Eq. (9.301) for μ_s and use this solution in Eq. (9.302) to give the adsorption isotherm. If we define V_{1s} by the relation

$$N_{sg}/V_{1s} = 2.612(2\pi m_s kT/h^2)^{3/2} \tag{9.303}$$

the result can be expressed as a power series in V_{1s}/V and we find

$$N_{sf}/A = (2\pi m_s kT/h^2) \sum_{n=1} a_n(V_{1s}/V)^n \tag{9.304}$$

where the coefficients are

$$a_1 = 2.612e^{W_s/kT}$$
$$a_2 = -2.412e^{W_s/kT} + 3.411e^{2W_s/kT}$$
$$a_3 = 1.025e^{W_s/kT} - 6.301e^{2W_s/kT} + 5.940e^{3W_s/kT}$$
$$a_4 = -0.2683e^{W_s/kT} + 5.588e^{2W_s/kT} - 16.46e^{3W_s/kT} + 11.64e^{4W_s/kT}$$
$$\text{etc.}$$

$$\tag{9.305}$$

The series converges theoretically if $V > V_{0s}$ and in practice converges rapidly enough for computation if

$$V \gg V_{1s} \times 2.612e^{W_s/kT} \tag{9.306}$$

To make certain that this condition is satisfied we may suppose that the Bose-Einstein component is present only in small concentrations relative to the Fermi-Dirac component:

$$N_s/N_a \ll 1 \tag{9.307}$$

The interesting point to discuss is the relative concentration of the two isotopes in the mobile monolayer in equilibrium with a given relative concentration in the gas. Let ρ be the density of the mixture in the gas, in grams per cubic centimeter, and x the relative concentration in the gas:

$$x = N_{sg}/N_{ag} \tag{9.308}$$

Then we can express N_{sg} in terms of x, ρ and the masses of the isotopes, put this expression into Eq. (9.303) and find

$$2.612 V_{1s}/V = [x\rho/(m_a + x m_s)](2\pi m_s kT/h^2)^{-\frac{3}{2}} \qquad (9.309)$$

A similar calculation yields

$$0.7643 V_{1a}/V = [\rho/(m_a + x m_s)](2\pi m_a kT/h^2)^{-\frac{3}{2}} \qquad (9.310)$$

Equation (9.309) used in Eq. (9.304) permits N_{sf}/A to be expressed in terms of the density ρ and the relative concentration x in the gas, while Eq. (9.310) used in Eq. (9.218) similarly permits the expression of N_{af}/A in terms of the same quantities ρ and x; hence we can compute the ratio:

$$y = N_{sf}/N_{af} \qquad (9.311)$$

in terms of x, ρ, T.

In the absence of quantum degeneracy, Eq. (9.221) applies to both components, and if the energies of adsorption are the same, the number of adsorbed particles is proportional to the inverse square root of the isotope mass:

$$y_{\text{class}} = x(m_a/m_s)^{\frac{1}{2}} \qquad (9.312)$$

Comparison of this ratio with the results obtained from Eq. (9.311), using the same energy of adsorption, gives a quantitative estimate of the effects of quantum degeneracy alone on the adsorption.

To illustrate this procedure we shall imagine a small percentage of He^4 added to saturated vapor He^3 and calculate the percentage of He^4 in a mobile film, assuming the same energy of adsorption for both isotopes, and confining ourselves to one temperature, 2.69 °K. From Eq. (9.303) we first evaluate V_{1s} per mole, finding $V_{1s} = 14.24$ cm^3. Then we find the volume V per mole from Eq. (9.306), beyond which our formulae become useful, to be 805 cm^3 per mole. The ratio between this and the volume per mole given in the Table for He^3 indicates that it is safe to use $x = 10$ per cent or less. We have in general from Eqs. (9.308), (9.303), and (9.212): $V_{1s}/V_{1a} = 0.2927x$, while V_{1a} is given in the Table. This permits direct calculation of the film density with respect to He^4 from Eq. (9.304), with the following results:

$$x = 10\% \qquad N_{sf}/A = 60.44 \times 10^{13}$$

$$x = 1\% \qquad N_{sf}/A = 4.125 \times 10^{13}$$

Comparing these with the values given in the foregoing Table we find the results displayed in the Table below. In other words, even though there may be only one-tenth as many He^4 atoms as He^3 in the vapor, there would be numerically

RELATIVE CONCENTRATION OF HE ISOTOPES IN ADSORBED FILM

$$T = 2.69 °K, \quad V_a = 271.8 \text{ cm}^3$$

x	y_{class}	$y_{q.m.}$	$y_{q.m.}/y_{\text{class}}$
0.1	0.0866	1.04	12.0
0.01	0.00866	0.05	5.8

a greater proportion of He^4 than He^3 in a mobile monolayer in equilibrium with the mixture, if adsorption energies were the same for both isotopes.

It is also easy to compute the volume V_{0s} at which adsorption of He^4 may become multilayer (see § 9.7) and completely swamp the adsorption of He^3. This turns out to be $V_{0s} = 1912$ cm^3 per mole at 2.69 °K, showing that a relative concentration of only 271.8:1912 = 14 per cent is sufficient to produce an avalanche adsorption of He^4 from the mixture.

Once again there are no data available in terms of which this theory can be tested as yet. Indeed, there is some doubt whether such data can be found. The only mobile film formed by adsorption from helium vapor is the film of superfluid below the *lambda*-temperature 2.19 °K, and it is not clear whether the above theory would apply qualitatively to the superfluid film. However, there are anomalies known to exist in the concentrations of the helium isotopes in the superfluid film that are qualitatively similar with those predicted above, and it seems reasonable to suppose that these anomalies are due to the kind of quantum degeneracy effects here elaborated.

9.4 Localized monolayers and Bose-Einstein parent gas. Adsorption into localized fixed sites presents a simpler problem than adsorption into a mobile monolayer. We shall assume that the sites are such that to each one there is only one state of adsorption, that the sites are mutually distinguishable, and that each has place for only one adsorbed particle. These are the same assumptions made in deducing the Langmuir isotherm in § 5.3; here we obtain the quantum degenerate form of Langmuir's isotherm by using Bose-Einstein statistics in the parent gas.

Because the atoms are indistinguishable from each other, there is only one way in which we may choose a given number N_f of atoms to put into the film; once chosen, these atoms can be placed among X sites in

$$X!/N_f!(X - N_f)! \tag{9.401}$$

different ways, because the sites are not permutable. If we are also given that n_{gr} atoms are in the rth energy level in the parent gas, the Bose-Einstein number of complexions for the gas is

$$C_g = \prod_r (n_{gr} + \omega_{gr})!/(n_{gr}!\omega_{gr}!) \tag{9.402}$$

The total number of complexions for the assembly is then the product:

$$C = [X!/N_f!(X - N_f)!] \prod_r (n_{gr} + \omega_{gr})!/(n_{gr}!\omega_{gr}!) \tag{9.403}$$

and the statistical problem is to maximize the logarithm of this under the restrictions that total number and total energy be conserved:

$$0 = \delta N = \sum_r \delta n_{gr} + \delta N_f \tag{9.404}$$

$$0 = \delta E = \sum_r \epsilon_r \delta n_{gr} - W \delta N_f \tag{9.405}$$

Here we have written W for the energy of adsorption relative to the lowest state in the gas. These restrictions are identical with Eq. (5.315) and Eq. (5.316), and the first factor in C is identical with that in Eq. (5.304); therefore the variations of N_f yield the same result here as in Eq. (5.324):

$$N_f = (X - N_f) \exp (\mu + W)/kT \tag{9.406}$$

The logarithm of the second factor in Eq. (9.403) is on the other hand identical with that in Eq. (9.101) for the isolated Bose-Einstein gas, and evidently leads through variations of n_{gr} to the same result, Eq. (9.109):

$$N_g = V(2\pi mkT/h^2)^{3/2} \sum_{j=1} (1/j^{3/2})e^{j\mu/kT} \tag{9.407}$$

We can now eliminate μ between the last two equations and find

$$N_g/V = (2\pi mkT/h^2)^{3/2} \sum_{j=1} (1/j^{3/2})[\theta/(1 - \theta)]^j e^{-jW/kT} \tag{9.408}$$

where

$$\theta = N_f/X \tag{9.409}$$

is the ratio of occupied sites to the total number of sites. This result is equivalent to the adsorption isotherm, because it relates θ to the density of the parent gas, and from the equation of state for the gas, we could put it into the form of a relation between θ and p. Indeed, from Eq. (9.111) the pressure of the gas is

$$p = kT(2\pi mkT/h^2)^{3/2} \sum_{j=1} (1/j^{5/2})e^{j\mu/kT} \tag{9.410}$$

and we can eliminate μ between this and Eq. (9.406) to get

$$p = kT(2\pi mkT/h^2)^{3/2} \sum_{j=1} (1/j^{5/2})[\theta/(1 - \theta)]^j e^{-jW/kT} \tag{9.411}$$

for the isothermal relation between pressure and fractional coverage.

If θ is much less than unity, or if the energy of adsorption is sufficiently great, this isotherm reduces to the classical Langmuir isotherm, Eqs. (5.327) and (5.328), because the series in Eq. (9.411) then converges so rapidly that we need to retain only the first term. But if the energy of adsorption is small, the fractional coverage given by Eq. (9.411) for a given pressure is less than that predicted by the Langmuir isotherm. This difference increases as θ increases, and while the Langmuir isotherm allows p to go to infinity and θ to go to unity, there is some question whether this can occur in the quantum degenerate theory. In fact Eq. (9.411) formally predicts that an infinite pressure is required to produce a fractional coverage θ^* where

$$\theta^*/(1 - \theta^*) = e^{W/kT} \tag{9.412}$$

so that no finite pressure could ever increase θ beyond this value:

$$\theta = \theta^* = 1/(1 + e^{-W/kT}) \tag{9.413}$$

This limiting adsorption evidently coincides with the *lambda*-transition in the gas phase, because if we write the value (9.412) into Eq. (9.408) we get just the result $N_g/V = 2.612(2\pi mkT/h^2)^{3/2}$, showing $T = T_0$, or $V = V_0$ for the given T. Since no actual gas can be compressed far enough to show this transition without first becoming liquid or solid, the situation is quite hypothetical.

It is a simple exercise to go through the foregoing argument in the Fermi-Dirac statistics, obtaining a formula like Eq. (9.411), but with the alternating

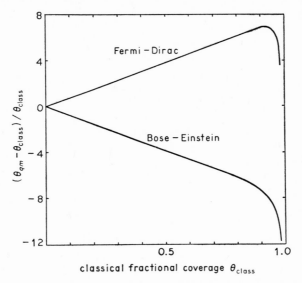

Fig. 9.41.   Quantum corrections on Langmuir's isotherm $\times\ 10^3$.

signs.   Whereas the pressure p required to produce a given value of θ is greater for Bose-Einstein statistics than in classical statistics, it is less for Fermi-Dirac statistics than in classical statistics.   It is of interest to find a quantitative estimate of these effects of quantum degeneracy.   To do this the values of θ on the three statistics produced by a given gas density N_g/V were computed, assuming the energy of adsorption in all cases was 28.9 cal per mole at 3 °K to correspond with the observed energy of adsorption of He^4 on charcoal.   A graph was drawn with the ratio $(\theta_{class} - \theta_{class})/\theta_{class}$ against θ_{class}.   The ratio is of the order 10^{-3}, so the effects of degeneracy are indeed very small.

9.5   Sublimation of a Bose-Einstein gas from an Einstein crystal.   Equilibrium between gas and solid crystal phase is evidently closely related with the equilibrium between gas and localized monolayer, the latter being essentially a two-dimensional solid crystal.   In the present problem, the solid is three-dimensional, and each atom in the solid phase has a whole spectrum of energies; if we use the Einstein model for the crystal, the atoms are mutually distinguishable harmonic oscillators.

The number of complexions in the combined assembly equals the number of ways the total number N of indistinguishable atoms can be divided into two parts N_g and N_s—which is just one—multiplied by the Boltzmann number of complexions of N_s oscillators and the Bose-Einstein number of complexions of N_g atoms in the gas. With the by now familiar notation, we therefore have [compare Eqs. (2.213), (2.223)]:

$$C = N_s! \prod_r \{\omega_{sr}{}^{n_{sr}}/n_{sr}!\} \prod_r (n_{gr} + \omega_{gr})!/(n_{gr}!\omega_{gr}!) \qquad (9.501)$$

where n_{sr} is the number of atomic oscillators in the rth oscillator level, and n_{gr} the number of atoms in the rth gas level. Write W_s for the energy depth of the lowest state of an atom in the crystal relative to the lowest state in the gas; then the total energy of the assembly is

$$E = \sum_r \epsilon_{gr} n_{gr} + \sum_r n_{sr}(\epsilon_{sr} - W_s) \qquad (9.502)$$

We have to maximize the logarithm of C by varying n_{gr} and n_{sr} under the restrictions that N and E remain fixed, where

$$N = N_s + N_g = \sum_r n_{sr} + \sum_r n_{gr} \qquad (9.503)$$

If we compare these equations with those used in § 5.6 for the sublimation of a classical gas from an Einstein crystal, we see that the factor in C pertaining to the crystal remains the same, while that pertaining to the gas is the same as for a Bose-Einstein gas phase considered alone; the two phases are connected simply through the Lagrangian multipliers required for conservation of N and E. The free energy Lagrangian parameter is determined exactly as before in Eq. (5.608), i.e., by

$$e^{-\mu/kT} = Q_s e^{W_s/kT} \qquad (9.504)$$

where W_s is present because the energy zero has been taken as the lowest energy state in the gas instead of that in the solid. The equations for the gas remain as for the separate phase, except that we now use Eq. (9.504) for its free energy:

$$N_g = V(2\pi mkT/h^2)^{3/2} \sum_{j=1} (1/j^{3/2})\{Q_s e^{W_s/kT}\}^{-j} \qquad (9.505)$$

and for the pressure of the gas:

$$p = kT(2\pi mkT/h^2)^{3/2} \sum_{j=1} (1/j^{5/2})(1/Q_s{}^j)e^{-jW_s/kT} \qquad (9.506)$$

For an Einstein crystal with characteristic frequency ν the partition function Q_s, referred to the same energy zero used above, is

$$Q_s = \{1 - e^{-h\nu/kT}\}^{-3} \qquad (9.507)$$

—compare Eq. (4.803). In Eq. (9.505) the factor $Q_s e^{W_s/kT}$ must become unity before a Bose-Einstein transition could occur in the gas phase, and inspection of Eq. (9.507) shows that this can never happen, even theoretically. It therefore follows that the availability of the solid crystal phase inhibits the occurrence of the condensation into the zero state of the Bose-Einstein gas. Physically this is because the atoms prefer to concentrate in the lowest available states, and these are now the solid states rather than the lowest state in the gas.

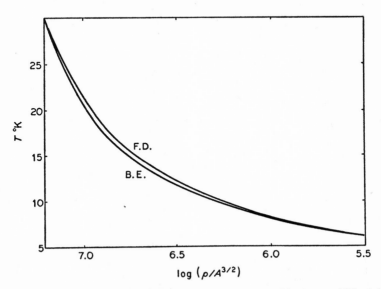

FIG. 9.51. Comparison between sublimation pressures p of isotopes of Einstein crystal in B.E. and F.D. vapor; calculated from Eqs. (9.506) and (9.507) with $h\nu/k = 25$, $W_s = 25$ cal/mole and m = atomic mass of H times atomic weight A. These constants correspond roughly to helium.

It may be noticed that the sublimation pressure of the Bose-Einstein gas, given by Eq. (9.506), is appreciably greater than that of the classical gas given by Eq. (5.612), when in equilibrium with a given crystal at a given temperature. In fact, the classical expression is just the first term of the series appearing in the Bose-Einstein expression. The difference is greatest when the factor $(1/Q_s)e^{-W_s/kT}$ is a maximum, and this is not at the lowest temperature. In fact the correction is evidently greatest when

$$(d/dT)\{(1/Q_s)e^{-W_s/kT}\} = 0$$

or

$$h\nu/kT = \ln(1 + 3h\nu/W_s) \qquad (9.508)$$

The effect vanishes both at very high and at very low temperatures. If for instance we take W_s about 400 cal/mole and the Einstein temperature $h\nu/k$ about 200 °K, we find the temperature at which quantum degeneracy effect is maximum to be about 144 °K, the increase in pressure due to the effect being about 10 per cent. It is left as an exercise to show that a Fermi-Dirac gas in equi-

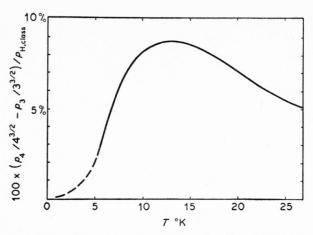

Fig. 9.52. Percentage difference between B.E. and F.D. sublimation pressures from an Einstein crystal; same constants as Figure 9.51.

librium with an Einstein crystal will have a lower sublimation pressure than classical, and to estimate the order of magnitude of the difference.

9.6 Saturated vapor and Bose–Einstein model liquid. We saw in § 8.6 that it is possible to set up a phenomenological theory of the liquid phase by treating the atoms as forming a gas trapped in a potential well whose depth is a constant. To consider the equilibrium between such a liquid model and its gas or vapor phase, we proceed just as in all the foregoing examples of phase equilibria: write down the product of the Bose–Einstein complexions in the two phases, maximize the logarithm of the product by varying the numbers in both sets of energy levels, under the two restrictions to conservation of total number and total energy, and arrive at the same expressions for the most probable populations in and liquid as if the two phases were completely separate, but with the same free energy and temperature in each. Just as in Eq. (8.605), we find

$$N_g = V_g (2\pi m k T/h^2)^{3/2} \sum_{j=1} (1/j^{3/2}) e^{j\mu/kT} \tag{9.601}$$

$$N_l = V_l (2\pi m k T/h^2)^{3/2} \sum_{j=1} (1/j^{3/2}) e^{j(\mu + W^*)/kT} \tag{9.602}$$

where, as before $W^* = W + N_l \partial W/\partial N$, W is the depth of the potential well in the liquid, and μ is the free energy determined by the total number $N = N_g + N_l$. Formally the above results determine the numbers in the two phases when we know W^*, but in practice we do not know W^*, so the theory is to be applied the other way round: from the observed density of the liquid we try to find W^* and the density of the saturated vapor.

Eq. (9.602) can be solved for $(\mu + W^*)/kT$ in the same way as Eq. (8.305) was solved for μ/kT, giving the same solution, Eq. (8.328), in the form

$$e^{(\mu+W^*)/kT} = 2.612(\rho_l/\rho_0)\{1 - 0.9235\rho_l/\rho_0 + 0.3926(\rho_l/\rho_0)^2$$

$$-0.1027(\rho_l/\rho_0)^3 + \cdots\} \quad (9.603)$$

where

$$\rho_l = N_l/V_l \quad \text{and} \quad \rho_0 = (2\pi mkT/h^2)^{3/2} \sum_{j=1} 1/j^{3/2} \quad (9.604)$$

The pressure of the vapor is given again by Eq. (8.337), where now the factor $e^{\mu/kT}$ is to be found in terms of W^*, etc., from Eq. (9.603). If we define T_0 by the relation

$$\rho_l = (2\pi mkT_0/h^2)^{3/2} \sum_{j=1} 1/j^{3/2} \quad (9.605)$$

so that

$$\rho_l/\rho_0 = (T_0/T)^{3/2} \quad (9.606)$$

we find from Eqs. (8.337) and (9.604) that

$$p_{\text{sat}} = \rho_l kT e^{-W^*/kT}\{1 - a(T_0/T)^{3/2} + b(T_0/T)^3 - c(T_0/T)^{9/2} + \cdots\} \quad (9.607)$$

where

$$a = 0.9235 - 0.4617e^{-W^*/kT}$$
$$b = 0.3926 - 0.9528e^{-W^*/kT} + 0.4377e^{-2W^*/kT}$$
$$c = 0.1027 - 0.7564e^{-W^*/kT} + 1.213e^{-2W^*/kT} - 0.5569e^{-3W^*/kT}$$

valid for all T greater than T_0.

In this result W^* is a phenomenological parameter to be chosen rather arbitrarily so as to give the best agreement with the known density of the liquid phase. To this end, consider first sufficiently high temperatures or low enough densities to allow the classical statistics to apply. In this limit, μ is large and negative, and the series both in Eq. (9.601) and Eq. (9.602) reduce to their first terms; hence we can write, practically,

$$\rho_l/\rho_g = e^{W^*/kT} \quad \text{or} \quad W^*/kT = \ln{(\rho_l/\rho_g)}, \quad \rho_g = N_g/V_g \quad (9.608)$$

From the discussion of § 8.6 we know that the pressure of this liquid model depends on $\partial W/\partial \rho_l$, and evidently the pressure as given by Eq. (8.607) should be the same as the vapor pressure given here in Eq. (9.607). Using the classical limit on both these equations leads to the following relation:

$$(\rho_l - \rho_g)kT = \rho_l^2 \partial W/\partial \rho_l \quad (9.609)$$

Eliminating $\partial W/\partial \rho_l$ from between Eqs. (9.608) and (9.609) we find

$$T \gg T_0: \qquad W/kT = \ln{(\rho_l/\rho_g)} - (1 - \rho_g/\rho_l) \quad (9.610)$$

The situation at very low temperatures comparable with or less than T_0 is essentially modified by the fact that the *lambda*-condensation occurs in the liquid model. From Eq. (9.608), it follows that W^* must be positive for all actual examples where the gas density is certainly less than the liquid density. Inspection then of Eq. (9.601) and Eq. (9.602) shows at once that, as μ increases from very large negative values towards zero with falling temperature, it will eventually reach the value $-W^*$ before it reaches zero. The series (9.602) then reaches its radius of convergence, and the liquid phase suffers its *lambda*-transition at the temperature T_0 determined by Eq. (9.605). Below T_0, the free energy μ approaches more and more closely to $-W^*$, and the number of atoms in the gas drops rapidly with decreasing T, according to the relation derived from Eq. (9.501), with $\mu = -W^*$:

$$T \leq T_0: \qquad \rho_g = (2\pi mkT/h^2)^{3/2} \sum_{j=1} (1/j^{3/2})e^{-jW^*/kT} \qquad (9.611)$$

The pressure of the vapor derived from Eq. (8.337) with the same μ is

$$T \leq T_0: \qquad p_{\text{sat}} = kT(2\pi mkT/h^2)^{3/2} \sum_{j=1} (1/j^{5/2})e^{-jW^*/kT} \qquad (9.612)$$

The pressure on the liquid given by Eq. (8.607), with $\mu = -W^*$, is

$$T \leq T_0: \qquad p_l = \rho_l kT(1.341/2.612)(T/T_0)^{3/2} - \rho_l^2(\partial W/\partial \rho_l) \qquad (9.613)$$

Equating these two pressures, we get an equation involving only W, T, and ρ_l:

$$kT(T/T_0)^{3/2}\{1.341 - \sum_{j=1} (1/j^{5/2})e^{-jW^*/kT}\} = 2.612 \, \rho_l \partial W/\partial \rho_l \qquad (9.614)$$

Unfortunately there is no direct way of eliminating $\partial W/\partial \rho_l$ from between this equation and Eq. (9.611), which was how we derived Eq. (9.610) in the high-temperature case. If for example we were to assume that at sufficiently low temperatures we could take $W^* \gg kT$, and so neglect all but the first term in the series of Eq. (9.614) and Eq. (9.611), we could work through the algebra to find a solution for W; but in fact W turns out not to be much greater than kT, thus violating the assumption made at the outset. Indeed, inspection of Eq. (9.614) shows that the left-hand side must approach zero with decreasing T; the only way the right-hand side can do the same is for the liquid to expand with decreasing temperature, its potential well becoming so shallow that $\rho_l \partial W/\partial \rho_l$ approaches zero as $T \to 0$. The liquid therefore must get "blown up" to anomalously small densities and behave more like a gas. This sounds impossible, but liquid helium does in fact behave very much like a gas and has a density much less than normal liquids; in fact it needs a pressure of some 25 atm to compress liquid helium far enough to solidify even in the neighborhood of absolute zero temperature. The model merits a detailed numerical comparison with the data on liquid helium; if it is found inadequate, two obvious improvements are available. First, the variable free volume parameter V_f may be adopted, as was done in the classical theory of § 7.6 in place of V of the present model; second, the pressure of the saturated vapor could be discussed in terms of the cluster theory to be developed in the next chapter, instead of as ideal Bose-Einstein gas.

9.7 Multilayer adsorption of a Bose-Einstein gas. In § 9.1 we saw that in the equilibrium between a Bose-Einstein gas and a mobile monolayer, there exists a critical density of the gas at which adsorption suddenly increases. At lower gas densities the adsorbed film is no more dense than one would expect from gaseous surface densities, while at slightly higher gas densities the film may have a density corresponding to liquid surface densities. To study this effect more closely, we note first that from Eq. (9.118) the increase in adsorption occurs at constant gas pressure, so long as W, the energy of adsorption, remains fixed. Also from Eq. (9.117) and Eq. (9.116) the number in the film, during the increase in adsorption, is a function of the volume of the gas:

$$N_f = N(1 - V/V_l) \tag{9.701}$$

In other words an increase in adsorption N_f is associated with a decrease in volume, $-\Delta V$ where

$$\Delta N_f/N = -\Delta V/V_l \tag{9.702}$$

A tenfold increase in N_f would still be a very small fraction of N, so that extremely small volume changes are involved. As the monolayer starts to fill up, two things must happen. First the energy of adsorption drops because of incapacity to accept more particles into the monolayer, and second, the filled monolayer becomes itself a suitable surface on which further adsorption can occur. This last fact is independent of whether the adsorbed atoms attract other adsorbed atoms, and it arises simply because the van der Waals forces between the original adsorbing surface can act at considerable distances compared with the thickness of the single monolayer. If this were the only force acting, the energy of adsorption would fall off with an inverse cube law with respect to the distance from a plane. We may represent the actual law parametrically by the formula:

$$W_n - W_\infty = (W_1 - W_\infty)/n^q \tag{9.703}$$

where W_1 is the energy of adsorption in the first monolayer, W_n the energy of adsorption in the nth monolayer, and q a number which would be 3 if the original adsorbing surface alone attracted the film. Because there is naturally a mutual attraction between adsorbed particles as well, we cannot expect that $q = 3$. In fact W_∞ is evidently the energy of adsorption in a film of "infinite" thickness and contains no contribution from the original adsorbing surface. We may equate W_∞ to the energy of latent heat for evaporation from the liquid phase, because such a thick film would essentially be a thin layer of bulk liquid.

Consider now the situation where the first monolayer is almost full. The pressure of the gas is given by Eq. (9.118) with W_1 written in place of W:

$$V_2 \leq V \leq V_1: \qquad p = kT(2\pi mkT/h^2)^{3/2} \sum_{j=1}^{\infty} (1/j^{5/2})e^{-jW_1/kT} \tag{9.704}$$

where V_1 is defined by the analog of Eq. (9.116):

$$N = V_1(2\pi mkT/h^2)^{3/2} \sum_{j=1}^{\infty} (1/j^{3/2})e^{-jW_1/kT} \tag{9.705}$$

The meaning of V_2 will be explained in a moment. As V decreases below V_1, the population in the film fills rapidly and eventually W begins to decrease, and by virtue of Eq. (9.704), this requires an increase in pressure p if we wish to continue increasing the adsorption. As soon as W decreases to the value W_2, given by Eq. (9.703), the pressure must have reached the value needed for a sudden increase in adsorption into the second monolayer on top of the first. Instead of further adsorption into the first monolayer, the second layer now begins to form with further compression of the gas:

$$V_3 \leq V \leq V_2: \qquad p = kT(2\pi mkT/h^2)^{3/2} \sum_{j=1} (1/j^{5/2})e^{-jW_2/kT} \qquad (9.706)$$

where V_2 is defined by

$$N = V_2(2\pi mkT/h^2)^{3/2} \sum_{j=1} (1/j^{3/2})e^{-jW_2/kT} \qquad (9.707)$$

This step by step process may be continued indefinitely; as each layer fills up, the pressure in the gas must be increased to give additional adsorption, and this induces the sudden increase in adsorption in the next layer up. Formally this would seem to suggest a discontinuously jumping pressure, and the model is evidently too crude in this respect. The energy of adsorption should instead be regarded as a continuous function of population in the film, instead of a step function. We can write the general relation, replacing Eq. (9.706):

$$p_n = kT(2\pi mkT/h^2)^{3/2} \sum_{j=1} (1/j^{5/2})e^{-jW_n/kT} \qquad (9.708)$$

where by W_n we mean the energy of adsorption into the nth layer when that layer first begins to form, and by p_n the critical pressure of the gas needed to initiate this adsorption into the nth layer. This formula is true even when the energy of adsorption is a continuous function of population; it merely selects a discrete set of points on a continuous curve, corresponding to the onset of each layer. If for n we write ∞, we get the saturated vapor pressure for the liquid phase:

$$p_\infty = p_{\text{sat}} = kT(2\pi mkT/h^2)^{3/2} \sum_{j=1} (1/j^{5/2})e^{-jW_\infty/kT} \qquad (9.709)$$

Taking the ratio between p_n and p_{sat} from these last two equations, we have

$$p_n/p_{\text{sat}} = X_n(\tfrac{5}{2};T)/X_\infty(\tfrac{5}{2};T) \qquad (9.710)$$

where

$$X_n(\tfrac{5}{2};T) = \sum_{j=1} (1/j^{5/2})e^{-jW_n/kT} \qquad (9.711)$$

This equation (9.710) is a relation between the relative pressure of the gas to the saturated vapor pressure and the number of layers in the film, and it is therefore nothing but the isotherm equation for adsorption in the multilayer film. If we use Eq. (9.703) with any assumed value of q to calculate W_n and hence the series X_n in Eq. (9.711), we can plot a graph of the isotherm when we know W_∞.

In applying this theory to a study of helium adsorption at low temperatures, two complications arise. In the first place, it is found that the first adsorbed layer is not mobile, but localized; it is only after the second or perhaps even the third layer is present that sufficient mobility exists to make the present model acceptable. In the second place, true mobility occurs only below the *lambda*-transition when the film is superfluid, and this again makes the model of the film as a two-dimensional gas of doubtful validity. However, if one uses the BET isotherm for the first part of the adsorption, and the present theory for the adsorption beyond the second layer, agreement is fairly good with $q = 2$.

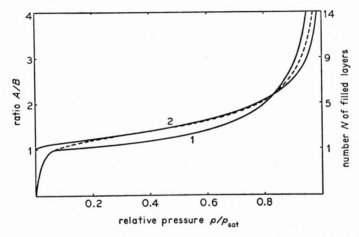

FIG. 9.71.   Multilayer adsorption isotherms for helium: Curve 1: B.E.T. isotherm modified to include anomalous packing in first layer; Curve 2: Bose-Einstein theory with mobility in second and higher layers; Curve 3: observed isotherm at about 2.4 °K.

The adsorption isotherm derived in this way by treating the mobile film as an ideal gas is really in no better agreement with the data on helium adsorption than that derived from the BET theory (§ 5.5), which treats the adsorbed film as a solid phase. To decide between the two models it is necessary to consider their implications for adsorption of mixtures of the two isotopes He^3 and He^4. On the BET theory the mixtures should behave normally, whereas on the ideal gas model, He^4 should swamp He^3 in the film, as was pointed out in § 9.3. When the superfluid film is formed by flow from bulk liquid, this swamping effect does apparently occur, but some significant experimental work completed recently at Chicago * on unsaturated films, both below and above the *lambda*-temperature, formed by pure adsorption without mass flow from bulk liquid, gives a contrary result. The unsaturated film appears to be entirely normal in isotopic content at all temperatures. Clearly the behavior of the unsaturated film is the proper test of any adsorption theory, and the data appear to be completely

* M. S. Inghram, E. Long, and L. Meyer, *Phys. Rev.*, **97** (1955), p. 1453.

consistent with the BET theory where the film is treated as a solid phase, even when the film is known to be superfluid! There are indeed good reasons for thinking of the superfluid as a solid having zero rigidity, none of the atoms possessing any random motion characteristic of normal liquids and gases. This point will arise again in § 12.3.

EXERCISES AND PROBLEMS

1. Investigate the adsorption isotherm for an ideal Bose-Einstein gas adsorbed into a monolayer with an energy spectrum like that found in Problem 9 of Chapter VIII.

2. Verify Eqs. (9.113) and (9.114); express Eq. (9.113) in terms of the pressure of the parent gas, as suggested in the text.

3. Verify Eq. (9.206) in detail.

4. From Eq. (9.210) show that $kT_1 = 1.535\ \mu_0$.

5. Check the developments given in Eqs. (9.214), (9.215), and (9.217).

6. Check the coefficients found in Eqs. (9.218) and (9.219).

7. Discuss the equilibrium of a Fermi-Dirac gas between a set of three-dimensional states like those in Problem 6 of Chapter VIII, and a set of two-dimensional states of the same type at some arbitrary energy of adsorption.

8. Check the coefficients in Eqs. (9.305) and (9.304).

9. Repeat Problem 1 above for a Fermi-Dirac gas, and for a mixture of Fermi-Dirac and Bose-Einstein components.

10. Repeat the analysis of § 9.4 for a Fermi-Dirac gas.

11. Modify the analysis of § 9.4 for the case where the adsorbed particle occupies two adjacent sites.

12. Study the sublimation of a Fermi-Dirac gas from an Einstein crystal.

13. Check the development given for Eq. (9.607).

14. In § 9.6 it has been assumed that the whole volume of the liquid is a "free volume"; discuss the improvements possible if we use instead the variable free volume, like that introduced in § 7.6 and § 7.7.

15. Develop the theory of the saturated vapor of a Fermi-Dirac liquid.

16. Discuss the saturated vapor of a mixture of two isotopes like He^3 and He^4, and develop formulae for the relative concentrations in the two phases, liquid and vapor.

17. Develop the formal modification of the multilayer adsorption theory of § 9.7 required to include immobility in the first layer.

REFERENCES FOR FURTHER STUDY

"Liquid-Solid Transformation in Helium near Absolute Zero," C. A. Swenson, *Phys. Rev.*, **79** (1950), p. 626.

"Solidification of He^3," Osborne, Abraham, and Weinstock, *Phys. Rev.*, **82** (1951), p. 263.

"Solid-Fluid Equilibrium of Helium above 5000 Atm. Pressure," Holland, Huggill, and Jones, *Proc. Roy. Soc.*, **A207** (1951), p. 268.

"Bose-Einstein Condensation for Thin Films," M. F. M. Osborne, *Phys. Rev.*, **76** (1949), p. 396.

"Mobile Multilayer Adsorption of B. E. Gas: Helium," W. Band, *J. Chem. Phys.*, **19** (1951), p. 435.

"The Unsaturated Helium Film," Earl Long and Lothar Meyer, *Advances in Physics*, **2** (1953), p. 1.

Chapter X

DISSOCIATIVE EQUILIBRIUM AMONG QUANTUM DEGENERATE SYSTEMS

10.1 Clustering phenomena in Bose-Einstein gas. In this section we give the Bose-Einstein analog of the problem worked out in § 6.4 for classical statistics. A Bose-Einstein gas whose molecules can form clusters under the action of their mutual van der Waals forces can, to the same approximation as that used in classical statistics, be treated as a mixture of a number of subassemblies, each subassembly consisting of clusters all of the same size forming an ideal gas. Each subassembly is subject to the Bose-Einstein statistics, and we count the number of complexions as follows: Because all the molecules are identical and indistinguishable, there is only one way in which the total number of molecules N can be split into N_s clusters each containing s molecules, all values of s. The number of ways in which we can assign N_s clusters, any one particular value of s, to their possible energy levels, n_{sr} to the rth level, is given by the Bose-Einstein count, Eq. (2.223):

$$C_s = \prod_r (n_{sr} + \omega_{sr})!/(n_{sr}!\omega_{sr}!) \qquad (10.101)$$

and the total number of complexions for the whole assembly corresponding to the distribution-in-energy specified by the set of numbers n_{sr}, all s and r, is simply the product of Eq. (10.101) over all s-values. We then maximize the logarithm of this under the restrictions, total number and total energy conserved, the variables being n_{sr}. This leads to the Bose-Einstein analog of Eq. (6.409):

$$\sum_s \{\delta \ln C_s - s\alpha \sum_r \delta n_{sr} - \beta \sum_r \delta n_{sr}(\epsilon_{sr} - W_s)\} = 0 \qquad (10.102)$$

where of course C_s is now given by Eq. (10.101). Again we can treat the different s-values separately, and each subassembly yields its own distribution-in-energy of maximum probability, all subassemblies having the same free energy and temperature. Because the quantities C_s are Bose-Einstein, the distributions are Bose-Einstein; hence we have in place of Eq. (6.410):

$$n_{sr} = \omega_{sr}\{\exp(\epsilon_{sr} - W_s - s\mu)/kT - 1\}^{-1} \qquad (10.103)$$

This distribution is formally identical with that for a simple ideal Bose-Einstein gas, Eq. (8.301), except that $W_s + s\mu$ replaces μ. Treating the present problem by the same integration approximation as used in § 8.3, we find an equation analogous to Eq. (8.305) for each value of s:

$$N_s = V(2\pi smkT/h^2)^{3/2} \sum_{j=1} (1/j^{3/2}) e^{j(s\mu+W_s)/kT} \tag{10.104}$$

and the equation determining μ is given by writing this into

$$N = \sum_s sN_s \tag{10.105}$$

In deriving Eq. (10.104), we note that the mass of each cluster is sm, and the internal energy of the cluster of size s is written $-W_s$.

For the partial pressure of each subassembly, we find the analog of Eq. (8.337) to be

$$p_s = kT(2\pi smkT/h^2)^{3/2} \sum_{j=1} (1/j^{5/2}) e^{j(s\mu+W_s)/kT} \tag{10.106}$$

and the total pressure is the sum of these

$$p = \sum_s p_s \tag{10.107}$$

In § 7.4 we showed that in classical statistics clustering leads to an avalanche of clusters at the saturation pressure, and leads to an equation for the saturated vapor pressure: the pressure at which large clusters suddenly become the most probable. Here we shall see a similar result and obtain the equation for the saturated vapor pressure of a Bose-Einstein vapor. From Eq. (10.104), it is obvious that at sufficiently high T or large V the free energy μ is lower than $-W_s/s$ for every s, and that if either V or T is decreased, μ must increase. The ratio of the total number of clusters to the number of unclustered particles is

$$\frac{\sum_{s=2} N_s}{N_1} = \frac{\sum_{s=2} \sum_{j=1} (s/j)^{3/2} e^{j(s\mu+W_s)/kT}}{\sum_{j=1} (1/j)^{3/2} e^{j(\mu+W_1)/kT}} \tag{10.108}$$

However, W_1, the energy of a cluster of size one, is obviously zero, so the series in the denominator would remain finite until $\mu = 0$. But the series in the numerator, all energies W_s being positive, would diverge as soon as μ increased above $-W_s/s$; that value of s that makes W_s/s a maximum would control the situation. It therefore follows that as we compress the gas into a smaller and smaller volume, we shall eventually arrive at a volume where the series in the numerator of Eq. (10.108) tends to diverge, the denominator remaining strictly finite. This evidently can be interpreted as the onset of a clustering avalanche. To study this in detail we have to decide on the dependence of W_s on s as was done in Eq. (6.420), but before doing this let us first discuss the probability of a *lambda*-transition due to statistical degeneracy.

As the student may already have noticed, the situation we have just described as bringing on a clustering avalanche is precisely the same as that which brings on a degeneracy transition (at T_0) in the ideal Bose-Einstein gas, or at least an obvious analogy to it, viz., that the free energy μ shall be such that the series in Eq. (10.104) reaches its radius of convergence. If we try to compress the assembly further, the free energy cannot further increase, and particles are forced into the lowest state. Here, however, the lowest state is not the zeroth state of the unclustered gas, but the large clusters, or the liquid phase, so the degeneracy *lambda*-transition is really identical with the condensation into the liquid phase. We thus arrive at the interesting theorem that a Bose-Einstein gas in which van der Waals forces can cause clustering, cannot undergo the ideal *lambda*-transition into the zeroth state, but must always condense first into its liquid phase.

Proceeding again as in § 6.4, Eqs. (6.420) and (6.421), we assume that the energy W_s has the simple relation to cluster size:

$$W_s = sW - Xs^{2/3} \tag{10.109}$$

Asymptotically, for large values of s, both W and X are constant. Using this relation in Eq. (10.104), we see that the convergence of the series depends only on the value of the factor,

$$e^{s(\mu+W)/kT} \tag{10.110}$$

The avalanche occurs when the double series involved in Eq. (10.105) and Eq. (10.104) reaches a radius of convergence. The ratio of the $s + 1$ term to the s-term for any particular j-value when $s \gg 1$ is easily shown to be

$$e^{j(\mu+W)/kT} \tag{10.111}$$

Comparison with (10.110) shows that the radius of convergence of the s- and the j-series is the same, given by

$$\mu = -W \tag{10.112}$$

The large clusters coalesce to form the liquid phase, or the assembly undergoes the *lambda*-transition into the lowest (liquid) state, according to one's arbitrary point of view; the two processes necessarily coincide. Putting this critical value of the free energy into Eqs. (10.106) and (10.107), we get the equation for the saturated vapor pressure:

$$p_{\text{sat}} = kT(2\pi mkT/h^2)^{3/2} \sum_{s=1} \sum_{j=1} (1/j^{5/2}) s^{3/2} e^{-jXs^{2/3}/kT} \tag{10.113}$$

This equation has been used to describe the observed saturated vapor pressure of liquid helium with fairly good results in spite of the crude nature of the theory. The method of procedure was as follows:

Note first that Eqs. (10.104) and (10.105) yield an equation for the numerical density of the saturated vapor:

$$(N/V)_{\text{sat}} = (2\pi mkT/h^2)^{3/2} \sum_{s=1} \sum_{j=1} (1/j^{3/2})s^{5/2}e^{-jXs^{2/3}/kT} \qquad (10.114)$$

We then find the energy X as a function of T so as to make p_{sat}, given in Eq. (10.113), agree with the observed saturated vapor pressure curve; we then use this energy X in Eq. (10.114) and compare the predicted density with the known

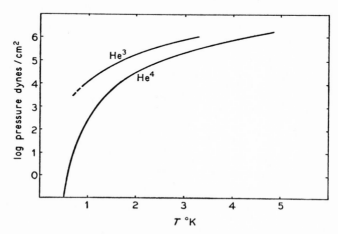

FIG. 10.11.   Observed saturated vapor pressures of helium isotopes.

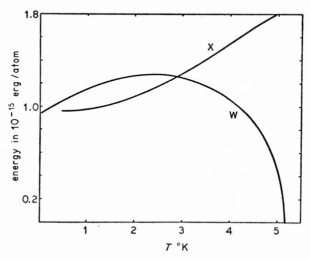

FIG. 10.12.   Cluster theory of helium vapor pressure.   Curve X is the energy term in Eq. (10.113) needed to fit the observed data on vapor pressure, He^4, and Curve W is the observed energy of vaporization.

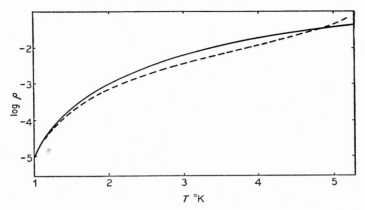

FIG. 10.13. Cluster theory of helium vapor density He^4. The theoretical curve (full line) is drawn from Eq. (10.114) using the X-values of Figure 10.12. The observed curve (broken line) is drawn from published data and virial coefficients.

density of the saturated vapor. The energy X is presumably comparable with the surface tension in large clusters, but in small clusters it must be more nearly equal to the energy of vaporization. In the series of Eq. (10.113), the dominant terms are the first few, so that the value of X should compare rather with the energy of vaporization than the surface tension. These comparisons are shown in the accompanying figures.

The chief weakness of this theory is its neglect of the finite size and internal structure of the clusters. In the classical theory given in § 6.4, the structure of the clusters was formally included through the internal partition function Q_{si}. Here the partition function method fails, and the correction must be made *ab initio*. Let the energy of a cluster be expressed as the sum of two terms, $\epsilon_{sr} + \epsilon'_{su}$, the kinetic energy of its center of mass plus internal energy (rotation); at the same time, the weight is expressed as the product $\omega_{sr}\omega'_{su}$. The distribution-in-energy is

$$n_{sru} = \omega_{sr}\omega'_{su}\{\exp{(\epsilon_{sr} + \epsilon'_{su} - s\mu)/kT} - 1\}^{-1} \qquad (10.115)$$

The number of clusters of size s is then found by the double sum over all r and u. Taking a particular value of u first, we treat this expression just as we did Eq. (10.103), to derive Eq. (10.104) and find

$$\sum_r n_{sru} = V(2\pi smkT/h^2)^{3/2} \sum_{j=1} (1/j^{3/2})\omega'_{su}e^{j(s\mu-\epsilon'_{su})/kT} \qquad (10.116)$$

Summing over all internal states u then gives the total number N. If we write

$$Q(s,j) = \sum_u \omega'_{su}e^{-j\epsilon'_{su}/kT} \qquad (10.117)$$

we have

$$N_s = V(2\pi smkT/h^2)^{3/2} \sum_{j=1} (1/j^{3/2})Q(s,j)e^{js\mu/kT} \qquad (10.118)$$

Evidently $Q(s,j)$ is identical with the internal partition function, except that T/j replaces T; it is thus a simple matter to express it in terms of the same physical parameters used in § 4.5. To develop the whole theory of the saturated vapor in terms of $Q(s,j)$, instead of the single energy W_s, would involve considerably more difficult computational work, but the results might well repay the effort.

10.2   Clustering phenomena in Fermi-Dirac gas.   Consider a Fermi-Dirac gas, e.g., helium isotope of mass 3, which can form clusters under the action of their mutual van der Waals forces. A cluster that contains an even number of atoms, having even mass number, is a member of a subassembly obeying Bose-Einstein statistics; clusters containing an odd number of atoms would still obey Fermi-Dirac statistics. The analog of Eq. (10.101) is therefore

s even:
$$C_s = \prod_r (n_{sr} + \omega_{sr})!/(n_{sr}!\omega_{sr}!)$$

(10.201)

s odd:
$$C_s = \prod_r \omega_{sr}!/\{(\omega_{sr} - n_{sr})!n_{sr}!\}$$

The reasoning is then the same as in the last section. Each subassembly can be treated separately, yielding its own most probable distribution-in-energy; even clusters have a Bose-Einstein distribution, and odd clusters, a Fermi-Dirac:

s even: $n_{sr} = \omega_{sr}\{\exp(\epsilon_{sr} - W_s - s\mu)/kT - 1\}^{-1}$

s odd: $n_{sr} = \omega_{sr}\{\exp(\epsilon_{sr} - W_s - s\mu)/kT + 1\}^{-1}$

(10.202)

Summing these over all energy levels, we again use the integration approximation, obtaining Eq. (10.104) for the even clusters and an equation analogous with Eq. (8.409) for the odd clusters. It is not difficult to see that both forms are included with the proper alternations of sign in the following expression, for any parity of s:

$$N_s = V(2\pi smkT/h^2)^{3/2} \sum_{j=1} (-1)^{s(j-1)}(1/j^{3/2})e^{j(s\mu + W_s)/kT}$$

(10.203)

The free energy μ is determined by writing this expression into the numerical sum of Eq. (10.105), which gives the density in terms of μ. The partial pressure of the s-subassembly is easily shown to be:

$$p_s = kT(2\pi smkT/h^2)^{3/2} \sum_{j=1} (-1)^{s(j-1)}(1/j^{5/2})e^{j(s\mu + W_s)/kT}$$

(10.204)

If only odd values of s were counted in Eq. (10.203) there would be no degeneracy transition, any more than there is in an ideal Fermi-Dirac gas; but because even values of s are present, Eq. (10.203) becomes similar to Eq. (10.104), and a transition may occur. However, just as in the clustering Bose-Einstein problem, the condensation into the liquid phase via a clustering avalanche always occurs first. To see this we look at Eqs. (10.105) and (10.203) again, reverse the order of the two sums, summing first over all s-values, and only afterwards over the j-values. Summing over s for any odd value of j gives a series without alternating signs. Such a series has a finite sum at its radius of convergence, but becomes discontinuously infinite beyond. This forces the free energy to remain at the value giving the radius of convergence and induces exactly the same kind of clustering avalanche as before. The fact that there are also present some s-series, with even values of j, that do not diverge, does not alter this; one diverging series is enough to make the total infinite.

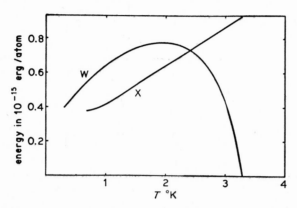

FIG. 10.21. Cluster theory of helium vapor pressure. Curve X is the energy term in Eq. (10.206) needed to fit the observed data on vapor pressure, He^3, and Curve W is the observed energy of vaporization.

Again assuming Eq. (10.109) for W_s, the critical value of μ is $-W$, and so the critical cluster concentrations are given by Eq. (10.203) with this value of the free energy. Then the density of the vapor is found from Eq. (10.105):

$$(N/V)_{\text{sat}} = (2\pi m kT/h^2)^{3/2} \sum_j \sum_{s=1} (-1)^{s(j-1)} s^{5/2}(1/j^{3/2})e^{-jXs^{2/3}/kT} \quad (10.205)$$

The saturated vapor pressure is found similarly by putting the critical value of μ into Eq. (10.204) and summing over all cluster sizes:

$$p_{\text{sat}} = kT(2\pi m kT/h^2)^{3/2} \sum_s \sum_{j=1} (-1)^{s(j-1)} s^{3/2}(1/j^{5/2})e^{-jXs^{2/3}/kT} \quad (10.206)$$

The saturated vapor pressure of pure He^3 has recently been measured, but not the density of the saturated vapor. We may proceed as for He^4 in the previous section, find X as a function of T from the observed pressure, and proceed to predict the density of the vapor. The results are shown in the accompanying figure.

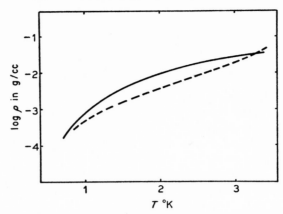

FIG. 10.22.   Cluster theory of helium vapor density, He³. Solid line: theoretical curve drawn from Eq. (10.205) using X-values of Figure 10.21. Broken line: experimental curve.

10.3   Saturated vapor pressure of isotopic mixtures.   In the foregoing two sections we have made use of the law of partial pressures, and it would seem timely at this point to indicate the general proof that this law holds in quantum degenerate gases.   A direct proof on the lines given in § 6.2 for classical statistics is troublesome in quantum degenerate assemblies, because the partition function formalism is no longer valid.   However, if we use the general theorems of thermodynamics, the law becomes almost obvious.   Referring to the argument preceding Eq. (8.337) for the pressure of the Bose-Einstein gas, we may note that, from their definitions, energy E, free energy F, and entropy S are all necessarily extensive (or additive) quantities with respect to contributions from the various parts of the assembly, provided only that there are no interaction energies between the parts concerned.   It then follows that because $pV = TS + F - E$, the pressure p is also additive in the same sense—since all the parts are in one and the same volume V.   The student can easily provide the proof that the same remarks apply equally well to the Fermi-Dirac assembly.

Chemical equilibria in gaseous mixtures with quantum degeneracy are of no more than formal interest.   This is because at low enough temperatures to make quantum degeneracy significant, no chemical reactions can in practice occur. Apart from this, the law of mass action cannot be stated in the simple manner of classical statistics, because the partition function formalism is not valid.   The required formalism is extremely involved and we shall not discuss it here.   One problem in gas mixtures, however, arises naturally from the work of the last two sections—that of the behavior of mixtures of isotopes in which clustering can occur.   We shall discuss the saturated vapor pressure of such mixtures as a clustering avalanche problem.

Any cluster has now to be specified by an ordered pair of numbers, say (s,t), in which the first number represents the number of He⁴ atoms in the cluster, and the second number, that of He³ atoms in it.   We have subassemblies for each type of cluster. Any cluster of an even number of He^3 atoms will belong to a Bose-Einstein subassembly; any cluster containing an odd number of He^3 atoms belongs to a Fermi-Dirac subassembly. The parity of the number of He^4 atoms in the cluster has no effect on the statistics. In maximizing the probability for an assembly of this kind, there are two independent numerical restrictions, one for each isotopic component, yielding two free energy parameters μ_3 and μ_4 respectively. The mass of a cluster of type (s,t) is evidently $(sM_4 + tM_3)$, and the free energy of the subassembly of clusters of this type is $(s\mu_4 + t\mu_3)$. Keeping these remarks in mind, the student will have little difficulty in generalizing Eq. (10.203) to fit the present problem, finding

$$N(s.t) = V(2\pi kT/h^2)^{3/2}(sM_4 + tM_3)^{3/2} \times \sum_{j=1} (-1)^{t(j-1)}(1/j^{3/2})e^{j(s\mu_4+t\mu_3+W_{st})/kT}$$

$$(10.301)$$

where W_{st} means the energy of dissociation of the cluster of type (s,t) and $N(s,t)$ is the total number of such clusters. The two free energies μ_4 and μ_3 are determined by equating the sum over all s and over all t respectively to N_4 and N_3:

$$N_4 = \sum_t \sum_s sN(s,t); \quad N_3 = \sum_s \sum_t tN(s,t) \qquad (10.302)$$

where s and t may each start from zero. A clustering avalanche occurs if either of the free energies reaches its critical value, and the discussion of this possibility follows the assumption analogous to Eq. (10.109):

$$W_{st} = sW_4 + tW_3 - X(s,t) \qquad (10.303)$$

where $X(s,t)$ is a surface term roughly proportional to $(s + t)^{2/3}$. The series in Eq. (10.302) diverges if either μ_4 exceeds $-W_4$ or if μ_3 exceeds $-W_3$, and either the one or the other of these two possibilities may be responsible for the avalanche accompanying the saturation of the vapor. Actual determination of the free energies from Eq. (10.302) presents practically insurmountable difficulties, and the best we can do is to restrict ourselves to several limiting cases—in particular where the concentration of one isotope is extremely small compared with the other.

Careful examination of Eq. (10.301) will make it apparent that if, for example, $N_3 \ll N_4$, it is necessary for μ_3 to be much more negative than μ_4. If we consider an isothermal compression of the mixture, both free energies tend to increase towards zero as V decreases; but of course μ_4 increases to its critical value $-W_4$ before μ_3 reaches its critical value $-W_3$, provided only that N_3 is sufficiently small compared with N_4. Any further decrease in volume cannot cause μ_4 to increase beyond its critical value, and it remains practically fixed. This removes one variable and it becomes impossible to satisfy both Eqs. (10.302) for smaller volumes simply by increasing μ_3. Atoms then condense out of the vapor into a liquid phase on further compression; however, without a definite theory of the liquid phase, it is not possible to say what proportion of each isotope goes into the liquid. If we are interested only in the condition of the saturated vapor, we do not need to discuss what happens beyond the initial onset of saturation. The present theory is sufficient for this but is inadequate to discuss the relative concentrations in the liquid phase in equilibrium with the vapor.

First let us suppose that N_3 is so small that the isotope behaves effectively like an ideal classical gas; this means that $-\mu_3$ is so large that any term in a series containing a factor $e^{\mu_3/kT}$ to the second or higher power can be neglected. Then setting $\mu_4 = -W_4$, Eqs. (10.302) reduce to the following first approximation to the saturation densities:

$$(N_4/V)_{sat} = (2\pi kT/h^2)^{3/2} \left\{ \sum_s s(sM_4)^{3/2} \sum_{j=1} (1/j^{3/2})e^{-jX(s,0)/kT} \right.$$

$$\left. + \sum_s s(sM_4 + M_3)^{3/2} \exp\left[\mu_3 + W_3 - X(s,1)\right]/kT \right\} \quad (10.304)$$

$$(N_3/V)_{sat} = (2\pi kT/h^2)^{3/2} \sum_{s=0} (sM_4 + M_3)^{3/2} \exp\left[\mu_3 + W_3 - X(s,1)\right]/kT$$

$$(10.305)$$

This last equation determines μ_3 in terms of N_3 at saturation, and we can use Eq. (10.305) to eliminate the factor $\exp{(\mu_3 + W_3)}/kT$ from the second part of Eq. (10.304), yielding a linear relation between (N_4/V) and (N_3/V) at saturation. Noting that the saturation density of the mixture is

$$\rho_{sat} = M_4(N_4/V) + M_3(N_3/V) \quad (10.306)$$

A few simple algebraic steps transform the linear relation into:

$$\rho_{sat} = \cfrac{(M_4 + xM_3)(2\pi M_4 kT/h^2)^{3/2} \sum_{s,j} (s^{5/2}/j^{3/2})e^{-jX(s,0)/kT}}{1 - x\cfrac{\sum_s s(sM_4 + M_3)^{3/2} \exp\left[-X(s,1)/kT\right]}{\sum_s (sM_4 + M_3)^{3/2} \exp\left[-X(s,1)/kT\right]}} \quad (10.307)$$

where x stands for the ratio N_3/N_4, and so is much less than unity in the present discussion in order for the formula to be valid.

To find the saturated vapor pressure, it is fairly obvious how to generalize Eq. (10.204) for the partial pressure of clusters of type (s,t) and then to find the total pressure from the law of partial pressures:

$$p_{sat} = \sum_{s=0} \sum_{t=0} p(s,t) \quad (10.308)$$

Under the same approximation that holds for Eqs. (10.304) and (10.305), this gives

$$p_{sat} = kT(2\pi kT/h^2)^{3/2} \left\{ \sum_{s,j} (sM_4)^{3/2}(1/j^{5/2})e^{-jX(s,0)/kT} \right.$$

$$\left. + \sum_{s=0} (sM_4 + M_3)^{3/2} \exp\left[\mu_3 + W_3 - X(s,1)\right]/kT \right\} \quad (10.310)$$

Using Eq. (10.305) in the second part of this reduces it immediately to $N_3 kT/V$, while the first part is precisely the same as Eq. (10.113) for the pure Bose-Einstein gas, with $X(s,0)$ substituted for $Xs^{2/3}$. So on this approximation the two components simply contribute independent partial pressures:

$$N_3 \ll N_4 : \qquad\qquad p_{sat} = p_4{}^0 + N_3 kT/V \qquad\qquad (10.311)$$

where $p_4{}^0$ is an expression derived from Eq. (10.113), with a modified energy term.

The corresponding formulae for the case that $N_4 \ll N_3$ are easily written down, and their detailed deduction is left as an exercise:

$$p_{sat} = \frac{(M_3 + yM_4)(2\pi M_3 kT/h^2)^{3/2} \sum_{t,j} (t^{5/2}/j^{3/2})(-1)^{t(j-1)} e^{-jX(0,t)/kT}}{1 - y \dfrac{\sum_t t(M_4 + tM_3)^{3/2} \exp\left[-X(1,t)/kT\right]}{\sum_t (M_4 + tM_3)^{3/2} \exp\left[-X(1,t)/kT\right]}} \qquad (10.312)$$

where $y = N_4/N_3$ and must be much less than unity for the formula to be valid. Equation (10.311) is replaced by

$$N_4 \ll N_3 : \qquad\qquad p_{sat} = p_3{}^0 + N_4 kT/V \qquad\qquad (10.313)$$

where $p_3{}^0$ is the same as Eq. (10.206), with $X(0,t)$ replacing $Xt^{2/3}$.

Second approximations can be obtained for Eqs. (10.307) and (10.310) by writing

$$\left. \begin{aligned} N_4 &= \sum_s sN(s,0) + \sum_s sN(s,1) + \sum_s sN(s,2) \\ N_3 &= \sum_s N(s,1) + 2\sum_s N(s,2) \quad \text{(include } s = 0) \end{aligned} \right\} \qquad (10.314)$$

and

$$p_{sat} = \sum_s \{p(s,0) + p(s,1) + p(s,2)\} \qquad (10.315)$$

The development of this is tedious, and is omitted here. Details can be found outlined in the literature quoted in subsequent paragraphs. The figures have been drawn from the second approximation.

In applying these formulae to a discussion of the data, we have to find $X(s,t)$ as a reasonable interpolation formula between the two pure isotopes, restricted at least to being proportional to the number of particles in the surface of a cluster of size $s + t$, and therefore to $(s + t)^{2/3}$. However, it is to be noticed that W_{st}, of which $X(s,t)$ is a part, is the energy required to dissociate the cluster and distribute its atoms in the vapor—not into empty space. In practice, therefore, the surface energy of a cluster of pure He^4 in a mixed vapor is not the same as the surface energy of such a cluster in pure He^4 vapor; in other words, $X(s,0)$ is not equal to $X_4 s^{2/3}$, and $X(0,t)$ is not equal to $X_3 t^{2/3}$. The interpolation formula that seems a priori most reasonable is

$$X(s,t) = (s + t)^{2/3}\{(1 - C)X_4 + CX_3\} \qquad (10.319)$$

where

$$C = N_3/(N_3 + N_4) = x/(1 + x)$$

This formula essentially assumes that on average the concentration of He^3 in the cluster surfaces is the same as in the vapor. Actually, Eq. (10.319) gave results * for the saturated vapor pressure much higher than those observed.† To obtain better agreement the following formula was employed: ‡

$$X(s,t) = (s + t)^{2/3}\{X_4(1 - C)^n + X_3 C^n\} \qquad (10.320)$$

where n has some value chosen to give the best fit with the data. By using for X_4 the value of X in § 10.1 for He^4, and for X_3 the value of X in § 10.2 for He^3, we can construct $X(s,t)$ for any desired value of n from Eq. (10.320) and hence find the theoretical saturated vapor pressure for the mixture, both at small C and small values of $1 - C$. To fit the data exactly at $C = 10$ per cent, it was found necessary to choose n as a function of T: for the isotherm at 2 °K, $n = 0.79$; $T = 1.7$ °K, $n = 0.78$; $T = 1.55$ °K, $n = 0.77$. The predicted pressures are quite sensitive to the value of n, n being fixed to within 0.5 per cent by the experimental data. By using Eq. (10.315) one can then obtain predictions for $C = 95$ per cent and rough ones for $C = 90$ per cent. The theoretical curves are shown in Figure 10.31 compared with smoothed experimental data. Experimental data are lacking between 78 and 100 per cent so that exact comparison at 95 per cent is not possible. However, it is quite obvious that the curves fitted at 10 per cent are too low at the higher concentrations. For the 2 °K isotherm, the deviation becomes significant at about 40 per cent; for the 1.7 °K isotherm, at about 65 per cent; and for the 1.55 °K isotherm, at about 80 per cent. These vapor concentrations can be translated roughly into liquid phase concentrations at the same pressures, and they turn out to be about 10 per cent at 2°, 24 per cent at 1.7°, and 30 per cent at 1.55°. These are actually quite close to the *lambda*-transition points in the liquid mixtures. §

Now the liquid phase does not enter our analysis as such—the saturation is an effect of clustering in the vapor. There does remain the possibility that small

* R. A. Nelson and W. Band, *Phys. Rev.*, **88** (1952), p. 1431.

† H. S. Sommers, Jr., *Phys. Rev.*, **88** (1952), p. 113.

‡ W. Band and R. A. Nelson, *Phys. Rev.*, **90** (1953), p. 744.

§ Abraham, Weinstock, and Osborne, *Phys. Rev.,* **76** (1949), p. 864; Daunt and Heer, *Phys. Rev.*, **81** (1951), p. 447.

droplets or large clusters may on average exhibit an anomaly at or near the *lambda*-transition in the liquid. In our formula Eq. (10.320) with $n < 1$, the He^3 isotope does indeed play a reduced role in determining the surface energy of small clusters, compared with that in the linear formula Eq. (10.319). This may be interpreted as due to an average deficiency of He^3 in cluster surfaces, and may be related to the effects discussed in § 9.3. Above the *lambda*-points our formula Eq. (10.320) is apparently overcorrected: to obtain the observed

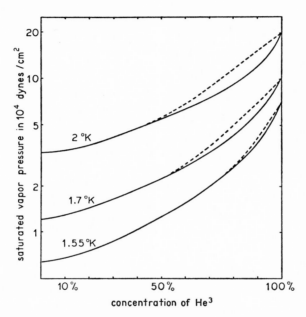

Fig. 10.31. Cluster theory of vapor pressure of helium isotope mixtures. Full lines, theoretical curves; dotted lines, smoothed data.

curve, n would have to be nearer unity at smaller values of $(1 - C)$. This means that He^3 plays a greater part in determining the surface term above the *lambda*-transition than below.

The transition in the droplets, if it exists, appears to be quite gradual; no breaks have been observed in the isotherms at the *lambda*-points. This might be explained as due to a dependence of a sudden transition in a cluster on the cluster size. On the other hand, the fact that the deviations appear to set in at the *lambda*-points may be fortuitous. To decide this question it would be necessary to have an observed isotherm above 2.2 °K, where the *lambda*-transition could not occur at all. Unfortunately cryogenic techniques for maintaining isotherm temperatures by means of liquid helium rely strongly on the existence of the superfluid helium for maintaining uniform temperature, and isothermal data above 2.2 °K are much more troublesome to obtain.

10.4   Nuclear reactions.   It was mentioned in the last section that quantum degeneracy has no practical effect on chemical equilibria because chemical reactions do not occur at the low temperatures where quantum effects become significant. We must qualify this statement, however, if we include nuclear reactions. If we recall the criterion for validity of classical statistics in § 3.6 and write for N/V the numerical density of matter within a nucleus, we find that significant quantum effects are to be expected at all temperatures below about 10^{10} °K, which includes temperatures sufficient to permit thermonuclear reactions.

Nuclei containing more than 50 nucleons can be treated as assemblies of large numbers of systems, although we can hardly expect the statistical results to have as sharp a meaning as they do for macroscopic assemblies containing many billions of atoms.   The major difficulty encountered in applying statistics to such nuclear assemblies is that so little is yet known of the internal energy states of the nuclei.   Nevertheless the statistical consequences of various models of nuclear structure are used to check the models in question, and there is no doubt that the statistical method will be increasingly employed in the future, as nuclear structure becomes better known.   We shall not discuss this aspect of statistical mechanics further, but refer the interested student to other sources in the literature.

According to astronomical evidence, there exist stars, called white dwarfs, that have densities comparable to nuclear matter, and which are apparently quantum degenerate assemblies of nucleons—protons and neutrons—they are supernuclei.   If their temperatures are lower than 10^{10} °K, the nucleons must all be in their lowest energy states, and so far as the kinetic energy of the nucleons is concerned, the white dwarfs are "dead." However, the supernucleus is unstable with respect to transmutations of neutrons into electron and proton plus neutrino, and it decays just like any other radioactive nucleus, emitting fragments that have high enough energy to escape from the star's gravitational field. Recent speculations about the origin of the elements as we now know them have suggested that the nuclei familiar in elementary chemistry are remnants of the fission and decay of one or more such supernuclei. This picture accounts qualitatively for the observed relative abundances of the heavier elements, but it fails to account for those of the lighter elements from about atomic weight 80 down.   In fact the abundance of H is about 10^9 times too great to be understood in this way.

The abundance of the lighter elements up to about atomic weight 60 have been explained tentatively in terms of an equilibrium theory.   Considering all nuclei as composed only of protons and neutrons, and neglecting electrons around the nuclei and all electrical forces, the relative probability of a cluster (nucleus) of z protons and n neutrons should be proportional to the Boltzmann factor $e^{-W/kT}$ where W is the energy of binding in the nucleus, $-W(z,n)$. The mathematical theory is identical with that given in § 6.3 in connection with ordinary chemical reactions in gases; the physical interpretation is different.   The most probable number of clusters containing z protons and n neutrons is given by an obvious generalization of Eq. (6.319):

$$N(z,n) = V\{2\pi m(z,n)kT/h^2\}^{3/2} \exp (z\mu_p + n\mu_n + W_{z,n})/kT \quad (10.401)$$

where $m(z,n)$ is the mass of the nucleus, and μ_p and μ_n are the free energies per proton and per neutron respectively. By adjusting the three unknowns, μ_p, μ_n, and T, a good fit can be secured for the relative abundances $N(z,n)$ in terms of the known binding energies $W(z,n)$ up to atomic weights about 60, with $kT \sim$ 1 mev, $\mu_p = -11.6$, $\mu_n = -7.6$ mev.

These two very different pictures regarding the origin of the heavier elements on the one hand and the lighter elements on the other may possibly be reconciled in one broader picture in the following way. We start with a primordial neutron-rich fluid of greater than nuclear densities, and at even higher temperature than 10^{10} °K, exploding and cooling until it separates into two phases: a nuclear liquid phase and a nuclear gaseous phase, or saturated vapor. The terms "liquid" and "vapor" are here the analogs of the same terms used ordinarily, but the forces responsible for the condensation and phase separation are nuclear forces of extremely short range compared with the van der Waals forces. An ordinary solid would be counted as a nuclear gas according to this terminology. After cooling and separation into the two phases, the temperature of the assembly is supposed to be still high enough to permit thermonuclear reactions. Going over from ordinary temperatures, densities, and van der Waals forces, to these high temperatures, densities, and nuclear forces, we see that the clustering approximation to the saturated vapor carries over also, and that the statistical problem of calculating the relative abundances of small nuclear clusters is mathematically identical with that of finding the relative abundances of clusters in the saturated vapor; we do not need to know anything about the nature of nuclear forces beyond the simple fact that they are of short range and sufficient to form stable clusters. The small nuclear clusters are of course nothing but the chemical elements, or rather their nuclei.

Before such a calculation can have any meaning we must be sure that the atmosphere or nuclear vapor would be held around the liquid core by gravitation, even though the temperature is as high as required to permit nuclear reactions. There is a minimum mass below which the supernucleus could not exist in two separate but contiguous phases: the condensed phase or core must be at least massive enough to hold, by its gravitational attraction, an atmosphere at the saturated vapor pressure corresponding to the required temperature. Indeed, the kinetic energy per nucleon in the atmosphere will have to be of the order of several million electron volts, and before this can be held in the gravitational field of the central mass, the latter must produce a gravitational potential at least 10^{18} erg/g. The gravitational field of a sphere of mass M and density ρ at its surface is $10.7 \times 10^{-8}\rho^{1/3}M^{2/3}$ erg/g. Assuming nuclear densities $\rho \sim 10^8$ g/cm³, the minimum mass M turns out to be of the same order of magnitude as the white dwarfs, 10^{34} g; the supernucleus is possibly 2,000 km in radius.

To handle the statistical problem, the atmosphere is treated as a mixture of ideal gases—the particles of which are composed of the nuclear clusters between which dissociative equilibrium exists. Each nuclear species or cluster type forms a subassembly. There exist only neutrons and protons in the mixture, and each cluster type is specified by an ordered pair of numbers, (n,z), of which the first represents the number of neutrons, and the second the number of protons in the cluster. The masses of the neutron and proton can be taken as equal, so that the mass of the cluster is $(n + z)m$, where m is the proton mass. If the free energies are written μ_n and μ_z respectively, the free energy of the cluster of type (n,z) is $n\mu_n + z\mu_z$. Evidently the reasoning proceeds exactly as in the previous section, except that all clusters with an odd number, $n + z$ are Fermi-Dirac and result in alternating signs:

$$N(n,z) = V(2\pi mkT/h^2)^{3/2}(n + z)^{3/2} \times \sum_{j=1} (-1)^{(n+z)(j-1)}(1/j^{3/2})e^{j(n\mu_n+z\mu_z+W_{n,z})/kT}$$

$$(10.402)$$

The free energies are determined then by the expressions:

$$N_n = \sum_{z,n} nN(n,z); \quad N_z = \sum_{n,z} zN(n,z) \qquad (10.403)$$

for the total numbers of neutrons and protons, assuming that these numbers are fixed, and ignoring the occurrence of pair formation by neutron decay.|

The clustering avalanche sets in when one of the free energies causes the corresponding series to reach its radius of convergence, and the relative abundances of the clusters are found from Eq. (10.401) with the critical value of the free energy. Suppose the assembly is neutron-rich; then it is the free energy μ_n that controls the saturation, and which must be equated to its critical value; the other, μ_z, is determined by the second of Eqs. (10.403), or rather, we can eliminate μ_z from between Eqs. (10.403) and (10.402). This leads to an equation for the relative abundances of the clusters as a function of the ratio N_z/N_n, like the derivation of Eq. (10.307) from Eqs. (10.305) and (10.304). As an example of the order of magnitude of the resulting abundances, we may assume that N_z/N_n has such a value that both free energies reach their critical values simultaneously. Let

$$W_{n,z} = (n + z)W - X(n,z) \qquad (10.404)$$

and put the free energies equal to their critical values:

$$\mu_n = \mu_z = -W \qquad (10.405)$$

The total number of clusters of type (n,z) in the vapor at saturation is then

$$N(n,z) = V(2\pi mkT/h^2)^{3/2}(n + z)^{3/2} \sum_{j=1} (-1)^{(n+z)(j-1)}(1/j^{3/2})e^{-jX(n,z)/kT}$$

$$(10.406)$$

The energies $X(n,z)$ are the nonlinear terms in the mass defects of the nuclei and so are approximately known. The exponent in this equation in practice is so large that all the j-series can be dropped after the first terms, and quantum degeneracy be completely neglected. We then have the classical formula:

$$N(n,z) = V(2\pi mkT/h^2)^{3/2}(n + z)^{3/2}e^{-X(n,z)/kT} \tag{10.407}$$

Comparing this with Eq. (10.401) of the original equilibrium theory, we note that the latter equation contained three arbitrary (unknown) parameters, whereas Eq. (10.407) has only one, viz., T. The quantities $X(n,z)$ are the non-linear terms in the binding energies (mass defects) and are not known as exactly as the total binding energies; they are in fact somewhat hypothetical because derived from a smoothed mass-defect curve versus atomic weight. The observed abundances are well enough represented by Eq. (10.407) with $kT \sim 5$ mev up to atomic weight about 80 mass units. Such a temperature is adequate to permit thermonuclear reactions and so maintain equilibrium concentrations in the atmosphere during its formation. When the universe cools below where the nuclei have enough kinetic energy for these reactions, the distribution gets frozen in; hence one would expect the observed distribution to correspond to the lowest temperature permitting thermonuclear reactions.

The main advantage of this modified equilibrium theory over the simpler equilibrium theory is that it includes the heavy nuclei in the same picture, as eventual fission products of the liquid phase core. Of course the whole concept of an equilibrium situation persisting during the origin of the elements in the universe is highly questionable.

Returning for a moment to the general problem of nuclear theory, it must be emphasized that the quantum statistical method so far developed in this text is inadequate on two major counts. First, nuclear problems usually involve high energies where relativistic corrections are important. This affects both the quasi-classical expression for energy in terms of momentum, e.g., Eq. (4.216), and, because the quantum mechanics employed (Chapter I) is so far completely non-relativistic, drastic revision is necessary. Second, nuclear processes include transformation of matter into radiation, and nuclear assemblies in general necessarily include both nucleons and photons, with no very strict conservation of the total number of either type of system. This complicates the accessory restrictions, like Eqs. (2.301). The Lagrangian parameters associated with these restrictions yield the statistical definitions of the chemical potential and the temperature, which therefore need careful revision when we are dealing with such thermonuclear assemblies. Under the agreed limitations of the present text, these very interesting questions will not be discussed further.

EXERCISES AND PROBLEMS

1. Carry through the reasoning of § 10.1 for a clustering Bose-Einstein two-dimensional gas or monolayer, like Problem 5 of Chapter VI. Show that no sudden avalanche occurs, the condensation of the vapor into a condensed film taking place gradually as T approaches zero.

2. Develop the clustering theory for a Bose-Einstein gas with the energy spectrum of Problem 9, Chapter VIII. Is the condensation sudden in this case?

3. With a view towards the eventual development of the cluster theory in terms of Eq. (10.118), calculate $Q(s,j)$ at 2 °K for helium (a) for $s = 2$, and (b) for large values of s, assuming interatomic distances of 3×10^{-8} cm and that the large clusters are spherical.

4. Check Eq. (10.204) for the pressure.

5. Carry through the same arguments as in § 10.2 for a monolayer.

6. Check Eqs. (10.307) and (10.312).

7. Find the ratio N_3/N_4 such that the free energies μ_3 and μ_4 arrive at their critical values $-W_3$ and $-W_4$ simultaneously, from Eq. (10.302). Find the corresponding density and saturated vapor pressure.

8. If relativistic mechanics are used, Eq. (3.204) for the density of states becomes $\omega(\epsilon) = 8\pi(L/h)^3(\epsilon^2/c^2 - m^2c^2)^{\frac{1}{2}}\epsilon/c^2$, where c is the velocity of light, m the rest mass, ϵ the energy, including the rest energy mc^2. The expression under the square root is the relativistic momentum (squared). Use this in the Bose-Einstein expression, Eq. (3.511), and obtain the relativistic modification of Eq. (8.304), noting that the energy starts from mc^2 instead of zero. Discuss the possibility of a *lambda*-transition in the relativistic Bose-Einstein gas.

REFERENCES FOR FURTHER STUDY

"Condensation Phenomena in a Clustering Bose-Einstein Gas," W. Band, *Phys. Rev.*, **79** (1950), p. 871.

"The Origin of the Lighter Elements," W. Band, *Phys. Rev.*, **80** (1950), p. 813.

"Theory of the Origin and Relative Abundance Distribution of the Elements," R. A. Alpher and R. C. Herman, *Revs. Modern Phys.*, **22** (1950), p. 153.

Chapter XI

QUANTUM DEGENERATE ASSEMBLIES OF DEPENDENT SYSTEMS

11.1 The Slater-sum. The last three chapters have covered many quantum degenerate problems where one may assume the systems to be independent, and now we turn to quantum degenerate assemblies in which the systems interact. This calls for a generalization of the method of the assembly partition function that was introduced in Chapter VII. In § 7.5 we used a quasi-classical method to evaluate the assembly partition function for an imperfect gas and this naturally left the results inapplicable to quantum degenerate assemblies. The general method of the assembly partition function and the basic concepts of the Gibbs ensemble are however equally valid whether the assemblies are quantum degenerate or not. It is only the evaluation of the assembly partition function that has to be generalized to include quantum corrections. Throughout the whole discussion of § 7.1 there is no assumption regarding the absence of quantum degeneracy, until the results of the assembly partition function method are compared with those of the ordinary partition function method in the classical gas: specifically Eq. (7.121), where the classical complexion count was used. In particular, the thermodynamic relation Eq. (7.114),

$$A = -kT \ln \mathbf{Q}$$

is generally valid, as is the definition of the assembly partition function, Eq. (7.119):

$$\mathbf{Q} = \sum_j \Omega_j \exp\left(-E_j/kT\right) \tag{11.101}$$

Slater has shown how to evaluate $\mathbf{Q}$ for quantum degenerate assemblies, and we present his method here.

Let u_n, $n = 1, 2, \cdots$ represent the entire spectrum of energy eigenfunctions for the assembly as a whole, and E_n be the eigenvalue of the nth eigenfunction. In reading Eq. (11.101), we understand by E_j the jth energy level of the whole assembly, and by Ω_j the number of eigenfunctions u_n belonging to this eigenvalue:

$$E_j = E_n, \quad n = j_1, j_2, \cdots j_{\Omega_j} \tag{11.102}$$

225

Moreover if we write $d\tau$ for the $3N$-dimensional volume element in the configuration space of the assembly, we know that

$$\frac{1}{N!} \sum_{n=1}^{\Omega_j} \int \cdots \int \bar{u}_n u_n d\tau = \Omega_j \qquad (11.103)$$

because of the orthonormality of the eigenfunctions. Therefore, if we sum over all the eigenfunctions we find, comparing with Eq. (11.101):

$$\frac{1}{N!} \sum_n \exp\left(-E_n/kT\right) \int \cdots \int \bar{u}_n u_n d\tau = \mathbf{Q} \qquad (11.104)$$

We next note that E_n is a constant, and the factor preceding this integral can be included in the integrand:

$$\mathbf{Q} = \frac{1}{N!} \sum_n \int \cdots \int \bar{u}_n e^{-E_n/kT} u_n d\tau \qquad (11.105)$$

The functions u_n are eigenfunctions of the Hamiltonian operator for the whole assembly, so we may write the Schrödinger equation

$$H u_n = E_n u_n \qquad (11.106)$$

Indeed any function of the operator H can operate on the eigenfunctions of H, yielding the same kind of result, in particular,

$$e^{-H/kT} u_n = e^{-E_n/kT} u_n \qquad (11.107)$$

where the operator $e^{-H/kT}$ is defined in terms of H by the ordinary exponential series:

$$e^{-H/kT} = 1 - H/kT + \tfrac{1}{2}(H/kT)^2 + \cdots \qquad (11.108)$$

Thus we can write instead of Eq. (11.105), the operational equation:

$$\mathbf{Q} = \frac{1}{N!} \sum_n \int \cdots \int \bar{u}_n e^{-H/kT} u_n d\tau \qquad (11.109)$$

This, however, is exactly the sum over all the diagonal elements of the matrix representation of the operator (11.108), namely the matrix:

$$\|e^{-H/kT}\|_{n,m} = \int \cdots \int \bar{u}_n e^{-H/kT} u_m d\tau \qquad (11.110)$$

This sum, the spur of the matrix, is invariant for all linear transformations in the function space of which the u's are base vectors. Thus we have in general:

$$\mathbf{Q} = \frac{1}{N!} \sum_n \int \cdots \int \bar{v}_n e^{-H/kT} v_n d\tau \qquad (11.111)$$

where v_n, $n = 1, 2, \cdots$ is any closed orthonormal set of functions in the same configuration space as the u's, and not necessarily eigenfunctions of the operator H. Because we are free to choose any member of the family of closed orthonormal sets of functions for the v's, Eq. (11.111) is a much more powerful theorem than Eq. (11.102) from which we started. This form of the assembly partition function is known as the Slater-sum of the assembly.

The importance of the Slater-sum lies in the fact that we often do not know the exact eigenfunctions for the assembly, so that we could not set up the assembly partition function in its ordinary form. Even though we might be able to find the degeneracy numbers from group-theoretical considerations, we do not usually know the eigenvalues if we do not know the eigenfunctions. However, we can always set up the operator H, and we can always choose some arbitrary set of orthonormal functions v_n, and so at least formally set up the assembly partition function as a Slater-sum.

Before using this method to study assemblies of interacting systems, we show that when applied to ideal quantum degenerate gases it gives the same results as before in § 8.3 and § 8.4. To do this we can choose the actual exact eigenfunctions for the ideal gas as outlined in Eqs. (1.436) and (1.438):

$$u(\mathbf{p,r}) = N!^{-\frac{1}{2}}V^{-\frac{1}{2}N} \sum_P (\pm 1)^P \exp\left\{(2\pi i/h) \sum_{j=1}^N (\mathbf{p}_j \cdot \mathbf{r}_{Pj})\right\} \quad (11.112)$$

On the left side of this equation, we regard u as a function of all the momentum vectors of the assembly of particles represented by $\mathbf{p}$, and all the position vectors represented by $\mathbf{r}$. The momenta $\mathbf{p}$ take the place of the subscript n in Eq. (11.111). If the gas is confined to a box of side L, the momenta have discrete allowed values:

$$\mathbf{p}_j = h\mathbf{n}_j/L \quad (11.113)$$

where $\mathbf{n}_j$ is a vector having integer components. Thus the sum over n in Eq. (11.111) is translated into a sum over allowed momenta, or over the vectors $\mathbf{n}_j$. On the right-hand side of Eq. (11.112), we have written a sum over all permutations P, and the symbol $(\pm 1)^P$ assumes the upper sign if we are dealing with symmetrical eigenfunctions, or Bose-Einstein statistics, or the lower sign if with Fermi-Dirac statistics. In the latter case it signifies an alternating sign, positive for even permutations P and negative for odd permutations P. In the Bose-Einstein statistics it is always positive and can be dropped. The Hamiltonian operator is derived from the classical Hamiltonian in the usual way, the classical form being

$$H = \sum_j \mathbf{p}_j{}^2/2m \quad (11.114)$$

However because we have chosen the actual eigenfunctions of the assembly we can go back to Eq. (11.105) to find the assembly partition function, instead of using the operational form of Slater-sum in Eq. (11.111). Of course E_n is then replaced by

$$E(\mathbf{p}) = \sum_j \mathbf{p}_j{}^2/2m \quad (11.115)$$

The sum over all the energy levels can be written as an integral over all the momenta if we use the weight factor already found in Eqs. (3.204) and (8.303), expressed in terms of momentum instead of energy. It is easy to see that

$$\omega(p)dp = 4\pi V h^{-3} p^2 dp \qquad (11.116)$$

Then we can form the assembly partition function $\mathbf{Q}$ and find

$$N! h^{3N} \mathbf{Q} = \frac{1}{N!} \sum_P \sum_{P'} (\pm 1)^{P+P'} \int \cdots \int \exp\left\{-(2\pi i/h) \sum_{j=1}^{N} \mathbf{p}_j \cdot \mathbf{r}_{Pj}\right\}$$

$$\times \exp\left\{\sum_{j=1}^{N} -p_j^2/2mkT\right\} \exp\left\{(2\pi i/h) \sum_{j=1}^{N} \mathbf{p}_j \cdot \mathbf{r}_{P'j}\right\} \Pi\, 4\pi p_j^2 dp_j\, \Pi\, d\tau_j \qquad (11.117)$$

The index j in this expression indicates which particle the terms refer to, and Pj refers to another particle obtained from the jth particle by the permutation P. In evaluating this expression we find the following elementary integral over the momenta which goes through at once if we change to Cartesian co-ordinates: $4\pi p^2 dp \rightarrow dp_x dp_y dp_z$ for each particle.

$$\int \cdots \int_{-\infty}^{\infty} \exp\left\{(2\pi i/h) \sum_{j=1}^{N} (\mathbf{p}_j \cdot [\mathbf{r}_{P'j} - \mathbf{r}_{Pj}]) - \sum_{j=1}^{N} p_j^2/2mkT\right\} \Pi\, dp_{jx} dp_{jy} dp_{jz}$$

$$= (2\pi mkT/h^2)^{3N/2} \exp\left\{-(2\pi^2 mkT/h^2) \sum_{j=1}^{N} (\mathbf{r}_{Pj} - \mathbf{r}_{P'j})^2\right\} \qquad (11.118)$$

Therefore we may write Eq. (11.117) as follows:

$$N!^2 \mathbf{Q} = \sum_P \sum_{P'} (\pm 1)^{P+P'} (2\pi mkT/h^2)^{3N/2}$$

$$\times \int \cdots \int \exp\left\{-(2\pi^2 mkT/h^2) \sum_{j=1}^{N} (\mathbf{r}_{Pj} - \mathbf{r}_{P'j})^2\right\} \Pi\, d\tau_j \qquad (11.119)$$

From this it follows that

$$\mathbf{Q} = \frac{1}{N!} \sum_P (\pm 1)^P (2\pi mkT/h^2)^{3N/2}$$

$$\times \int \cdots \int \exp\left\{-(2\pi^2 mkT/h^2 \sum_{j=1}^{N} (\mathbf{r}_j - \mathbf{r}_{Pj})^2\right\} \Pi\, d\tau_j \qquad (11.120)$$

To see this we must note that the parity of the double permutation P' followed by the reciprocal of P is the same as the parity of P plus the parity of P'; then we write P in place of $P'P^{-1}$ and j in place of Pj in Eq. (11.119), and note that one of the sums merely multiplies the result by $N!$ as the total number of permutations, thanks to the symmetry of the integral with respect to the particles.

In the last integral over configuration space, the sum in the exponent, viz.,

$$\sum_{j=1}^{N} (\mathbf{r}_j - \mathbf{r}_{Pj})^2$$

breaks up into loops in some arbitrary pattern depending on the permutation P, each loop being self-contained and not connected with any other loop, e.g.,

$$(\mathbf{r}_1 - \mathbf{r}_2)^2 + (\mathbf{r}_2 - \mathbf{r}_3)^2 + \cdots + (\mathbf{r}_{s-1} - \mathbf{r}_s)^2 + (\mathbf{r}_s - \mathbf{r}_1)^2$$

The integral thus breaks up into a product of smaller integrals, each over the volume elements of the s particles in the loop. Each permutation determines a loop pattern, specified, say, by the number m_s of loops each containing s particles. The numbers m_s necessarily satisfy the relation:

$$\sum_s s m_s = N \tag{11.121}$$

because all the N particles are present in the exponent. Summing over all the permutations P in Eq. (11.120) means summing over all ways in which loops can be formed, or over all sets of numbers m_s that satisfy Eq. (11.121), and all ways in which the particles can be arranged in each set of numbers m_s. For the integral over any one loop, we write:

$$B_s = \int \cdots \int \exp \left\{ -(2\pi^2 mkT/h^2)(\mathbf{r}_{12}{}^2 + \mathbf{r}_{23}{}^2 + \cdots + \mathbf{r}_{s1}{}^2) \right\} d\tau_1 \cdots d\tau_s \tag{11.122}$$

where

$$\mathbf{r}_{12} = \mathbf{r}_1 - \mathbf{r}_2, \quad \text{etc.} \cdots$$

Note that the value of this integral over the co-ordinate space is independent of which particles are involved, and depends only on the number s. We evaluate this integral later. The integral occurs in Eq. (11.120) as a factor m_s times, for the corresponding permutation P. The number of permutations yielding the given set of numbers m_s is easily shown to be $N!/\{\prod_s m_s! s^{m_s}\}$. The factor s^{m_s} occurs here instead of $s!^{m_s}$ because only the cyclic permutations are allowed in a loop. Collecting together all the above information, we can rewrite Eq. (11.121) as

$$Q = (2\pi mkT/h^2)^{3N/2} \sum_{\{m_s\}N} (\pm 1)^P \prod_{s=1} (1/m_s!)(B_s/s)^{m_s} \tag{11.123}$$

where the sign is positive for Bose-Einstein statistics, but for Fermi-Dirac statistics the sign is negative whenever the permutation P producing the set m_s is odd. The summation sign means over all sets m_s satisfying Eq. (11.121).

It is clear that a loop containing an odd number of particles could be generated by an even number of steps, so that if we were to write a factor $(-1)^{s-1}$ for each loop of size s, the whole product would automatically give the proper sign for the permutation among all N particles in the Fermi-Dirac case. It is also to be noted that when $s = 1$ in the above expressions, a "loop" of one particle occurs whenever $Pj = j$, and the exponent vanishes; the loop integral then reduces simply to the total volume for that one particle:

$$B_1 = V \tag{11.124}$$

Incidentally, as will be shown shortly, every B_s contains a factor V, so it is convenient to introduce the following notation:

$$Vb_s = B_s/s \tag{11.125}$$

In terms of this notation Eq. (11.123) becomes

$$\mathbf{Q} = (2\pi mkT/h^2)^{3N/2} \sum_{\{m_s\}N} \prod_{s=1} (1/m_s!)\{Vb_s(\pm 1)^{s-1}\}^{m_s} \tag{11.126}$$

There are two ways in which we can now proceed. The more rigorous way is to form the generating function of some real variable X:

$$F(X) = \exp\left\{\sum_{s=1} Vb_s(\pm 1)^{s-1}(2\pi mkT/h^2)^{3/2}X^s\right\} \tag{11.127}$$

and we note that $\mathbf{Q}$ is the coefficient of X^N in the expansion of $F(X)$ as a power series in X. We then go over into the complex Z plane, of which X is the real axis, and evaluate the coefficient by the theorem of residues. The student is referred to other works for further details of this method. Instead we shall follow a less rigorous and mathematically simpler method that gives the same results. Looking at Eq. (11.126) as a series over all sets $\{m_s\}$, we note that there must exist some particular set $\{m_s\}$ that contributes the maximum term to the sum. It can be proved that if we take the logarithm of the series, the logarithm of its maximum term gives a first approximation to the result; and this approximation is the more precise, the larger N. The theorem may be stated in the form:

$$\lim N \to \infty: \quad \ln \mathbf{Q} = (3N/2) \ln (2\pi mkT/h^2)$$
$$+ \sum_{s=1} [\bar{m}_s \ln \{Vb_s(\pm 1)^{s-1}\} - \ln \bar{m}_s!] \tag{11.128}$$

where $\bar{m}_s$ is the most probable, or maximizing, value of m_s. This maximizing value $\bar{m}_s$ is to be found by making variations in m_s and equating to zero the resulting variations of $\ln \mathbf{Q}$; the variations δm_s are subject to the condition Eq. (11.121), so that we need one Lagrangian parameter, say γ. Multiplying Eq. (11.121) by γ, subtracting from Eq. (11.128), and taking the variations and equating to zero, we find, after making free use of the Stirling approximation on the factorials:

$$\delta m_s[\ln \{Vb_s(\pm 1)^{s-1}\} - \ln m_s - s\gamma] = 0$$

which solves to yield

$$\bar{m}_s = (\pm 1)^{s-1}Vb_se^{-s\gamma} \tag{11.129}$$

Putting this into Eq. (11.121) gives the equation determining γ:

$$N = \sum_s (\pm 1)^{s-1} s V b_s e^{-s\gamma} \tag{11.130}$$

Writing $\ln m_s! = m_s \ln m_s - m_s$ on the right side of Eq. (11.128) and using Eq. (11.129), we find the logarithm terms cancel and get simply:

$$\ln \mathbf{Q} = (3N/2) \ln (2\pi mkT/h^2) + \sum_s (\pm 1)^{s-1} V b_s e^{-s\gamma} + N\gamma \tag{11.131}$$

Applying to this the theorem of Eq. (11.101) and using the thermodynamic relation Eq. (7.116), we find the pressure:

$$p = kT \sum_{s=1} (\pm 1)^{s-1} b_s e^{-s\gamma} \tag{11.132}$$

To compare these results with those obtained previously, viz., Eq. (8.303) and Eq. (8.337) for Bose-Einstein and Eq. (8.409) for Fermi-Dirac statistics, we have finally to evaluate the integrals B_s of Eq. (11.122) or b_s of Eq. (11.125).

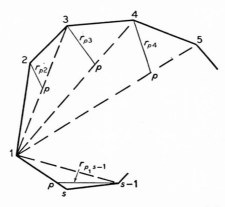

FIG. 11.11.   Illustrating evaluation of the loop integral B_s in Eq. (11.133).

To do this, first draw a polygon with s corners numbered $1, 2, \cdots s$. Complete the triangle $1, m, m+1$ and choose some point p on the side joining the corners 1 and $m+1$. Then

$$r^2{}_{1m} = r^2{}_{1p} + r^2{}_{pm} - 2r_{1p}r_{pm} \cos (\angle 1pm)$$

and

$$r^2{}_{m,m+1} = r^2{}_{p,m+1} + r^2{}_{pm} + 2r_{p,m+1}r_{pm} \cos (\angle 1pm)$$

Multiply the first of these by the ratio $a_m = r_{p,m+1}/r_{1p}$ and add the result to the second equation to eliminate the angle:

$$a_m r^2{}_{1m} + r^2{}_{m,m+1} = (1 + a_m)r^2{}_{pm} + a_m r^2{}_{1,m+1}/(1 + a_m)$$

Apply this equation successively starting from $m = 2$:

$$r^2_{12} + r^2_{23} = 2r^2_{p2} + \tfrac{1}{2}r^2_{13}$$

and with the point p on the line joining the corners 1 and 3, midway between them. Again with $m = 3$:

$$\tfrac{1}{2}r^2_{13} + r^2_{34} = \tfrac{3}{2}r^2_{p3} + \tfrac{1}{3}r^2_{14}$$

and the point p on the line joining the corners 1 and 4, such that $a_4 = \tfrac{1}{2}$. By choosing the points p successively in the appropriate places, we can set up a series of equations of which the typical one is

$$r^2_{1n}/(n - 1) + r^2_{n,n+1} = nr^2_{pn}/(n - 1) + r^2_{1,n+1}/n$$

Adding all these equations together for the values of $n = 2$ up to $s - 1$, we find

$$r^2_{12} + r^2_{23} + \cdots + r^2_{s-1,s} = 2r^2_{p2} + \cdots + (s - 1)r^2_{p,s-1}/(s - 2) + r^2_{1s}/(s - 1)$$

If to both sides of this equation we add r^2_{1s}, we get the expression appearing in the integrand of B_s on the left, which is therefore expressed, on the right, with separated variables. The origin of co-ordinates can be transferred to the corresponding point p for each integration, and we then find B_s to be a product of elementary integrals (Pierce's Tables #494):

$$B_s = 4\pi \prod_{n=2}^{s} \int \cdots \int \exp\{-nr_n^2/[(n-1)g^2]\}r_n^2 dr_n d\tau_1 = Vg^{3(s-1)}/s^{5/2} \quad (11.133)$$

where

$$g = (2\pi mkT/h^2)^{-1/2}$$

Dividing this by sV, we have from Eq. (11.125):

$$b_s = g^{3(s-1)}s^{-5/2} \quad (11.134)$$

If these integrals are put into Eq. (11.130), we can solve this equation for the parameter γ. However, we do not actually need to carry out this solution; for if we compare the equation with Eq. (8.305), which determined the free energy, we see that the two become identical if we write

$$e^{-\gamma} = g^{-3}e^{+\mu/kT} \quad (11.135)$$

so the solution we obtained before for μ will give γ. Putting this transformation from γ to μ into Eq. (11.132), we find that this equation reduces exactly to the equation of state (8.337) we found before. This completes the verification of the new formalism as it applies to the simplest case of an ideal quantum degenerate gas. It also demonstrates effectively that it is pointless to use a high-power formalism to solve a low-grade problem. We have done it here because the solution gives some insight into how the new formalism works, before we come to apply it to new problems that are insoluble by the earlier methods.

11.2   Quantum degenerate imperfect gas: theory of Kahn and Uhlenbeck.
In setting up the quantum mechanical generalization of § 7.5 and § 7.4 on imperfect gases, we use the Slater-sum Eq. (11.111) and the operational form of Hamiltonian Eq. (7.303):

$$H = - \sum_j \hbar^2 \nabla_j{}^2 / 2m + U(\mathbf{q}) \tag{11.201}$$

This permits the Slater-sum to be written in the form:

$$Q = \frac{1}{N!} \int \cdots \int G(\mathbf{q}) e^{-U(\mathbf{q})/kT} \Pi dq \tag{11.202}$$

where Πdq is intended to indicate the volume elements of all particles, and

$$G(\mathbf{q}) = \int \cdots \int \bar{u}(\mathbf{p,q}) \exp \left\{ \sum_j \hbar^2 \nabla_j{}^2 / 2mkT \right\} u(\mathbf{p,q}) V^N h^{-3N} \Pi dp \tag{11.203}$$

The factor $(V/h^3)^N$ takes care of the number of eigenstates per unit cell in momentum space when the eigenfunctions are normalized in the volume V, as in Eq. (11.116). The function $G(\mathbf{q})$ is a function of all the co-ordinates of all the N particles.

During the integration over $3N$ co-ordinate space, the particles form all conceivable cluster patterns. In any particular cluster pattern the energy breaks up into additive contributions, one from each cluster, and because interaction between particles is assumed short range, there is no interaction term between different clusters. Therefore the Hamiltonian corresponding to any cluster pattern also splits into clusters between which no interaction occurs. Similarly, the corresponding variables in the Schrödinger equation will separate and the corresponding eigenfunctions separate into congruent clusters. Because of this the function $G(\mathbf{q})$ splits into separate factors, one for each cluster. Thus in carrying out the integration in Eq. (11.202), any clustering of the variables that factorizes the term $e^{-U(\mathbf{q})/kT}$ automatically factorizes the term $G(\mathbf{q})$ in the same cluster pattern, and the integrand of Q therefore behaves in the same way as it did in the classical Mayer theory of Chapter VII. Note specially that in reaching this conclusion no assumption has been implied as to the pair-by-pair nature of the interaction forces; the result is therefore more general than the equivalent clustering in the Mayer theory of Chapter VII. Because of the factor $G(\mathbf{q})$, the contribution from each cluster has to be re-evaluated, and we need a more general formalism than in § 7.5. We introduce the following functions:

$$\begin{aligned}
f(q_1) &= g^3 G(q_1) \\
f(q_1,q_2) &= g^6 \{ G(q_1,q_2) e^{-u(q_1,q_2)/kT} - G(q_1)G(q_2) \} \\
f(q_1,q_2,q_3) &= g^9 \{ G(q_1,q_2,q_3) e^{-u(q_1,q_2,q_3)/kT} + 2G(q_1)G(q_2)G(q_3) \\
&\quad - \sum G(q_1)G(q_2,q_3) e^{-u(q_2,q_3)/kT} \}
\end{aligned} \tag{11.204}$$

The sum in the last expression is over the three cyclic permutations of the subscripts. The g-factors normalize the f's to unity as in the classical theory. Subscripts indicate particles. The functions are to be defined for all particles, all pairs, all triplets, etc., the above being typical examples only.

These f-functions have the important property that they become zero if the particles indicated by their subscripts do not form a close cluster. Thus if q_1 and q_2 are too far apart to be counted as a clustered pair, the function $f(q_1,q_2)$ vanishes because the function $G(q_1,q_2)$ factorizes into $G(q_1)G(q_2)$, as discussed above, and the interaction energy $u(q_1,q_2)$ vanishes. Similarly, if the third particle is too far from either the first or second to give any interaction energy, the function $f(q_1,q_2,q_3)$ vanishes identically, because the G's all factorize with respect to the third particle.

Equations (11.204) can be reversed to read

$$\left.\begin{aligned}
G(q_1) &= g^{-3}f(q_1) \\
G(q_1,q_2)e^{-u(q_1,q_2)/kT} &= g^{-6}\{f(q_1,q_2) + f(q_1)f(q_2)\} \\
G(q_1,q_2,q_3)e^{-u(q_1,q_2,q_3)/kT} &= g^{-9}\{f(q_1,q_2,q_3) + \sum f(q_1)f(q_2,q_3) \\
&\qquad\qquad + f(q_1)f(q_2)f(q_3)\}
\end{aligned}\right\} \quad (11.205)$$

etc.

In carrying out the integration of Eq. (11.202), there will be some definite region of co-ordinate space corresponding to each cluster pattern, and the integrand factorizes into this pattern; each factor in the integrand has the form of one of the expressions on the left side of the series of equations, Eq. (11.205). If we substitute the right sides of Eq. (11.205) for these factors in the integrand, the latter becomes the sum of a large number of f-products. Because of the cluster property of the f-functions, the integral over any one of these products splits into separate integrals over each factor in the product, and these integrals do not depend on which particles appear in the subscripts, only on how many. Moreover, because of the short range character of the interactions within each cluster, the integral over any one f-factor is proportional to V, and otherwise depends only on the number of particles in the factor. The general product contains m_1 factors like $f(q_1)$, m_2 factors like $f(q_1,q_2)$, and in general m_n factors with n particles. On integrating out the product, all these similar factors give identical integrals, so we may write the integral of an f-factor in which n particles are present in the form:

$$\int \cdots \int f(q_1,\cdots q_n)\, \Pi^n\, dq = n!Vb^*_n \qquad (11.206)$$

where $\Pi^n\, dq$ indicates the volume elements of all n particles. The product obtained from some one cluster pattern specified by the set of numbers m_n is

$$\prod_n \{n!Vb^*_n\}^{m_n} \qquad (11.207)$$

The number of identical cluster patterns formed by permuting the particles among themselves is

$$N!/\{\prod_n m_n!(n!)^{m_n}\} \tag{11.208}$$

so that the total value of $\mathbf{Q}$ is found by summing the product of the last two expressions over all sets of numbers m_n:

$$\mathbf{Q} = \sum_{\{m\}N} \prod_n (1/m_n!) \{Vb^*_n\}^{m_n} g^{-3N} \tag{11.209}$$

The sum over the sets m_n is restricted by the condition

$$N = \sum_n nm_n \tag{11.210}$$

Comparing this result with Eqs. (7.512) and (7.520), we notice the exact formal identity between the classical potential partition function $Q(\mathbf{q})/N!$ and the quantum mechanical $\mathbf{Q}g^{3N}$. The most important difference is that in the quantum mechanical formalism the momentum integrations, corrected for by the normalization factor g^3, occur in the integrals b^*, whereas in the classical formalism the momentum integrations were carried out before factorization and are absent from the b's. The most probable cluster numbers are evidently given by the analog of Eq. (7.517), which reads

$$m_n = V(b^*_n/g^n)e^{-n\gamma} \tag{11.211}$$

where γ is the Lagrangian multiplier determined by Eq. (11.210) in the form:

$$N = \sum_n nV(b^*_n/g^n)e^{-n\gamma} \tag{11.212}$$

If these equations can be solved, we can use the resulting values of m_n in Eq. (11.209) to find the logarithm of the assembly partition function, and hence the thermodynamic properties of the assembly.

The formal identity with the classical theory permits us to take over the classical results and merely reinterpret the coefficients. The work goes exactly as before and we find first that the analog of Eq. (7.526) is

$$(1/N) \ln (g^{3N}\mathbf{Q}) = \ln (Vb^*_1/N) + 1 + (b^*_2/b^*_1{}^2)(N/V)$$
$$+ (b^*_3/b^*_1{}^3 - 2b^*_2/b^*_1{}^4)(N/V)^2 + \cdots \tag{11.213}$$

It will be shown later, Eq. (11.217), that $b^*_1 = 1$, compare Eq. (7.524), and this simplifies Eq. (11.213). If the range of interatomic forces is small compared with the dimensions of the enclosure we can again accept the b^*'s as independent of the volume and proceed to find the pressure of the assembly from Eqs. (11.101) and (7.116). The result is

$$pV/NkT = 1 - b^*_2(N/V) - (2b^*_3 - 4b^*_2{}^2)(N/V)^2 - \cdots \tag{11.214}$$

Note that the full effects of quantum degeneracy are formally included in this result: quantum degeneracy of binary collisions affects all the virial coefficients from the second up, degeneracy of triple collisions affects all the virials from the third up, etc.

Before applying this result to calculate the effects of quantum degeneracy on the virial coefficients, it is again worthwhile to check that when applied to an ideal gas it yields identical results with those already obtained by the more elementary methods. In setting up the Slater-sum for an ideal gas, we know the eigenfunctions exactly, so we do not need to use the operational form Eq. (11.111), but can use the form Eq. (11.105) directly. To calculate $b*_1$ we first choose the eigenfunction for a single particle:

$$u(\mathbf{p},\mathbf{q}) = V^{-\frac{1}{2}} \exp{(i\mathbf{p}\cdot\mathbf{q}/\hbar)} \tag{11.215}$$

and evaluate the integral $G(\mathbf{q})$ from Eq. (11.203) for one particle:

$$G(\mathbf{q}) = h^{-3}\int\cdots\int \exp{\{-i\mathbf{p}\cdot\mathbf{q}/\hbar - p^2/2mkT + i\mathbf{p}\cdot\mathbf{q}/\hbar\}}dp_1 dp_2 dp_3$$

$$= h^{-3}\int\cdots\int e^{-p^2/2mkT}dp_1 dp_2 dp_3 = (2\pi mkT/h^2)^{\frac{3}{2}} \tag{11.216}$$

From Eqs. (11.206) and (11.205), the value of $Vb*_1$ is the volume integral of $G(\mathbf{q})g^3$, and because $G(\mathbf{q})$ as given here is independent of position, this yields

$$b*_1 = g^3(2\pi mkT/h^2)^{\frac{3}{2}} = 1 \tag{11.217}$$

Evidently the interaction energy does not enter this calculation anyway, so that this result is true also for the imperfect gas.

To calculate $b*_2$ for the ideal gas, we choose eigenfunctions for a pair of particles:

$$u(\mathbf{p}_1,\mathbf{p}_2,\mathbf{q}_1,\mathbf{q}_2) = (1/V2^{\frac{1}{2}})\{e^{i(\mathbf{p}_1\cdot\mathbf{q}_1+\mathbf{p}_2\cdot\mathbf{q}_2)/\hbar} \pm e^{i(\mathbf{p}_1\cdot\mathbf{q}_2+\mathbf{p}_2\cdot\mathbf{q}_1)/\hbar}\} \tag{11.218}$$

where the positive sign applies to the Bose-Einstein statistics and symmetrical eigenfunctions, and the negative sign gives antisymmetry; compare Eqs. (1.421) and (1.422). Writing $\mathbf{r} = \mathbf{q}_1 - \mathbf{q}_2$, it is easy to show that the square modulus of these eigenfunctions is:

$$\left.\begin{aligned}(\bar{u}u)_s &= (2/V^2)\cos^2{\{\pi(\mathbf{p}_1 - \mathbf{p}_2)\cdot\mathbf{r}/h\}}\\(\bar{u}u)_a &= (2/V^2)\sin^2{\{\pi(\mathbf{p}_1 - \mathbf{p}_2)\cdot\mathbf{r}/h\}}\end{aligned}\right\} \tag{11.219}$$

To find $G(q_1,q_2)$, we have to evaluate the integrals:

$$G(q_1,q_2) = 2h^{-6}\int\cdots\int\binom{\cos}{\sin}^2\{\pi(\mathbf{p}_1 - \mathbf{p}_2)\cdot\mathbf{r}/h\}e^{-(p_1{}^2+p_2{}^2)/2mkT}dp_1 dp_2 \tag{11.220}$$

over 6-dimensional momentum space. The easiest way to do this is to transform to new momentum variables defined by

$$p^2 = (\mathbf{p}_1 - \mathbf{p}_2)^2, \quad P^2 = (\mathbf{p}_1 + \mathbf{p}_2)^2 \tag{11.221}$$

The Jacobian of this transformation is 8, so the new 6-dimensional element is $(4\pi p^2 dp)(4\pi P^2 dP)/8$, and the integration is straightforward. The result is

$$G(q_1, q_2) = (2\pi mkT/h^2)^3 \{1 \pm \exp(-4\pi^2 mkTr^2/h^2)\} \tag{11.222}$$

where the positive sign corresponds to the cosine in Eq. (11.220) and symmetric eigenfunctions, and the negative sign to the sine in Eq. (11.220) and antisymmetric eigenfunctions. Applying this result to the second of Eqs. (11.204) with zero interaction energy, $u(q_1, q_2) = 0$, we find, from Eq. (11.216):

$$f(q_1, q_2) = \pm \exp(-4\pi^2 mkTr^2/h^2) \tag{11.223}$$

Putting this into Eq. (11.206) to find b^*_2, we must integrate over 6-dimensional co-ordinate space to get

$$\int \cdots \int f(q_1, q_2) d\tau_1 d\tau_2 = \pm V(\pi mkT/h^2)^{-\frac{3}{2}} \tag{11.224}$$

so that we find finally that

$$b^*_2 = \pm \tfrac{1}{16}(\pi mkT/h^2)^{-\frac{3}{2}} \tag{11.225}$$

It may easily be verified that this is equal to

$$b^*_2 = \pm 0.462(V/N)(T_0/T)^{\frac{3}{2}} \tag{11.226}$$

where T_0 is defined by Eq. (8.308), so that the second term on the right of Eq. (11.214) for the equation of state is identical with that in Eq. (8.340) derived previously. The evaluation of the third term is more tedious, but involves no new principles; it can also be shown to coincide with the corresponding term in Eq. (8.340) when no forces exist between the particles. This general method is evidently not convenient when applied to the ideal gas, but it does give the correct results. In the next section, we apply this new method to the problem for which it was designed, a study of imperfect gases with quantum degeneracy.

11.3   The second virial coefficient in quantum degenerate gases. If we write the imperfect gas equation (11.214) in the form:

$$pV/NkT = 1 + B/V + C/V^2 + \cdots \tag{11.301}$$

the quantity B is the second virial coefficient, C the third, etc. We have already seen in Eq. (11.225) that even for the ideal quantum degenerate gas, B is not zero, but has the value:

$$B_{id} = \mp(N/16)(\pi mkT/h^2)^{-\frac{3}{2}} \tag{11.302}$$

the sign depending on the statistics. Interaction forces between atoms may alter the value of B, and we now proceed to compute this effect:

$$B = B' + B_{id} \qquad (11.303)$$

It is evident from Eq. (11.214), remembering Eqs. (11.217) and (11.206), that

$$B = -\tfrac{1}{2}(N/V)(h^2/2\pi mkT)^3 \int \cdots \int \{G(q_1,q_2)e^{-u(q_1,q_2)/kT} - G(q_1)G(q_2)\}d\tau_1 d\tau_2$$

$$(11.304)$$

The second part of this can be integrated at once, and we find

$$B = \tfrac{1}{2}NV - \tfrac{1}{2}(N/V)(h^2/2\pi mkT)^3 \int \cdots \int G(q_1,q_2)e^{-u(q_1,q_2)/kT}d\tau_1 d\tau_2 \qquad (11.305)$$

The corresponding expression for the ideal gas is identical with this but has $u(q_1,q_2) = 0$, and $G_0(q_1,q_2)$ written in place of $G(q_1,q_2)$, defined in the same way as $G(q_1,q_2)$ except in terms of the free-particle eigenfunctions $u_0(q_1,q_2)$ in Eq. (11.203). Therefore we have

$$B' = -\tfrac{1}{2}(N/V)(h^2/2\pi mkT)^3 \int \cdots \int \{G(q_1,q_2)e^{-u(q_1,q_2)/kT} - G_0(q_1,q_2)\}d\tau_1 d\tau_2$$

$$(11.306)$$

Because these calculations involve a single pair of particles only, they are closely similar to those met with in the quantum mechanical theory of collisions,* and we find the method of partial waves familiar in the latter problem most appropriate here.

The integrals in Eq. (11.306) are essentially of the same form as those in Eq. (11.111), with the momentum integral implied in $G(q_1,q_2)$, replacing the sum over states in Eq. (11.111). It turns out to be easier to evaluate Eq. (11.306) if we go back to the earlier form Eq. (11.102), instead of Eq. (11.111), and write in place of Eq. (11.306):

$$B' = \tfrac{1}{2}(N/V)(h^2/2\pi mkT)^3 2! \left\{ \sum_n e^{-E_n/kT} - \sum_n e^{-E_n^0/kT} \right\} \qquad (11.307)$$

where the factor 2! is to take care of the degeneracy due to the identity of the two particles, there being on this account two states with each energy eigenvalue; the integer n is to be given a different value for each of the eigenstates of one of the particles, with respect to the other. The eigenvalues for interacting particles are E_n, and E_n^0 are those for noninteracting ones.

Expressing the co-ordinates of the pair in terms of their center of mass, the energy separates into kinetic energy of the center of mass motion, and energy

* *Quantum Mechanics*, L. I. Schiff, McGraw-Hill, 1949; Chapter V.

of relative motion. Summing over all states of the center of mass motion yields the classical factor for a body of mass $2m$:

$$V(4\pi mkT/h^2)^{3/2} \tag{11.308}$$

The energy of relative motion possesses the eigenvalues of the angular momentum equations in a spherically symmetrical field:
(a) no force field:

$$-(\hbar^2/m)d^2(ru^0{}_{nl})/dr^2 + \{\hbar^2l(l+1)/mr^2\}(ru^0{}_{nl}) = E^0{}_{nl}(ru^0{}_{nl}) \tag{11.309}$$

(b) central field $U(r)$:

$$-(\hbar^2/m)d^2(ru_{nl})/dr^2 + U(r)(ru_{nl}) + \{h^2l(l+1)/mr^2\}(ru_{nl}) = E_{nl}(ru_{nl}) \tag{11.310}$$

The number of eigenfunctions, either u_{nl} or $u^0{}_{nl}$, for each value of l is $2l + 1$. Therefore,

$$B' = -N(h^2/\pi mkT)^{3/2} \sum_l (2l+1) \left\{ \sum_n e^{-E_{nl}/kT} - \sum_n e^{-E^0{}_{nl}/kT} \right\} \tag{11.311}$$

To distinguish between Bose-Einstein and Fermi-Dirac statistics one has to include only eigenfunctions that are symmetrical or antisymmetrical respectively between the two particles. This means summing only over even values of l or only over odd values respectively. The detailed calculations for helium at low temperatures based on this method may be found in the literature; agreement between computed and observed coefficients is satisfactory when the Lennard-Jones potential function is used for $U(r)$.

As a much simpler example illustrating the method, we consider here a model gas of impenetrable spheres in which the potential function has the form:

$$U(r) = 0, \quad r > \sigma; \quad U(r) = \infty, \quad r \le \sigma \tag{11.312}$$

The eigenfunctions of Eq. (11.310) for such a field are linear combinations of the Bessel functions with arbitrary coefficients $A_l(k)$ and $B_l(k)$:

$$r > \sigma: \quad ru_{nl}(r) = A_l(k)(\tfrac{1}{2}\pi kr)^{1/2}J_{l+1/2}(kr) + B_l(k)(\tfrac{1}{2}\pi kr)^{1/2}J_{-l-1/2}(kr) \tag{11.313}$$

where k is determined by $\hbar^2k^2/2m = E_{nl}$ and so depends both on n and l. The ratio of A_l to B_l is determined by the condition:

$$r \le \sigma: \qquad\qquad ru_{nl}(r) = 0 \tag{11.314}$$

The eigenfunctions of the field free case, (11.309) are also linear combinations of the Bessel functions, but because the functions with negative coefficients become infinite at the origin, the arbitrary constants B_l have to vanish:

$$ru^0{}_{nl}(r) = A_l(k_0)(\tfrac{1}{2}\pi k_0 r)^{1/2}J_{l+1/2}(k_0 r) \tag{11.315}$$

where

$$\hbar^2k_0{}^2/2m = E^0{}_{nl}$$

Asymptotically at large radius the field free functions become

$$r \gg \sigma: \qquad\qquad ru^0{}_{nl}(r) = A_l(k_0) \sin (k_0 r - \tfrac{1}{2}l\pi) \qquad\qquad (11.316)$$

while the other functions become

$$r \gg \sigma: \qquad\qquad ru_{nl}(r) = (A_l{}^2 + B_l{}^2)^{\frac{1}{2}} \sin \{kr - \tfrac{1}{2}l\pi + \eta_l(k)\} \qquad (11.317)$$

where

$$\tan \eta_l(k) = (-1)^l B_l/A_l = (-1)^{l+1}\{J_{l+\frac{1}{2}}(k\sigma)/J_{-l-\frac{1}{2}}(k\sigma)\} \quad (11.318)$$

To use these functions in Eq. (11.311), we note that the sum over n in that equation may be transformed into an integration over k. To effect this transformation, we first enclose the field concentrically in a sphere of radius R and demand that $Ru(R) = 0$. This has the effect of forcing a discrete spectrum on the k-values, with a one-to-one correspondence between the k- and the n-values. We find that the transformation from n to k is independent of R, so that we can then let R approach infinity, thus allowing the k-spectrum to become continuous and its sums become integrals that can be evaluated in closed form. The provisional boundary condition:

$$Ru(R) = 0 \qquad\qquad (11.319)$$

applied to Eqs. (11.316) and (11.317) yields

and
$$\left.\begin{array}{l} k_0 R - \tfrac{1}{2}l\pi = n\pi \\ kR - \tfrac{1}{2}l\pi + \eta_l(k) = n\pi \end{array}\right\} \qquad\qquad (11.320)$$

so that in the two fields,

and
$$\left.\begin{array}{l} \Delta n = (R/\pi)\Delta k_0 \\ \Delta n = (R/\pi)\Delta k + (1/\pi)(d\eta_l/dk)\Delta k \end{array}\right\} \qquad (11.321)$$

To use these in Eq. (11.311), we note that

$$\sum_n e^{-E_{nl}/kT} \rightarrow (R/\pi)\int_0^\infty e^{-\hbar^2 k^2/mkT}\{dk + (1/R)(d\eta_l/dk)dk\} \quad (11.322)$$

and

$$\sum_n e^{-E^0{}_{nl}/kT} \rightarrow (R/\pi)\int_0^\infty e^{-\hbar^2 k_0{}^2/mkT}dk_0 \qquad\qquad (11.323)$$

The first integral of Eq. (11.322) is identical with Eq. (11.323), so that there remains only

$$B' = -N(h^2/\pi mkT)^{\frac{3}{2}}(1/\pi)\sum_l (2l + 1)\int_0^\infty e^{-\hbar^2 k^2/mkT}(d\eta_l/dk)dk \quad (11.324)$$

The details of this integration can be found in the literature, and if the entire

l-sum is included, it leads to the quantum mechanical evaluation of the virial coefficient in Boltzmann statistics:

$$B'_{Boltz} = B_{class} = (2\pi N\sigma^3/3)\{3\hbar^2/m\sigma^2 kT + \tfrac{9}{2}$$

$$- \tfrac{11}{2}(m\sigma^2 kT/\hbar^2) + \tfrac{1921}{120}(m\sigma^2 kT/\hbar^2)^2 - \cdots\} \quad (11.325)$$

It is convenient to use the dimensionless quantities,

$$T^* = kT/\mathcal{E}, \quad V^* = V/(2\pi N\sigma^3/3), \quad L^* = h/[\sigma(m\mathcal{E})^{1/2}] \quad (11.326)$$

where $\mathcal{E}$ is an arbitrary energy later identified with the minimum energy of interaction between two particles. In terms of these we find

$$B'_{Boltz} = (V/V^*)\{(3/4\pi^2)L^{*2}/T^* + \tfrac{9}{2}$$

$$- 22\pi^2 T^*/L^{*2} + (3842\pi^4/15)T^{*2}/L^{*4}\} \quad (11.327)$$

In the Bose-Einstein case we sum over only even l-values and find

$$B'_{B.E.} = (V/V^*)\{(3/2\pi^2)L^{*2}/T^* - 44\pi^2 T^*/L^{*2} + \cdots\} \quad (11.328)$$

and with the antisymmetrical case, summed only over odd l-values, we have

$$B'_{F.D.} = (V/V^*)\{9 + (7684\pi^4/15)T^{*2}/L^{*4} + \cdots\} \quad (11.329)$$

Combined with Eq. (11.302) in the form:

$$B_{id} = \mp(V/V^*)(3/32\pi^{5/2})L^{*3}/T^{*3/2} \quad (11.330)$$

these results permit us to find the second virial coefficient for either kind of statistics at temperatures such that $T^*/L^{*2} \ll 1$.

These quantum effects are generally quite negligible, but for the lightweight elements like hydrogen and helium, they can be appreciable even at ordinary temperatures. The corrections on the virial coefficients depend on the mass through L^*, increasing with decreasing mass. Thus a comparison between the virial coefficients of H_2 and D_2 can be used to test the theory. There is every reason to believe that the intermolecular potentials for hydrogen and deuterium are the same, so the difference between their second virial coefficients $B(H_2) - B(D_2)$ should be due entirely to the quantum correction. The dominant term in this is the first one in Eq. (11.328), so that

$$B(H_2) - B(D_2) = (3/2\pi^2)(V/V^*)\{L^{*2}(H_2) - L^{*2}(D_2)\}/T^* \quad (11.331)$$

Actually it appears that the hard-sphere model on which this formula is based is not realistic enough for a proper comparison with experimental data. However, a similar result has been worked out in terms of the exp-six potential discussed briefly in § 7.4, and a good check has been obtained.*

* E. A. Mason and W. E. Rice, *J. Chem. Phys.*, **22** (1954), p. 522.

It is of some theoretical interest to consider the effect of the second virial co-efficient on the *lambda*-transition temperature in a Bose-Einstein gas, particularly when the forces are repulsive. The transition occurs when the series of Eq. (11.212) reaches its radius of convergence; in the absence of interatomic forces, this series is the same as Eq. (11.130) and Eq. (8.305). The radius of convergence for Eq. (11.212) occurs when $\gamma = 0$, so the equation determining the transition temperature T_0 is now

$$N/V = \sum_j jb^*_j(2\pi mkT_0/h^2)^{3j/2} \tag{11.332}$$

From equation (11.217) the first term in this series is the same as for an ideal gas, because it is calculated from the eigenfunctions for an isolated particle in each case. The second term can be expressed in terms of the second virial coefficient through Eq. (11.214):

$$b^*_2 = -B/N \quad \text{or} \quad b^*_2 = -(B_{\text{id}} + B')/N \tag{11.333}$$

The term B_{id} leads to the same as the second term in an ideal gas, Eq. (8.305), and the B' term is an added correction due to interatomic forces. We could proceed to higher corrections from the third virial, etc., but shall include here only that due to the second virial. Evidently the series so corrected reads:

$$N/V = (2\pi mkT_0/h^2)^{3/2} \left\{ \sum_j 1/j^{3/2} - 2B'/Ng^3 + \cdots \right\} \tag{11.334}$$

Using Eqs. (11.326) and (11.328), we can show that this becomes

$$N/V = (2\pi mkT_0/h^2)^{3/2}\{2.612 + \text{correction}\} \tag{11.335}$$

where the correction term is

$$-4(2\pi T^*_0)^{1/2}/L^* + (88\pi^2/3)(2\pi T^*_0)^{5/2}/L^{*5} \tag{11.336}$$

$T^*_0 = kT_0/\varepsilon$.

The numerical values of the parameters ε and σ obtained from the equation of state for helium are approximately

$$\varepsilon = 14 \times 10^{-16} \text{ erg}, \quad \sigma = 2.6 \times 10^{-8} \text{ cm}$$

From these and Eq. (11.326), we find $T^* = T/10$, $L^* = 2.6$. Using these values in Eq. (11.336), we find the correction term as a function of T_0, and then if we substitute the density of liquid helium for N/V, we can solve the equation for the corrected *lambda*-transition temperature T_0. The result turns out to be very nearly 2.1 °K, which is to be compared with the observed *lambda*-transition in liquid helium at 2.19 °K. The student may recall from the discussion of § 8.3 that the uncorrected (ideal gas) calculation of the *lambda*-temperature gave a result 3.14 °K, and that various devices have been employed (see § 8.6) in at-

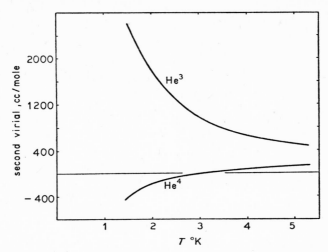

F$_{IG}$. 11.31. Second virial coefficients for impenetrable sphere model liquid comparing Bose-Einstein and Fermi-Dirac theories of liquid helium isotopes. Radius of sphere is taken as 2×10^{-8} cm for either isotope.

tempts to lower this towards the observed value. The present method seems to have the most success, and is moreover perhaps the most logical.

11.4   The von Neumann matrix method. This is an alternative and very fruitful generalization of the method of the assembly partition function to quantum mechanical problems, which at first appears to be quite remote from the method of the Slater-sum. We shall outline this generalization briefly and show its relationship to the Slater-sum.

Turning back to § 7.1, we can reinterpret Eq. (7.110) as indicating that

$$\rho_j = (1/\mathbf{Q})e^{-E_j/kT} \qquad (11.401)$$

is the normalized probability that the assembly is in any one of the Ω_j states that have the energy E_j. The normalization is such that the total probability of finding the assembly in some state is unity. If the energies are renumbered $j \rightarrow r$, so that the suffix r is different for every eigenstate, whether the energies differ or not, $\sum_j \rho_j \Omega_j \rightarrow \sum_r \rho_r$, and we have

$$\sum_r \rho_r = (1/\mathbf{Q}) \sum_r e^{-E_r/kT} = (1/\mathbf{Q}) \sum_j \Omega_j e^{-E_j/kT} = 1 \qquad (11.402)$$

from the definition Eq. (7.108) of the assembly partition function $\mathbf{Q}$. Alternatively, we may use Eqs. (7.109) and (7.115) to rewrite Eq. (11.401) in the form:

$$\rho_r = e^{(A-E_r)/kT} \qquad (11.403)$$

This is the probability of finding the assembly in the rth eigenstate. We recall that this probability is defined in § 7.1 in terms of an ensemble of N assemblies.

Let u_r be the rth member of a closed orthonormal family of assembly eigenfunctions, the family that gives the eigenvalues E_r of the Hamiltonian for the assembly. Let v_k be a possible wave function describing the quantum state of the kth assembly in the ensemble, $k = 1, 2, \cdots N$. Each such v_k can be expanded as a linear sum of the eigenfunctions:

$$v_k = \sum_r a_{rk} u_r \tag{11.404}$$

compare with Eq. (1.243). If all N functions v_k are given, we can obtain the probability of finding an assembly in the rth eigenstate. The total probability of finding the kth assembly in some state is

$$\int \bar{v}_k v_k d\tau = \int \sum_r \bar{a}_{rk} \bar{u}_r \sum_s a_{sk} u_s d\tau = \sum_r \sum_s \bar{a}_{rk} a_{sk} \int \bar{u}_r u_s d\tau$$

$$= \sum_r \bar{a}_{rk} a_{rk} = \sum_r |a_{rk}|^2 \tag{11.405}$$

This is interpreted as the sum of probabilities $|a_{rk}|^2$ of finding the kth assembly in the various eigenstates, r.

Now the essential problem of quantum statistics is that we do not know the exact state v_k for the kth assembly under observation, so we have to accept all those states v_k not inconsistent with our information and set up the ensemble so as to give equal probability to finding an assembly in the ensemble in any of these v_k states. This means that the probability Eq. (11.405) is the same throughout the ensemble, i.e., for every value of k, and so we can normalize to unity:

$$\sum_r |a_{rk}|^2 = 1, \quad \text{all } k \text{ in the ensemble} \tag{11.406}$$

Now we have interpreted $|a_{rk}|^2$ as the probability of finding the kth assembly in the rth eigenstate; and we can in consequence write

$$\rho_r = (1/N) \sum_k |a_{rk}|^2 \tag{11.407}$$

for the mean probability of finding some assembly of the ensemble in the rth state. The normalization of this can be checked by summing over r and using Eq. (11.406) to show that $\sum_r \rho_r = 1$.

We now make the fundamental generalization of the theory: from the matrix formulation of quantum mechanics briefly outlined in § 1.6, we are familiar with the idea that any physical observable may be represented by a matrix, and that, when the representation is such that the matrix is diagonal, the possible measured values of the observable appear as the diagonal matrix elements. We now assert that the probability of finding an assembly in the rth eigenstate is a physical observable, and therefore ought to be the diagonal element of a matrix. Looking at Eq. (11.407) from this point of view, we notice that indeed this would be the diagonal element of the matrix ρ, whose elements are in general:

$$\rho_{mn} = (1/N) \sum_k \bar{a}_{mk} a_{nk} \tag{11.408}$$

Only when it is reduced to a diagonal form by a suitable representation will its diagonal elements give correctly the observable probabilities, but the sum over the diagonal elements is invariant, the same in all representations:

$$\text{trace } \rho = (1/N) \sum_k \sum_r \bar{a}_{rk} a_{rk} = \sum_r \rho_r = e^{A/kT} Q \tag{11.410}$$

This makes direct connection with the Slater-sum through Eq. (11.111). The matrix ρ is evidently given by the elements,

$$\rho_{mn} = \frac{1}{N!} e^{A/kT} \int \bar{u}_m e^{-H/kT} u_n d\tau \tag{11.411}$$

where H is the Hamiltonian operator for the assembly.

The von Neumann density matrix ρ permits us to apply the quantum mechanical equations of motion, Eq. (1.606), to the ensemble:

$$i\hbar d\rho/dt = H\rho - \rho H \tag{11.412}$$

and to study the changes in the ensemble in the course of time. We can now state several important theorems as a result of this equation of motion. An ensemble is in equilibrium if $d\rho/dt = 0$, and therefore if ρ and H commute. Any constant of the motion of the ensemble commutes with H and with ρ. The average in the ensemble of any observable represented by a matrix F is given by:

$$\text{trace } (\rho F) = \langle F \rangle \tag{11.413}$$

In an equilibrium ensemble, any representation that diagonalizes ρ also diagonalizes H simultaneously; we interpret this physically to mean that we can measure simultaneously the energy of an assembly in a steady state along with determining the probability that it remains in this state. In a nonequilibrium ensemble, ρ does not commute with H, and it is impossible to measure the energy of an assembly in a steady state simultaneously with determining the probability that it remains in this state. Any function F defined in the ensemble has a matrix that commutes with ρ. The mean rate of change of such a function due to changes in the ensemble is given by

$$\text{trace } (\dot{\rho} F) = \langle dF/dt \rangle \tag{11.414}$$

This is the basis of a quantum mechanical proof of the ergodic hypothesis, and also leads to a study of a very wide field of nonequilibrium problems.

EXERCISES AND PROBLEMS

1. Check the integrals in Eq. (11.118).

2. Provide the missing steps between Eqs. (11.128) and (11.129).

3. Develop the Slater-sum method for the two-dimensional ideal quantum degenerate gas and show that the analog of Eq. (11.132) agrees with Eq. (8.519).

4. Show that the function $f(q_1, q_2, q_3)$ defined in Eq. (11.204) vanishes identically if any one of the three particles is outside the field of the other two.

5. Verify Eq. (11.205).

6. Check the development in Eq. (11.213).

7. Prove Eqs. (11.222), (11.225), and (11.226).

8. Prove Eq. (11.335).

9. Consider a nonideal Bose-Einstein gas of hard spheres whose radii are 2×10^{-8} cm. Find T at which $B_{\text{B.E.}}$ vanishes, and find $B_{\text{F.D.}}$ at this temperature for the same hard spheres; compare with B_{class}.

REFERENCES FOR FURTHER STUDY

"The Quantum Theory of the Equation of State," J. C. Slater, *Phys. Rev.*, **38** (1931), p. 237.

"On the Theory of Condensation," B. Kahn and G. Uhlenbeck, *Physica*, **5** (1938), p. 399.

"Quantum Theory of Non-Ideal Gases," G. E. Uhlenbeck and E. Beth, *Physica*, **3** (1936), p. 729; 4 (1937), p. 915.

"On Quantum Corrections for Thermodynamic Equilibrium," J. G. Kirkwood, *Phys. Rev.*, **44** (1933), p. 31; J. E. Mayer and W. Band, *J. Chem. Phys.*, **15** (1947), p. 141.

"H and D Equations of State in Quantum Theory," J. de Boer, *Physica*, **10** (1943), p. 357.

"Equation of State of Gaseous He³," Kranendonk, Compaan, and de Boer, *Phys. Rev.*, **76** (1949), pp. 998; 1728.

"Theory of Degenerate Non-Ideal Gases," L. I. Schiff, *Phys. Rev.*, **59** (1941), pp. 751; 758.

"Quantum Corrections to the Thermodynamic Properties of Liquids: Neon," O. K. Rice, *J. Chem. Phys.*, **16** (1948), p. 141.

"The Quantum-Mechanical Partition Function," G. V. Chester, *Phys. Rev.*, **93** (1954), p. 606.

"The Quantum-Mechanical Partition Function," H. S. Green, *J. Chem. Phys.*, **20** (1952), p. 1274.

"An Expansion Theorem of the Density Matrix," Ryogo Kubo, *J. Chem. Phys.*, **20** (1952), p. 770.

"The Configurational Distribution Function in Quantum Statistics," M. L. Goldberger and E. N. Adams, II, *J. Chem. Phys.*, **20** (1952), p. 240.

"Space-Time Approach to Non-Relativistic Quantum Mechanics," R. P. Feynman, *Revs. of Modern Phys.*, **20** (1948), p. 367.

"Bose-Einstein Condensation of Imperfect Gas," M. H. Friedman and S. T. Butler, *Phys. Rev.*, **91** (1953), p. 465.

Chapter XII

THE GRAND PARTITION FUNCTION
AND ITS APPLICATIONS

12.1 Formalism of the grand partition function. The method of the grand partition function was developed originally to handle assemblies containing two or more phases, composed of several different molecular species or components in which the molecules are interacting. In our previous discussions of assemblies of interacting systems we set up an assembly partition function, and calculated averages over an ensemble of assemblies composed of a single phase and containing but one component. Here we need a more general formalism and proceed at once to set up the appropriate symbolism.

Let one sample assembly contain n_1, n_2, $\cdots$ molecules of species n in the first, second, $\cdots$ phases respectively, and m_1, m_2, $\cdots$ molecules of species m in the first, second, $\cdots$ phases, and so on through all species. Let our sample assembly contain a total energy E_1 in the first phase, E_2 in the second phase, etc. We note particularly that these energies are not assigned to individual molecules, but belong to the phases as a whole. The phases may exchange energy and molecules, but do not influence each other's possible energy spectra. The state of the sample assembly is specified by two sets of numbers (a) the set of populations $n = (n_1, n_2, \cdots)$, $m = (m_1, m_2, \cdots)$, etc.; and (b) the set of energies $E = (E_1, E_2, \cdots)$. The statistical problem is to determine the most probable state of the assembly as so specified, in terms of a suitable ensemble.

The grand ensemble of Gibbs, designed to handle this situation, contains a fixed number, X, of complete assemblies, each assembly being a "copy" of the assembly under study, in the sense that it contains the same species and same set of phases, and has the same geometrical characteristics. The assemblies in the Gibbs grand ensemble are provided with means by which they can exchange molecules and heat, but cannot influence each other in any other way. At any moment the ensemble may contain a number $N_{E,n,m}$ of assemblies in the state specified by the sets E, n, and m. If these numbers $N_{E,n,m}$ are written down for every set E, every set n, every set m, etc. in the ensemble, the set of numbers $N_{E,n,m}$ so formed specify the distribution-in-ensemble of the assemblies. The number of complexions of the ensemble with the given distribution is equal to the Boltzmann count, because all the assemblies are distinct and distinguish-able:

$$C = X! \prod_E \prod_n \prod_m \{\Omega_{Enm}\}^{N_{Enm}}/N_{Enm}! \tag{12.101}$$

where Ω_{Enm} is the number of quantum states of an assembly specified by E, n, and m. It is assumed that the ensemble in the course of time will take on every possible complexion with equal probability—the ergodic hypothesis, and that therefore the most probable distribution numbers N_{Enm} are found by maximizing the logarithm of C. After finding the most probable distribution, we calculate the average properties of the assemblies in terms of the most probable ensemble, exactly as we did in § 7.1 for the single-phase, one-component assembly. The student may find the present formalism confusing at the start; it may repay one's effort to rewrite the whole of this section in terms of a single phase single component assembly; and we shall in fact apply the results to this simple example later.

In maximizing $\ln C$, there are three kinds of restriction imposed. The total number of assemblies remains fixed:

$$\sum_E \sum_n \sum_m N_{Enm} = X \tag{12.102}$$

The total energy in the ensemble is conserved:

$$\sum_E \sum_n \sum_m (E_1 + E_2 + \cdots)N_{Enm} = X\bar{E} \tag{12.103}$$

The total number of each species of molecule is fixed in the ensemble:

$$\sum_E \sum_n \sum_m (n_1 + n_2 + \cdots)N_{Enm} = X\bar{N} \tag{12.104}$$

and

$$\sum_E \sum_n \sum_m (m_1 + m_2 + \cdots)N_{Enm} = X\bar{M} \tag{12.105}$$

and so forth through all the species represented. Making virtual variations δN_{Enm}, using Lagrangian multipliers α, $1/kT$, $-\nu/kT$, $-\mu/kT$, etc., on the re-strictions, Eqs. (12.102) through (12.105), respectively, and subtracting from the variations of $\ln C$ and equating to zero, one obtains the most probable distribution in the ensemble analogous with Eq. (7.104):

$$N_{Enm} = X\Omega_{Enm}e^{-\alpha} \exp\left[-\{E_1 + E_2 + \cdots - \nu(n_1 + n_2 + \cdots)\right.$$
$$\left. - \mu(m_1 + m_2 + \cdots)\}/kT\right] \tag{12.106}$$

Summing over all E, n, and m, and using Eq. (12.102) on the left, we find

$$1 = e^{-\alpha} \sum_E \sum_n \sum_m \Omega_{Enm} \exp\left[-\sum_j (E_j - \nu n_j - \mu m_j)/kT\right] \tag{12.107}$$

At this point it is convenient to note that, because the phases do not influence each other, the number of quantum states Ω_{Enm} can be factorized into parts assigned to each phase separately:

$$\Omega_{Enm} = \prod_j \Omega_{E_jn_jm_j} \qquad (12.108)$$

Eq. (12.107) can now be written in the form of a product over all the phases:

$$e^\alpha = \mathbf{Q} = \prod_j \mathbf{Q}_j \qquad (12.109)$$

Here $\mathbf{Q}$ is the grand partition function for the assembly, and $\mathbf{Q}_j$ is the grand partition function for the jth phase:

$$\mathbf{Q}_j = \sum_{E_j} \sum_{n_j} \sum_{m_j} \Omega_{E_jn_jm_j} \exp\left[-\{E_j - \nu n_j - \mu m_j\}/kT\right] \qquad (12.110)$$

$$\mathbf{Q}_j = \sum_{n_j} \sum_{m_j} e^{(\nu n_j + \mu m_j)/kT} \mathbf{Q}(n_j, m_j) \qquad (12.111)$$

Here $\mathbf{Q}(n_j, m_j)$ is the assembly partition function for the jth phase in which the populations are n_j, $m_j \cdots$ as defined in Eq. (7.108). Note that here the subscript j refers to the phase, not to an energy level; in the present notation we sum over all energies without indicating the discrete levels.

We now define the mean entropy per assembly in the ensemble as S, where

$$XS = k \ln C \qquad (12.112)$$

Also the mean energy of the jth phase is defined as $\overline{E}_j$, where

$$X\overline{E}_j = \sum_E \sum_n \sum_m E_j N_{Enm} \qquad (12.113)$$

The mean population in the jth phase of the species n is $\bar{n}_j$, where

$$X\bar{n}_j = \sum_E \sum_n \sum_m n_j N_{Enm} \qquad (12.114)$$

and of the species m, it is $\bar{m}_j$, where

$$X\bar{m}_j = \sum_E \sum_n \sum_m m_j N_{Enm} \qquad (12.115)$$

Writing down explicitly the logarithm of C from Eq. (12.101), making use of Eq. (12.106) to express $\ln N_{Enm}$ in detail, and using the above definitions, we find in place of Eq. (7.112):

$$S = k \sum_j \{\ln \mathbf{Q}_j + (\overline{E}_j - \nu\bar{n}_j - \mu\bar{m}_j)/kT\} \qquad (12.116)$$

the entropy being thus the sum of contributions from each phase.

The interpretation of T as the absolute temperature follows roughly the same steps as from Eq. (7.112) to (7.114). That of the parameters ν and μ follows from the definition of the partial chemical potentials ν_j of any phase, viz., Eq. (3.145), in the form:

$$\nu_j = -T(\partial S_j/\partial \bar{n}_j)_{V,E} \qquad (12.117)$$

Noting that the term $\ln \mathbf{Q}_j$ in Eq. (12.116) is not a function of $\bar{n}_j$, we see at once that

$$\nu_j = \nu, \quad \text{all } j; \qquad \mu_j = \mu, \quad \text{all } j \qquad (12.118)$$

This result is the familiar thermodynamic condition for equilibrium between two or more phases; that the free energy $\partial F/\partial N$ per particle shall be the same in all the phases.

To supplement the list of mean values in the ensemble, Eqs. (12.113)–(12.115), we may consider any function of the energy and populations, $F(E,n,m)$, and define its average over the ensemble by

$$X\bar{F}(E,n,m) = \sum_E \sum_n \sum_m F(E,n,m)N_{Enm} \qquad (12.119)$$

In most of what follows we shall not be concerned with the relation between different phases, and shall therefore drop the phase-indicating subscript. It is to be understood that all our equations apply to any one phase, there being similar equations valid for every phase in the assembly. We then write out the entropy of Eq. (12.116) in the form:

$$S = k \ln \mathbf{Q} + \bar{E}/T - \bar{n}\nu/T - \bar{m}\mu/T \qquad (12.120)$$

while Eq. (12.106) becomes

$$N_{Enm}/X = (1/\mathbf{Q})\Omega_{Enm} \exp \{-(E - n\nu - m\mu)/kT\} \qquad (12.121)$$

The definitions of mean values of E, n, and m in Eqs. (12.113)–(12.115) then yield the following results:

$$\bar{E} - \bar{n}\nu - \bar{m}\mu = (1/\mathbf{Q}) \sum_E \sum_n \sum_m (E - n\nu - m\mu)\Omega_{Enm}e^{-(E-n\nu-m\mu)/kT}$$

or

$$\bar{E} = \bar{n}\nu + \bar{m}\mu + kT^2\partial(\ln \mathbf{Q})/\partial T \qquad (12.122)$$

$$\bar{n}/kT = (1/\mathbf{Q}) \sum_E \sum_n \sum_m (n/kT)\Omega_{Enm}e^{-(E-n\nu-m\mu)/kT} = \partial(\ln \mathbf{Q})/\partial\nu \qquad (12.123)$$

and similarly

$$\bar{m}/kT = \partial(\ln \mathbf{Q})/\partial\mu \qquad (12.124)$$

The generalization of Eq. (7.118) is therefore

$$\bar{E}/kT = T\partial \ln \mathbf{Q}/\partial T + \nu\partial \ln \mathbf{Q}/\partial\nu + \mu\partial \ln \mathbf{Q}/\partial\mu \qquad (12.125)$$

Returning to the general equation (12.119), we may rewrite it in terms of a single phase, and suppose that F is a generalized force corresponding to some generalized co-ordinate x through the relation:

$$F = -\partial E/\partial x \tag{12.126}$$

The mean value of this, according to Eq. (12.119) and (12.121), is

$$\bar{F} = -(1/\mathsf{Q}) \sum_E \sum_n \sum_m (\partial E/\partial x)\Omega_{Enm} \exp\{-(E - n\nu - m\mu)/kT\}$$

or

$$\bar{F} = kT\partial \ln \mathsf{Q}/\partial x \tag{12.127}$$

If in particular we are interested in the pressure, $F \to p$, and $x \to V$, we have for the mean pressure of an assembly in the ensemble:

$$p = kT\partial \ln \mathsf{Q}/\partial V \tag{12.128}$$

Alternatively the Helmholtz free energy may be found from the thermodynamic definition $A = E - TS$, and using Eq. (12.116) for a single phase, we have

$$A = -kT \ln \mathsf{Q} + \nu\bar{n} + \mu\bar{m} \tag{12.129}$$

Then from the thermodynamic relation Eq. (3.144), $pV = \nu\bar{n} + \mu\bar{m} - A$, we derive

$$pV = kT \ln \mathsf{Q} \tag{12.130}$$

This result is not in fact inconsistent with Eq. (12.128) because $\ln \mathsf{Q}$ is necessarily proportional to V.

Explicitly [see Eq. (12.110)] the grand partition function for a single phase is

$$\mathsf{Q} = \sum_E \sum_n \sum_m \Omega_{Enm} e^{-(E - n\nu - m\mu)/kT} \tag{12.131}$$

and the theorem of Eq. (12.130) can be expressed in the form

$$\exp(pV/kT) = \sum_E \sum_n \sum_m \Omega_{Enm} e^{-(E - n\nu - m\mu)/kT} \tag{12.132}$$

As a corollary, the general relation Eq. (12.119) can be written in the form

$$\bar{F} = \exp(-pV/kT) \sum_E \sum_n \sum_m F(E,n,m)\Omega_{Enm} e^{-(E - n\nu - m\mu)/kT} \tag{12.133}$$

This may be regarded as the principal theorem of the grand partition function method, although for many applications Eq. (12.130) is most useful.

12.2 Quantum mechanical virial coefficients. In this section we obtain the equation of state of a nonideal gas in terms of the grand partition function, and show how the results are applicable to quantum degenerate gases.* For this purpose we condense the notation of § 12.1 to a single phase and single species, write Q_n for the assembly partition function of n molecules, and write for the absolute activity:

$$z = e^{\nu/kT} \tag{12.201}$$

* J. E. Kilpatrick, *J. Chem. Phys.*, **21** (1953), p. 274.

Equation (12.111) becomes

$$\mathbf{Q} = \sum_n \mathbf{Q}_n z^n \tag{12.202}$$

and Eq. (12.130) is

$$pV = kT \ln \sum_n \mathbf{Q}_n z^n \tag{12.203}$$

We wish to express this directly in the form of a power series in z, thus:

$$p = kT \sum_j b_j z^j \tag{12.204}$$

To do this we compare coefficients between the last two series:

$$\ln \sum_n \mathbf{Q}_n z^n = \sum_j V b_j z^j \tag{12.205}$$

and find, term by term:

$$\left.\begin{aligned} V b_1 &= \mathbf{Q}_1, \quad V b_2 = \mathbf{Q}_2 - \tfrac{1}{2}\mathbf{Q}_1{}^2 \\ V b_3 &= \mathbf{Q}_3 - \tfrac{1}{2}(\mathbf{Q}_2\mathbf{Q}_1 + \mathbf{Q}_1\mathbf{Q}_2) + \mathbf{Q}_1{}^3/3 \\ &\text{etc.} \end{aligned}\right\} \tag{12.206}$$

We can also express the density as a power series in z. Thus, Eq. (12.123) becomes

$$\bar{n} = z\partial \ln \mathbf{Q}/\partial z \tag{12.207}$$

and using this in Eq. (12.205), we have

$$\bar{n}/V = \sum_j j b_j z^j \tag{12.208}$$

To eliminate z between Eqs. (12.204) and (12.208), we invert the last series:

$$z = \sum_r c_r (\bar{n}/V)^r \tag{12.209}$$

where

$$c_1 = 1/b_1, \quad c_2 = -2b_2/b_1{}^3$$
$$c_3 = (8b_2{}^2 - 3b_1 b_3)/b_1{}^5 \tag{12.210}$$
$$\text{etc.}$$

Using this in Eq. (12.204) yields

$$p/kT = (\bar{n}/V) - b_2(\bar{n}/V)^2/b_1{}^2 - (2b_3 b_1 - 4b_2{}^2)(\bar{n}/V)^3/b_1{}^4 \cdots \tag{12.211}$$

By using complex variable theory, these coefficients can be extended indefinitely, and Kilpatrick obtained a general expression for the nth coefficient. We shall consider here only the second virial, given by comparing Eq. (12.211) with the usual virial form of Eq. (11.301):

$$B = b_2 \bar{n}/b_1{}^2 \tag{12.212}$$

and with Eq. (12.206), which expresses the b's in terms of the partition functions.

The partition function of an assembly of one single particle, Q_1, depends on its spin only through the nuclear spin degeneracy, as discussed in § 1.5. From Eq. (4.302) we have for a particle of spin s:

$$Q_1(s) = (2s + 1)V/g^3 \qquad (12.213)$$

recalling that $g = (2\pi mkT/h^2)^{-\frac{1}{2}}$. The partition function Q_2 of an assembly of two particles depends on the spins of the nuclei, according to the discussion of § 1.5 in the following way. Consider first Bose-Einstein statistics. In this case the eigenstates that are symmetrical with respect to interchange between the two particles have a weight $(s + 1)(2s + 1)$ equal to the number of symmetrical spin states of the pair, and the eigenstates that are antisymmetrical with respect to interchange between the two particles have a weight $s(2s + 1)$ equal to the number of antisymmetrical spin states of the pair. Thus we may write for the sum over all states in the Bose-Einstein case:

$$Q_2(s)_{\text{B.E.}} = (s + 1)(2s + 1)Q_2(0)_{\text{B.E.}} + s(2s + 1)Q_2(0)_{\text{F.D.}} \quad (12.214)$$

where $Q_2(0)$ are the sums over symmetrical (B.E.) or antisymmetrical (F.D.) states disregarding spin altogether. Consider next the Fermi-Dirac case. Here the combinations of nuclear spin states and eigenstates is reversed, and one finds

$$Q_2(s)_{\text{F.D.}} = (s + 1)(2s + 1)Q_2(0)_{\text{F.D.}} + s(2s + 1)Q_2(0)_{\text{B.E.}} \quad (12.215)$$

Using these results in Eqs. (12.206) and (12.212), it is not difficult to see that the second virial coefficients are

$$\left. \begin{aligned} B(s)_{\text{B.E.}} &= \{(s + 1)/(2s + 1)\}B(0)_{\text{B.E.}} + \{s/(2s + 1)\}B(0)_{\text{F.D.}} \\ B(s)_{\text{F.D.}} &= \{(s + 1)/(2s + 1)\}B(0)_{\text{F.D.}} + \{s/(2s + 1)\}B(0)_{\text{B.E.}} \end{aligned} \right\} \quad (12.216)$$

where $B(0)$ are the second virial coefficients calculated for zero spin:

$$B(0) = g^6(\bar{n}/V)(Q_2 - \tfrac{1}{2}Q_1{}^2) \qquad (12.217)$$

with the partition functions derived from symmetrical eigenstates for the B.E. and antisymmetrical eigenstates for the F.D., ignoring spin. These are just what we calculated in § 11.3, where spin was indeed ignored.

For example, in an ideal gas we may use Eq. (11.302), and find

$$B(s)_{\text{B.E.}} = -B(s)_{\text{F.D.}} = -\bar{n}g^3/\{(2s + 1)2^{\frac{5}{2}}\} \qquad (12.218)$$

This can also be derived from Eq. (12.217) without resorting to Eq. (11.302). In actual gases, the Bose-Einstein statistics is generally associated with spin zero, $s = 0$, while the Fermi-Dirac statistics, with $s = \frac{1}{2}$. Thus for an ideal gas of pure He^4 isotope, one would take

He^4: $\qquad\qquad\qquad B(0)_{\text{B.E.}} = -\bar{n}g^3 2^{-\frac{5}{2}} \qquad\qquad (12.219)$

while for an ideal gas of pure He^3 isotope, one would take

He^3: $\qquad\qquad\qquad B(\tfrac{1}{2})_{\text{F.D.}} = \bar{n}g^3 2^{-\frac{7}{2}} \qquad\qquad (12.220)$

This quantum mechanical discussion of the virial coefficients leads to revision of some of the calculations that we carried out previously, in particular Eq. (9.216), the equation of state of a Fermi-Dirac gas. This equation was obtained ignoring the symmetry of the spin states. If we compare the second virial coefficient in Eq. (9.216) for the Fermi-Dirac gas with that in Eq. (8.339) for the Bose-Einstein gas, using Eqs. (8.324) and (9.211) for the comparison between V_0 and V_1, we find they are just equal and opposite. According to Eqs. (12.220) and (12.219), the second virial for the Fermi-Dirac gas ought to be one-half that given in Eq. (9.216). The corrections for the higher virials are more complicated, and should be investigated individually.

12.3 Theory of the liquid phase. In § 7.6 we studied approximate theories of the liquid phase, in particular, the cell or cage model on the one hand, and the free volume model on the other. The cage model is solid-like, and most acceptable near the freezing point; the free volume model is gas-like, and most useful near the boiling point. Other models have been proposed which attempt to combine the advantages of both solid-like and gas-like models. An early one of this mixed type was proposed by F. London * to explain the behavior of liquid helium, as already mentioned briefly in § 8.6. In this model the liquid is supposed to populate a lattice that has twice as many lattice points as atoms, the atoms spending half their lives on the lattice points in solid-like states and the rest of the time in gas-like states of motion between the lattice points. Walter and Eyring † developed a similar idea, assuming that the molecules of the liquid are divided into two subphases, one solid-like and the other gas-like, with a continual exchange of molecules between the two subphases. The fraction of molecules in the solid-like states was taken arbitrarily to equal v_s/v, where v_s is the observed volume per molecule in the solid phase, and v, the observed volume per molecule in the liquid. The theory was applied successfully to argon, nitrogen, and benzene.

The method of the grand partition function permits a significant improvement in these "double-life" models; instead of assigning an arbitrary fraction of the population to the solid-like states, the more general theory allows us to determine the statistical equilibrium distribution of populations between the two subphases as a function of temperature, in terms of an energy parameter of the model. The general procedure is to set up the grand partition function for an assembly containing the two subphases, and use Eq. (12.123) for the population of each subphase.

The partition function for an atom in the gas-like states is given by Eq. (4.302):

$$Q_g = V_g(2\pi mkT/h^2)^{3/2} \tag{12.301}$$

where V_g is the free volume accessible to the gas-like states. The classical assembly partition function for n_g particles in these states is

---

* F. London, *J. Phys. Chem.*, **43** (1939), p. 49.
† J. Walter and H. Eyring, *J. Chem. Phys.*, **9** (1941), p. 393.

$$\mathbf{Q}(n_g) = Q_g{}^{n_g}/n_g! \tag{12.302}$$

where the factor $1/n_g!$ corrects for indistinguishability of the particles. The grand partition function for the gas subphase then follows from Eq. (12.111):

$$\mathbf{Q}_g = \sum_{n_g} \mathbf{Q}(n_g)e^{\mu n_g/kT} = \exp\{e^{\mu/kT}V_g(2\pi mkT/h^2)^{\frac{3}{2}}\} \tag{12.303}$$

The average population of these states is then given by Eq. (12.123):

$$\bar{n}_g = e^{\mu/kT}V_g(2\pi mkT/h^2)^{\frac{3}{2}} \tag{12.304}$$

The solid-like states may be treated in terms of an Einstein crystal; see § 4.8. The partition function for an atom in an Einstein crystal, Eq. (4.803), is:

$$Q_x = e^{-\epsilon_0/kT}\{1 - e^{-hw/kT}\}^{-3} \tag{12.305}$$

where ϵ_0 is the energy of the lowest solid-like state with respect to the lowest gas-like state in the liquid. The assembly partition function for n_x atoms in such states is simply $Q_x{}^{n_x}$, because the lattice points are to be treated as distinguishable. Therefore the grand partition function for this subphase is

$$\mathbf{Q}_x = \sum_{n_x} Q_x{}^{n_x}e^{\mu n_x/kT} = 1/(1 - e^{\mu/kT}Q_x) \tag{12.306}$$

The average population of these states given by Eq. (12.123) is

$$\bar{n}_x = Q_x/(e^{-\mu/kT} - Q_x) \tag{12.307}$$

which can be written instead in the form:

$$e^{-\mu/kT} = Q_x(1 + 1/\bar{n}_x)$$

Then because in practice $\bar{n}_x \gg 1$, we may neglect the last term here and write

$$e^{\mu/kT} \doteq 1/Q_x \tag{12.308}$$

The grand partition function of the whole liquid is of course

$$\mathbf{Q} = \mathbf{Q}_x\mathbf{Q}_g \tag{12.309}$$

From Eq. (12.122) the energy of the liquid is

$$E = (\bar{n}_g + \bar{n}_x)\mu + kT^2\partial \ln \mathbf{Q}/\partial T$$
$$= \tfrac{3}{2}\bar{n}_gkT + \bar{n}_x\{\epsilon_0 + 3hw/(e^{hw/kT} - 1)\} \tag{12.310}$$

The heat capacity is obtained by taking the temperature derivative:

$$C_v = \tfrac{3}{2}\bar{n}_gk + 3\bar{n}_xk(hw/kT)^2e^{hw/kT}/(e^{hw/kT} - 1)^2$$
$$+ (\partial\bar{n}_g/\partial T)\{3kT/2 - \epsilon_0 - 3hw/(e^{hw/kT} - 1)\} \tag{12.311}$$

As with the simpler models discussed in § 7.6 and § 7.7, a full test of the model requires a discussion of phase equilibrium, i.e., at the freezing and boiling points.

For the boiling point we set up the grand partition function for the vapor phase, regarded as an ideal classical gas; by analogy with Eq. (12.303), this is

$$\mathbf{Q}_v = \exp\{e^{(\mu-W)/kT}V_v(2\pi mkT/h^2)^{3/2}\} \qquad (12.312)$$

where W is the energy of an atom at rest in the vapor with respect to the lowest gas-like state in the liquid. The vapor pressure of the liquid is given by Eq. (12.130):

$$p_{\text{sat}} = kT(2\pi mkT/h^2)^{3/2}e^{(\mu-W)/kT} \qquad (12.313)$$

The energy W is related to the latent heat of evaporation as follows. If a number Δn_v of atoms is taken over into the vapor phase, the increase in energy is found from Eq. (12.310):

$$\Delta E = (3kT/2 + W)\Delta n_v + (3kT/2)\Delta n_g + \{\epsilon_0 + 3hw/(e^{hw/kT} - 1)\}\Delta n_x$$

$$(12.314)$$

where $\Delta n_v + \Delta n_x + \Delta n_g = 0$. Since the ratio $\bar{n}_x/\bar{n}_g$ is a function only of temperature, it stays constant during the transfer of atoms to the vapor, so we have

$$\Delta n_x/\Delta n_g = \bar{n}_x/\bar{n}_g = \beta \qquad (12.315)$$

and so

$$\Delta E/\Delta n_v = 3kT/2 + W - (3kT/2)/(1 + \beta) - \{\epsilon_0 + 3hw/(e^{hw/kT} - 1)\}\beta/(1 + \beta)$$

The latent heat per atom is $L = \Delta E/\Delta n_v + p\Delta V/\Delta n_v$, where ΔV is the change in volume occupied by the number Δn_v, due to its transfer from liquid to vapor:

$$L = p\Delta V + W + \{3kT/2 - \epsilon_0 - 3hw/(e^{hw/kT} - 1)\}\beta/(1 + \beta) \quad (12.316)$$

For the freezing point we set up the grand partition function for the solid phase, again using the Einstein model; by analogy with Eq. (12.307), this is

$$\mathbf{Q}_s = 1/(1 - e^{\mu/kT}Q_s) \qquad (12.317)$$

where

$$Q_s = e^{-U_s/kT}\{1 - e^{hv/kT}\}^{-3} \qquad (12.318)$$

Here U_s is the energy of the lowest state in the solid phase with respect to the lowest state in the gas-like states in the liquid, and v is the Einstein characteristic frequency of the solid. The energy involved in the freezing process, neglecting the work done by external pressure during the small volume changes involved, is

$$\Delta E = \{\epsilon_0 + 3hw/(e^{hw/kT} - 1)\}\Delta n_x + (3kT/2)\Delta n_g$$

$$+ \{U_s + 3hv/(e^{hv/kT} - 1)\}\Delta n_s \quad (12.319)$$

where

$$\Delta n_x + \Delta n_g + \Delta n_s = 0$$

The latent heat of fusion per atom is then $H_m = -\Delta E/\Delta n_s$, or

$$H_m = -U_s - 3h\nu/(e^{h\nu/kT} - 1) + (3kT/2)/(1 - \beta)$$

$$+ \{\epsilon_0 + 3hw/(e^{hw/kT} - 1)\}\beta/(1 - \beta) \quad (12.320)$$

In applying this theory one may assume that the numerical density $\bar{n}_g/V_g$ of atoms in the gas-like states is equal to the observed density of the liquid. One would be quite justified in questioning this identification, and taking a different value for the numerical density, specially in the light of the free volume model of § 7.6. As a first attack, however, we shall accept it. Also, the further simplifying assumption will be made that the characteristic Einstein frequency of the solid-like states of the liquid is the same as in the actual solid phase, and this is such that hw/k is about three-fourths of the Debye characteristic temperature, θ_D.

Substituting the numerical density $\bar{n}_g/V_g$ in Eq. (12.304), we can calculate μ. This value of μ is used in Eq. (12.308) and Eq. (12.305) to find ϵ_0. The value of μ is also used in Eq. (12.313) for the vapor pressure, and by comparison with the observed vapor pressure, we can calculate W. These values of ϵ_0 and W are then used in Eq. (12.316) for the latent heat, and from the observed values of L we can find the ratio β between the populations of the solid-like and gas-like states in the liquid. A similar program can be worked out for the freezing point. To check the theory, the values of ϵ_0 and β are used in Eq. (12.311) for the heat capacity and the result is compared with observation.

This program has been carried through only for argon.[*] The ratio $\beta = \bar{n}_x/\bar{n}_g$ for this liquid was found to have a value nearly unity at the boiling point, 87.4 °K under atmospheric pressure, and to fall steadily with increasing temperature to zero at about 145 °K under 40 atm, beyond which temperature the pure free-volume model would be appropriate. The heat capacity was calculated at the normal boiling point to be 7.80×10^{-16} erg/atom deg, compared with the experimental value 7.31×10^{-16} erg/atom deg. This agreement is thus far satisfactory, but more extensive checks on other liquids are needed to establish the theory.

One important advantage of this double-life picture is that the above grand partition function method is capable of immediate generalization to quantum liquids like helium. The grand partition function for a Debye crystal can be used for the solid-like states, and the grand partition function for a quantum degenerate gas (either Bose-Einstein or Fermi-Dirac) for the gas-like states. The grand partition function for a Debye crystal is

$$\mathbf{Q}_x = \sum_{n_x} \mathbf{Q}(n_x)e^{\mu n_x/kT} \quad (12.321)$$

where $\mathbf{Q}(n_x)$ is the particular form of $\mathbf{Q}$ in Eq. (7.206) when $N = n_x$. The

[*] R. A. Nelson, Thesis, State College of Washington, 1952.

grand partition function for the quantum degenerate gas is

$$Q_g = \sum_{n_g} Q(n_g) e^{\mu n_g / kT} \tag{12.322}$$

where $Q(n_g)$ is the same as the Q of Eq. (11.126), with $N = n_g$. It would also be possible to include gas imperfections in the gas-like states, by using Eq.

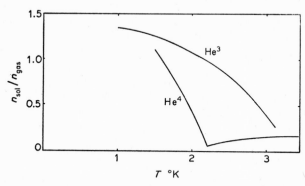

Fig. 12.31. Ratio of populations, solid-like and gas-like in liquid helium.

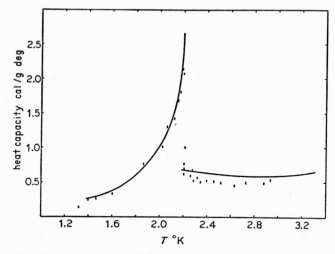

Fig. 12.32. Heat capacity of He⁴. Theoretical curve, experimental points.

(11.209) instead of Eq. (11.126). This program for a theory of liquid helium has just been completed * both for He³ and for He³, and is currently being extended to mixtures of the two isotopes. Figure 12.31 shows the ratio of the mean populations in the solid-like and the gas-like states for the two liquids, and Figures 12.32 and 12.33 show the heat-capacity curves derived from the

* Rudra Pal Singh, Thesis, State College of Washington, 1955.

model compared with the experimental data.   Evidently the *lambda*-type curve of He^4 arises from the apparent discontinuity in the population curve of Figure 12.31; the anomalous heat capacity is the heat required to dissolve the solid-like states with increasing temperature, and the analog with an order-disorder transition is significant.   If one adds the population of the solid-like states to that of the zeroth state of the Bose-Einstein gas-like states, the total matches quite closely the concentration of superfluid in liquid helium.   Recalling that the population of the zeroth state in a Bose-Einstein gas represents condensation in momentum space, this population has no random motion and may more appro-

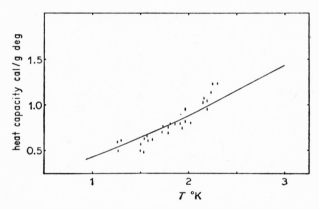

FIG. 12.33.   Heat capacity of He^3.   Theoretical curve, experimental points.

priately be pictured as a solid phase than a gas or liquid.   It is therefore not unreasonable to associate the solid-like states of the present model together with the zeroth-state of the gas-like states and to identify these with the superfluid.

12.4   Co-operative effects.   It is not easy to give a completely satisfactory definition of what physicists have come to mean by the term "co-operative effect".   Only one example has yet been discussed in this text; viz., the Langmuir isotherm when critical adsorption occurs, § 5.4.   In this theory the energy of an adsorbed atom was allowed to depend linearly on the number of atoms adsorbed. When the number of adsorbed atoms becomes large enough, the energy per adsorbed atom becomes so greatly modified that an avalanche sets in.   This type of avalanche is a typical co-operative effect.

The definition we shall adopt here for convenience is as follows: if the energy per particle in one or more of the eigenstates depends slightly on the distribution-in-energy as a whole, then the assembly is called a co-operative assembly, and the anomalous behavior of such an assembly, compared to the behavior expected in the absence of the co-operative term, is called the co-operative effect.   The kind of interaction leading to such an effect is evidently very weak; for if the interaction were too strong, it would already be impossible to set up the eigenstates of individual particles in the assembly.   From this point of view the "anomalous" behavior of an imperfect gas compared with the behavior of an ideal gas is not a co-operative effect. Examples of well-known phenomena that are usually classed as co-operative are: order-disorder transitions in binary alloys, ferromagnetism and the heat anomaly at the Curie point, the specific heat anomaly at the superconducting transition in metals, etc. These examples will be discussed in more detail in Chapter XIV.

A reinterpretation of the method of the grand partition function provides a natural technique for handling the general theory of co-operative effects. One in fact has only to regard each energy level of a single system as a "phase" in the grand ensemble, and nothing in the discussion of § 12.1 is changed by such a re-interpretation.

Let the energy of the jth level, replacing "phase," be written

$$E_j = n_j(\epsilon_j + y_j\{n\}) \tag{12.401}$$

where n_j is the number of systems in the jth level, ϵ_j the energy per system at zero occupancy, and y_j the co-operative term depending on the whole distribution, i.e., on the set of numbers n_j. It is assumed that y_j vanishes when the density approaches zero, but otherwise its dependency on populations is as yet unspecified.

The grand partition function is evidently

$$\mathbf{Q} = \sum_{\{n\}} \Omega_{\{n\}} \exp \{N\mu - \sum_j n_j(\epsilon_j + y_j\{n\}))\}/kT \tag{12.402}$$

No explicit summation over energies is required because the one expression in Eq. (12.401) takes care of all the possible energies when we sum over the sets of occupation numbers n_j in setting up the grand partition function. The number $\Omega_{\{n\}}$ depends on the kind of assembly partition function we start with. If it is classical, $\Omega_{\{n\}} = \prod_j \omega_j{}^{n_i}/n_j!$, if it is quantum degenerate, the corresponding weights for the Bose-Einstein or Fermi-Dirac statistics must be used.

The thermodynamic behavior of the assembly depends only on $\ln \mathbf{Q}$, so we have to evaluate the logarithm of the sum over all sets of numbers $\{n_j\}$ in Eq. (12.402). Most of the terms in this sum are large—they contain the number of complexions in an assembly—and once again it can be shown that the logarithm of the sum of very large terms is approximately equal to the logarithm of the largest term, and further that those values of n_j, that mark the largest term in $\ln \mathbf{Q}$, are the most probable values of n_j in the ensemble. We shall confirm these statements by an example, rather than attempt a general proof.

Consider a classical ideal gas with no co-operative term. The factor in the grand partition function corresponding to the jth level is

$$\mathbf{Q}_j = \sum_{n_j} (1/n_j!)\{\omega_j \exp (\mu - \epsilon_j)/kT\}^{n_i} \tag{12.403}$$

The value of n_j that marks the maximum term in this sum is such that changing

n_j by unity makes a negligible difference in the term:

$$(1/n_j!)\{\omega_j \exp (\mu - \epsilon_j)/kT\}^{n_i} \geq 1/(n_j\pm1)!\{\omega_j \exp (\mu - \epsilon_j)/kT\}^{(n_j\pm1)}$$

which yields the two alternatives:

$$n_j \leq \omega_j \exp (\mu - \epsilon_j)/kT \leq n_j + 1 \tag{12.404}$$

In the limit when n_j is large, this result is the familiar classical distribution, i.e., the known most probable numbers n_j. This confirms the second part of the theorem in question. To confirm the first part of the theorem, we may write $\ln \mathsf{Q}_j$ equal to the logarithm of the maximum term as now located, so that

$$\ln \mathsf{Q}_j = \ln \{(1/n_j)[\omega_j \exp (\mu - \epsilon_j)/kT]^{n_i}\} \tag{12.405}$$

and hence verify immediately that Eq. (12.213), for the mean number in the ensemble applied to Eq. (12.405), results at once in $\bar{n}_j = n_j$; the mean is equal to the number locating the maximum term and is given accurately by the approximate form, Eq. (12.405), for the logarithm of the grand partition function.

Returning now to the co-operative case, we can write $\ln \mathsf{Q}$ in Eq. (12.402), equal to the logarithm of its maximum term. First notice that $N = \sum_j n_j$ and $\Omega_{\{n\}} = \prod_j \Omega(n_j)$, so that $\mathsf{Q} = \prod_j \mathsf{Q}_j$, where

$$\mathsf{Q}_j = \sum_{n_j} \Omega(n_j) \exp [n_j(\mu - \epsilon_j + y_j\{n\})/kT] \tag{12.406}$$

Writing $\Omega(n_j) = (n_j + \omega_j - 1)!/n_j!(\omega_j - 1)!$ for the Bose-Einstein, and $\Omega(n_j) = \omega_j!/(\omega_j - n_j)!n_j!$ for the Fermi-Dirac case, and setting $\ln \mathsf{Q}_j$ equal to a single term in the sum of Eq. (12.406), we treat this term in the same way as we did Eq. (12.403) to derive Eq. (12.404) and come out with:

$$n_j = \omega_j\left\{\exp [(\epsilon_j - \mu + y_j\{n\} + \sum_i n_i y_{ji}\{n\})/kT] \mp 1\right\}^{-1} \tag{12.407}$$

for the most probable value of n_j. Here the term $y_{ji}\{n\}$ means the increase in $y_j\{n\}$ due to an increase of n_i by unity. The upper sign is for Bose-Einstein, and the lower for Fermi-Dirac, statistics. With these distribution numbers we can equate $\ln \mathsf{Q}$ to its maximum term:

$$kT \ln \mathsf{Q} = kT \ln \Omega\{n\} + N\mu - \sum_j n_j(\epsilon_j + y_j\{n\}) \tag{12.408}$$

and derive all the thermodynamic properties of the co-operative assembly from this by the rules developed in § 12.1. For example, Eq. (12.129) gives the Helmholtz free energy:

$$A = \sum_j n_j(\epsilon_j + y_j\{n\}) - kT \ln \Omega\{n\} \tag{12.409}$$

As a simple and amusing example, we take a classical gas with co-operative energy given, suppose, by

$$E_j = n_j(\epsilon_j - aN/V + bkTN/V) \qquad (12.410)$$

Here the co-operative term is such that, for all j-values,

$$y_j\{n\} = (-a + bkT)N/V \quad \text{and} \quad y_{ji}\{n\} = (-a + bkT)/V \quad (12.411)$$

From this we have $\sum_i n_i y_{ji}\{n\} = y_j\{n\}$ and the distribution becomes

$$n_j = \omega_j \exp\{-\epsilon_j + \mu + 2(a - bkT)N/V\}/kT \qquad (12.412)$$

Summing this over all j and equating the result to N, yields the free energy:

$$\mu = -2(a - bkT)N/V + \ln(N/V) + \tfrac{3}{2}\ln(2\pi mkT/h^2) \qquad (12.413)$$

Using this and the classical expression for $\Omega\{n\}$, it is not difficult to evaluate Eq. (12.408) for the grand partition function:

$$\ln \mathbf{Q} = N - (a - bkT)N^2/VkT \qquad (12.414)$$

Then from the theorem $pV = kT \ln \mathbf{Q}$, we find the equation of state:

$$pV = NkT(1 - aN/VkT + bN/V)$$

which is essentially equivalent to the familiar van der Waals equation:

$$(p + aN^2/V^2)(V - bN) = NkT \qquad (12.415)$$

provided the co-operative terms are small. The equation of state when quantum degeneracy is not neglected can also be found, but this is left as an exercise. The above examples serve to illustrate that the method of the co-operative assembly is a very useful device when either we do not know what interactions are at play, or do not wish to go into the complicated details required to handle them exactly.

12.5   The von Neumann matrix for the grand ensemble. Restrict Eq. (12.121) to one constituent, and rewrite it in the form:

$$\rho(E,n) = N_{En}/X\Omega_{En} = (1/\mathbf{Q})e^{(\Sigma n\mu - E)/kT} \qquad (12.501)$$

We can interpret $\rho(E,n)$ as the probability of finding the assembly in one of the states specified by E and n. Then from Eq. (12.129), we have

$$\rho(E,n) = e^{(A-E)/kT} \qquad (12.502)$$

formally identical with Eq. (11.411). This would go through in the same way as in § 11.4 to the matrix form of Eq. (11.411). However, a very significant generalization is usually made in Eq. (12.501) before the transition to Eq. (12.502). We note that n_j, the number of particles of an assembly in the jth phase, is a physical observable, and according to quantum mechanics, may be represented by a Hermitian matrix and its corresponding operator. To set up suitable operators, we need a "space" for them to operate in and functions in this space for them to operate on. For the familiar operators in the Schrödinger-Heisenberg quantum mechanics, the space is the classical phase space of Hamiltonian dynamics; for the spin matrices and operators, the space is abstract spinor space. For the operators representing populations, in our present problem, it turns out that the appropriate space is the set of integers (corresponding to the possible populations of the phases), and the number of "dimensions" in the space is equal to the number of phases in the assembly under study.

The distribution of an assembly among its phases is completely specified by a set of integers n_j, and we can in principle write down functions $\phi\{n\}$, depending on this set of integers to represent any complexion of the assembly that has such a distribution among the phases. We now define two sets of operators C_j and D_j, a pair for each phase, by the following operational relations:

$$C_j\phi(n_1, \cdots n_j, \cdots) = (n_j + 1)^{\frac{1}{2}}\phi(n_1, \cdots n_j + 1, \cdots) \qquad (12.503)$$

$$D_j\phi(n_1, \cdots n_j, \cdots) = n_j^{\frac{1}{2}}\phi(n_1, \cdots n_j - 1, \cdots) \qquad (12.504)$$

The operators C_j are "creation" operators; they have the effect of changing the complexion from one with a population n_j in the jth phase to one with a population $n_j + 1$, all the other phases remaining fixed in population. The operators D_j are "destruction" operators, reducing the population of the jth phase by unity. The numerical factors $n_j^{\frac{1}{2}}$ and $(n_j + 1)^{\frac{1}{2}}$ are included in the definitions for the following reason: given Eqs. (12.503) and (12.504), a double operation, first of destruction, followed by creation, leads to

$$C_jD_j\phi\{n\} = n_j\phi\{n\} \qquad (12.505)$$

which means that the functions $\phi\{n\}$ are the eigenfunctions of the operator C_jD_j, with eigenvalues equal to the population of the jth phase. This is just what we are seeking—operators to represent the populations.

The matrix representation of the creation and destruction operators in terms of the functions $\phi\{n\}$ are defined in a way analogous to the standard procedure described in § 1.6. Let $\{n\}$ and $\{n'\}$ be two in general different sets of integers, then the component matrix element corresponding to these two sets is

$$(C_j)_{\{n\}\{n'\}} = \int \phi^*\{n\}C_j\phi\{n'\}d\tau$$

$$= (n'_j + 1)^{\frac{1}{2}}\int \phi^*(n_1, \cdots n_j, \cdots)\phi(n'_1, \cdots n'_j + 1, \cdots)d\tau \qquad (12.506)$$

where the integration is over whatever other variables the functions ϕ may depend on. If these functions have been chosen at the outset to be orthonormal with respect to these integration variables, the integral in Eq. (12.506) vanishes unless $n_1 = n'_1, \cdots n_j = n'_j + 1, \cdots$; therefore, the component is

$$(C_j)_{\{n\}\{n'\}} \begin{cases} = (n'_j + 1)^{\frac{1}{2}}, & \text{if } n_j = n'_j + 1, \text{ all others equal} \\ = 0 \text{ otherwise} \end{cases} \qquad (12.507)$$

Similarly, it can be seen that

$$(D_j)_{\{n\}\{n'\}} \begin{cases} = n'_j{}^{\frac{1}{2}}, & \text{if } n_j = n'_j - 1, \text{ all others equal} \\ = 0 \text{ otherwise} \end{cases} \qquad (12.508)$$

The product matrix, $N_j = C_j D_j$, can easily be worked out and shown to have only diagonal elements that are not zero:

$$(N_j)_{\{n\}\{n'\}} = (C_j D_j)_{\{n\}\{n'\}} = n_j \delta\{n\}\{n'\} \qquad (12.509)$$

where $\delta\{n\}\{n'\}$ is an obvious generalization of the Kronecker *delta*-symbol. The eigenvalues of the operator N_j are the possible populations of the jth phase, as already pointed out.

It is easy to prove from the operational definitions, Eqs. (12.503) and (12.504), that the matrices C and D satisfy the following commutation rules:

$$D_j C_i - C_i D_j = \delta_{ij} \qquad (12.510)$$

These relations are analogous to the commutation relations obeyed by the conjugate dynamical variables P and Q of Eq. (1.608), and suggest that D and C can likewise be used as conjugate variables. This is in fact how the creation and destruction operators are first introduced in the theory of quantized wave fields. It is worth emphasizing that C and D are not Hermitian; they cannot be diagonalized in any representation, and therefore do not represent physical observables with measurable eigenvalues. The analogy with P and Q is therefore somewhat feeble.

A simple example will give this very abstract symbolism more particular content. Let the assembly possess two phases only, so there are only two operators C, and two operators D, and only two members in the set $\{n\}$. If there are N particles in the assembly, there are $\frac{1}{2}N(N + 1)$ sets $\{n\}$ when zero is included as a possible value for each n_j, and the matrices C and D therefore have $\frac{1}{2}N(N + 1)$ rows and columns each. We map out the top left-hand corner of the matrix C_1 in the following diagram. The columns are labeled (along the top) by the sets (pairs) $\{n\}$, and the rows are labeled (down the left side) by the pairs $\{n'\}$. This map is constructed in agreement with Eq. (12.507). It can be condensed into the simple form:

$$C_1 = \begin{matrix} 0 & 1 & 0 & 0 & \cdots \\ 0 & 0 & 2^{\frac{1}{2}} & 0 & \cdots \\ 0 & 0 & 0 & 3^{\frac{1}{2}} & \cdots \end{matrix} \qquad (12.511)$$

where each zero stands for a $(N + 1) \times (N + 1)$ null matrix, and each nonzero item stands for the $(N + 1) \times (N + 1)$ unit matrix times the number $n^{\frac{1}{2}}$.

Map of top left corner of the creation matrix C_1 in a two-phase assembly:

$\{n\} \rightarrow$	00	01	02	$\cdots$	10	11	12	$\cdots$	20	21	22	$\cdots$	30	31	32	$\cdots$
$\{n'\}$																
$\downarrow$																
00	0	0	0	$\cdots$	1	0	0	$\cdots$	0	0	0	$\cdots$	0	0	0	$\cdots$
01	0	0	0	$\cdots$	0	1	0	$\cdots$	0	0	0	$\cdots$	0	0	0	$\cdots$
02	0	0	0	$\cdots$	0	0	1	$\cdots$	0	0	0	$\cdots$	0	0	0	$\cdots$
$\cdots$																
10	0	0	0	$\cdots$	0	0	0	$\cdots$	$2^{\frac12}$	0	0	$\cdots$	0	0	0	$\cdots$
11	0	0	0	$\cdots$	0	0	0	$\cdots$	0	$2^{\frac12}$	0	$\cdots$	0	0	0	$\cdots$
12	0	0	0	$\cdots$	0	0	0	$\cdots$	0	0	$2^{\frac12}$	$\cdots$	0	0	0	$\cdots$
$\cdots$																
20	0	0	0	$\cdots$	0	0	0	$\cdots$	0	0	0	$\cdots$	$3^{\frac12}$	0	0	$\cdots$
21	0	0	0	$\cdots$	0	0	0	$\cdots$	0	0	0	$\cdots$	0	$3^{\frac12}$	0	$\cdots$
22	0	0	0	$\cdots$	0	0	0	$\cdots$	0	0	0	$\cdots$	0	0	$3^{\frac12}$	$\cdots$
$\cdots$																

The matrix C_2 is the transpose of the matrix C_1, while $D_1 = C_2$ and $D_2 = C_1$.

The double operator C_1D_2 is equivalent to a transfer of one particle from the second phase into the first phase, and C_2D_1 transfers a particle from the first phase into the second phase; we should therefore expect

$$C_2D_1 + C_1D_2 = 0 \qquad (12.512)$$

and in fact this is easily verified.

To see more clearly the relation between this formalism and that used in quantized wave fields, we have to reinterpret the notation of the grand ensemble in the same way as we did in § 12.4, replacing the word "phase" by energy level. Here again all the mathematical statements remain true, but with a new physical content. The function $\phi\{n\}$ can be interpreted as the wave function in the Schrödinger sense for the assembly, i.e., the functions discussed briefly in § 1.4. These functions do depend on the numbers n_j of particles in the various energy levels. For the Bose-Einstein statistics any values are permitted to the n_j; for Fermi-Dirac statistics, only the values 0 and 1 per energy state. Evidently the formalism of this section would be inapplicable to the Fermi-Dirac case, because all integral values of n_j have been allowed. For the Fermi-Dirac case, and nondegenerate energy levels, where $n_j = 0$ or 1, the population matrix operators evidently have to be set up differently. The appropriate definitions turn out to be more subtle than those for the Bose-Einstein case:

$$\left. \begin{aligned} C'_j\phi(n_1, \cdots n_j, \cdots) &= \theta_j(1 - n_j)^{\frac12}\phi(n_1, \cdots 1 - n_j, \cdots) \\ D'_j\phi(n_1, \cdots n_j, \cdots) &= \theta_j n_j^{\frac12}\phi(n_1, \cdots 1 - n_j, \cdots) \end{aligned} \right\} \qquad (12.513)$$

where θ_j is positive unity if the sum over the populations to the left of n_j is even, and negative unity if this sum is odd:

$$\theta_j = (-1)^{m_i}, \quad m_j = \sum_{i=1}^{j-1} n_j \tag{12.514}$$

Remembering that n_j can be either zero or unity (this will actually be proved a consequence of the definitions of C' and D' in a moment), we note that Eq. (12.513) makes D' remove a particle if one is present, but D' equals zero if there is no particle present—because of the numerical factor $n_j^{1/2}$. Also C' adds (or creates) a particle if there is none present initially, but it is equal to zero (by the factor $1 - n_j$) if there is already one present. From Eq. (12.513) we also have the following properties:

$$C'_iC'_j + C'_jC'_i = 0, \quad D'_iD'_j + D'_jD'_i = 0, \quad \text{any } i \text{ and } j, \left.\begin{array}{c} \\ \\ \end{array}\right\} \tag{12.515}$$
$$D'_iC'_j + C'_jD'_i = \delta_{ij}$$

These are called the "anticommutation" rules in contrast to the commutation rules obeyed by the Bose-Einstein operators, Eq. (12.510). The product $C'_jD'_j$ is the population matrix for the jth state:

$$N_j = C'_jD'_j = n_jI \tag{12.516}$$

where I is the unit matrix. The eigenvalues of N_j are indeed the possible populations of the jth state. We can now check that these numbers cannot be other than either zero or unity. Thus we have $\quad N_j{}^2 = C'_jD'_jC'_jD'_j = C'_j(1 - C'_jD'_j)D'_j = C'_jD'_j$, because $C'_jC'_j = 0$ from the first of Eqs. (12.515). Therefore

$$N_j{}^2 = N_j \tag{12.517}$$

Now put Eq. (12.516) into this and find $n_j{}^2 = n_j$ of which the only solutions are $n_j = 0,1$, as desired for the Fermi-Dirac statistics.

Again let us illustrate by means of a system with only two states. There are then only four possible populations or sets $\{n\}$, viz., 0,0, both empty, 0,1, the first empty and second filled, 1,0, the first filled and second empty, 1,1, both states filled. The matrices for C' and D' are thus 4×4 matrices and can be written down without much trouble. The same kind of procedure as we followed in Eq. (12.506) yields the following matrices for C'_1 and C'_2. The columns correspond respectively to the sets, 00; 01; 10; and 11, while the rows, to the same sets in order reading down:

$$C'_1 = \begin{array}{cccc} 0 & 0 & 1 & 0 \\ 0 & 0 & 0 & 1 \\ 0 & 0 & 0 & 0 \\ 0 & 0 & 0 & 0 \end{array} \qquad C'_2 = \begin{array}{cccc} 0 & 1 & 0 & 0 \\ 0 & 0 & 0 & 0 \\ 0 & 0 & 0 & -1 \\ 0 & 0 & 0 & 0 \end{array} \tag{12.518}$$

Also we find D'_1 is the same as the transpose of C'_1, while D'_2 is the transpose of C'_2. The product matrix $C'_1D'_2$ is a transfer from the second state to the first, provided one particle is initially in the second state; it has the matrix form:

$$C'_1 D'_2 = \begin{matrix} 0 & 0 & 0 & 0 \\ 0 & 0 & -1 & 0 \\ 0 & 0 & 0 & 0 \\ 0 & 0 & 0 & 0 \end{matrix} \tag{12.519}$$

The only nonzero element in this matrix is the one that connects the state of occupancy 1,0 with the state 0,1. It is easy to check that these 4×4 matrices satisfy the anticommutation rules, Eq. (12.515).

These creation and destruction operators, and others related to them, have become powerful tools in handling nuclear problems and in the theory of quantized wave fields. We have introduced them here from a point of view somewhat unlike that usually adopted in the literature of quantum mechanics. According to the usual point of view, the commutation and anticommutation rules of Eqs. (12.510) and (12.515) are considered basic, and held responsible for either the Bose-Einstein or Fermi-Dirac character of the systems. Here we have proceeded naturally from the opposite point of view; we regarded the statistics as given, and therefore have derived the commutational character of the population operators. Having now made clear where our statistical methods tie in with those of nuclear physics, we shall leave this subject and continue with the main line of our course.

EXERCISES AND PROBLEMS

1. Set up the grand partition function of a quantum degenerate gas using Eq. (11.131) for the assembly partition function. Show that Eq. (11.135) selects the maximum term in the grand partition function and discuss the significance of this.

2. Write down the grand partition function for a Debye crystal. Assume the logarithm of this series equals the logarithm of its maximum term and hence show that the chemical potential of the crystal is given by

$$\mu = 3h\nu_m/2 + 3kT \ln (1 - e^{-h\nu_m/kT})$$

where ν_m is the maximum frequency of the Debye spectrum of modes.

3. Write down the grand partition function for a classical ideal gas and show that the pressure of the gas is

$$p = kT(2\pi mkT/h^2)^{3/2} e^{\mu/kT}$$

4. Set up an equilibrium between a Debye crystal and a classical gas with an energy of sublimation equal to W; using the results of the last two problems, find the sublimation pressure of the crystal.

5. Check the details involved in Eqs. (12.205), (12.206), (12.209), and (12.210).

6. Prove Eqs. (12.216).

7. Prove Eq. (12.407).

8. Check Eq. (12.414).

9. Start from Eq. (12.410) for the energy with a co-operative term, and find the modification of the equation of state for Boss-Einstein and Fermi-Dirac statistics.

10. Prove $D_j C_j \phi\{n\} = (n_j + 1)\phi\{n\}$.

11. Verify Eq. (12.509).

12. Prove Eqs. (12.510), (12.512), and (12.515).

13. Show that Eqs. (12.518) satisfy Eq. (12.515).

14. Write out in detail the generalization of the Neumann matrix for $\rho(E,n)$ in the grand ensemble replacing Eq. (11.411) when the number operators are used.

REFERENCES FOR FURTHER STUDY

Mathematische Grundlagen der Quantenmechanik, J. von Neumann, Dover, 1943.
Statistical Mechanics, G. S. Rushbrooke, Oxford, 1949; Chapter XVII.
Elements of Statistical Mechanics, D. ter Haar, Rinehart, 1954; Chapter VII.

"The Quantization of Sound Waves," O. Penrose, *Phil. Mag.*, **45** (1954), p. 80.
"The Ergodic Theorem in Quantum Statistical Mechanics," M. J. Klein, *Phys. Rev.*, **87** (1952), p. 111.
"Perfect B. E. Gas in Q. M. Grand Canonical Ensembles," D. ter Haar, *Proc. Roy. Soc.* (London), **A212** (1952), p. 552.

Chapter XIII

GENERAL THEORY OF THE LIQUID PHASE

13.1 The condensation process. In § 7.5 we discussed the Mayer theory of the higher virial coefficients of an imperfect gas, and in § 6.4 we studied the dissociative cluster theory of the same problem. The dissociative theory leads naturally to a condensation process in which the large clusters suddenly become most probable, being then identified with the liquid phase. Mathematically, this occurred when the series in Eq. (6.422) reached its radius of convergence:

$$(N - N_1)/N_1 = e^{W/kT} \sum_{s=2} A_s z^{s-1} \qquad (13.101)$$

being the ratio of the number of atoms involved in clusters to those not involved in clusters. The Mayer theory is formally quite similar. The series in Eq. (7.522),

$$N = V \sum_{s=1} s\theta^s b_s \qquad (13.102)$$

can be interpreted as a sum over clusters, $N = \sum_s s N_s$, where $N_s = V b_s \theta^s$, and can be written in the form:

$$(N - N_1)/N_1 = V \sum_{s=2} s\theta^s b_s \qquad (13.103)$$

If this series, like Eq. (13.101), ceases to converge, the developments given following Eq. (7.522) become invalid, the density becomes a discontinuous function of pressure, and the assembly condenses into a smaller volume. The details of this condensation are determined by how the integrals b_s depend on s asymptotically at large values of s. The same kind of situation occurs in the quantum mechanical theory of Kahn and Uhlenbeck, outlined in § 11.2.

Above some temperature T_c the series fails to diverge at any finite density, and T_c is interpreted as the critical temperature above which there is no phase separation. Considerable controversy exists in the literature concerning this point, and we shall outline briefly what the situation now appears to be without going too far into the history of the discussion.

We note first that, since the assembly contains a finite number of particles, the series in Eq. (7.522) is in fact not infinite, but is nothing worse than a very long polynomial in θ, the highest power being θ^N. It is therefore strictly incorrect to speak of its divergence; to have a diverging series we would have to have an infinite number of particles. This suggests the use of the method of the grand ensemble of § 12.2. Here the grand partition function Q is a sum over all possible populations:

$$\mathsf{Q} = \sum_{n=1}^{M} \mathsf{Q}_n z^n \tag{13.104}$$

We have inserted an upper limit to the sum here, because in practice the volume of the assembly is finite and there must exist a maximum number of particles that can be crowded in.* However, in going over to the series expansion of Eq. (12.205), it is in principle necessary to include an infinite number of terms:

$$\bar{n} = \sum_{j} jVb_j z^j \tag{13.105}$$

This series is infinite, j does not have any physical meaning like the number of particles, and its radius of convergence can be properly discussed. To do so, however, requires that we go over into a complex plane for the variable z.

Alternatively, from Eq. (12.207), we may write

$$\bar{n} = (z/\mathsf{Q})(\partial \mathsf{Q}/\partial z) \tag{13.106}$$

so that the divergence of Eq. (13.105) is equivalent to a zero of Q. Now Q is a polynomial in z, as Eq. (13.104) shows, and may indeed have zeroes; but since the coefficients in the polynomial are all positive—they are ordinary partition functions—these zeroes cannot be positive real, but must in general be complex. In other words the infinities of the series of Eq. (13.105) occur at complex values of z; there are no infinities for real values of z, and therefore condensation cannot occur at all. However, if we now allow V to increase indefinitely, the maximum possible number M of particles in the assembly also increases indefinitely, and the order of the polynomial Q increases without limit. The zeroes of Q must obviously move about in some way in the complex plane as M and V increase, and it is in fact possible for one or more of these zeroes to approach the real axis indefinitely closely as V approaches infinity. In this case, in the limit $V \rightarrow \infty$, a singularity arrives on the real axis and a condensation will occur; the density becomes a discontinuous function at this point. Of course Q is a function of temperature, so the behavior of the zeroes of Q with increasing V depends on temperature. It is possible that a critical temperature T_c exists such that above this temperature the zero no longer approaches the real axis with increasing V. In this case T_c is the critical temperature above

* C. N. Yang and T. D. Lee, *Phys. Rev.*, **87** (1952), pp. 404, 410.

which no phase separation can occur. The logarithm of Q is analytic except at the zeroes of Q, so that there is no obstacle to going around the singularity in $\ln Q$ in the z-plane from one phase to the other.

Taking a somewhat less abstract point of view, we may say that if V is very large, but not actually infinite, i.e., large enough to contain a very great number of atoms, the singularity in the z-plane may be very close to the real axis, although not exactly on it. Then $\ln Q$ is analytic all along the real axis, and the density is a continuous function. However, on the real axis in the immediate neighborhood of the nearby singularity, $\ln Q$ may have a very sharp maximum and the series suddenly have a very large sum, the density increasing very rapidly. If the sharpness and suddenness of these changes increase with increasing V, we can identify the situation with a physical phase change: they may be so sharp and so sudden that, within the possible precision of physical measurements, they might just as well be discontinuous. This practical equivalence between very sudden and discontinuous is a concept that becomes very familiar in statistical mechanics; we have already discussed it once in connection with the *lambda*-transition in a Bose-Einstein gas, § 8.3.

So far we have merely indicated possibilities regarding the existence of phase transitions. To show that they actually must occur, given the usually accepted laws of interaction between atoms, is something quite different. Mayer's study showed that a discontinuity occurs with the pair interaction known to be valid in imperfect gases, but he arrived at what turned out to be some controversial conclusions regarding the critical temperature. From his work on the asymptotic forms of the b's it appears that a finite temperature range is required to go from the case where a discontinuous phase change can occur to the case where one does not occur, and that, in the intermediate transition range, a density difference can exist without a surface tension between the two parts of one and the same enclosure. This view has been challenged by other writers, and alternative explanations have been offered for the experimental data that give apparent support to Mayer's theory. It is indeed quite possible for example, on the approximate cluster theory of condensation, for gravitational sedimentation of the larger clusters, present just below the critical temperature, to settle down and blur the meniscus even while a density difference exists. Actually the mathematically necessary conditions for the existence of a critical temperature in terms of the complex-plane picture have not yet been thoroughly investigated. It is quite conceivable that the motion of the singularity of $\ln Q$ in the complex plane, with increasing V, does not have a definite limiting goal, but that the singularity may oscillate indefinitely with finite amplitude about some limiting position. Mayer's transition region could correspond to some such mathematical peculiarity: below the region the singularity definitely approaches the real axis; in the region it oscillates without a final goal; and above the region its goal is definitely off the real axis. Some of the limiting processes used by Mayer in his work have been criticized; other workers have investigated simpler models that can be solved exactly and found that no transition region exists. A final answer must wait for a more general theory of the motion of the singularities of ln Q in the complex plane.

13.2 Mayer's generalization of the grand partition function theorem. We have just seen in the last section that for any real assembly with a finite volume, the discontinuity between the gaseous and the condensed phase is "physical," rather than mathematical; the logarithm of the grand partition function is in fact a continuous function throughout the condensation process, except for the purely hypothetical case where V goes to infinity along with the maximum possible number of particles. Large changes in density occur in the real assembly during condensation, also the changes in pressure are so small that they are practically unmeasureable; mathematically, the density is a continuous function of the pressure. For this reason we may with confidence proceed in principle to apply the same functional form for ln Q in the condensed phase that we have used in studying the imperfect gas and build up an exact theory of the liquid phase. The mathematical difficulties obstructing such a program have been appreciably reduced by a generalization of the grand partition function theorem due to J. E. Mayer, and we proceed to give a somewhat simplified version of this development.

We shall first set up the grand partition function Eq. (12.131) in terms of the quasi-classical picture and the classical phase space, restricting ourselves to a single constituent and single phase. The weights become densities in phase space and the sums become integrals thus:

$$\sum_E \Omega_{En} \rightarrow \int \cdots \int \overset{n}{\Pi} dq \, \overset{n}{\Pi} dp (1/n! h^{3n}) \qquad (13.201)$$

and the energy is assumed to have the form:

$$E = \text{total kinetic energy plus } U_n(\mathbf{q}) \qquad (13.202)$$

where $U_n(\mathbf{q})$ is the total interaction energy among the n particles of the assembly. The integration over the momenta implied in the summation for Q goes through in the same way as in Eq. (4.217) for every particle, and we find

$$Q = \sum_n (1/n!)(2\pi MkT/h^2)^{3n/2} e^{n\mu/kT} \int \cdots \int e^{-U_n(\mathbf{q})/kT} \overset{n}{\Pi} dq \qquad (13.203)$$

where M is the mass of the particles. It is convenient to introduce the abbreviation:

$$Z = (2\pi MkT/h^2)^{3/2} e^{\mu/kT} \qquad (13.204)$$

in terms of which Eq. (13.203) becomes

$$Q = \sum_n (Z^n/n!) \int \cdots \int e^{-U_n(\mathbf{q})/kT} \overset{n}{\Pi} dq \qquad (13.205)$$

From Eq. (12.130) we then can write the grand partition function theorem as

$$\exp (pV/kT) = \sum_n (Z^n/n!) \int \cdots \int e^{-U_n(\mathbf{q})/kT} \overset{n}{\Pi} \, dq \qquad (13.206)$$

The variable Z is a function of the partial potential μ and is known as the fugacity of the assembly. In an ideal gas, it is simply the numerical density N/V, as is evident from a comparison between Eq. (13.204) and the partition function of a classical gas; see Eqs. (4.101) and (4.202). We can also prove this directly by letting $U_n(\mathbf{q})$ approach zero in Eq. (13.206), when the integration yields just V^n and we find $\exp (pV/kT) = \sum_n Z^n V^n/n! = \exp (ZV)$, so that $Z = p/kT = N/V$. If the gas has quantum degeneracy, this result fails, and it is necessary to remove both the imperfections and the anomalies due to quantum effects on the statistics before Z approaches N/V. This may be secured by simply asking that N/V approach zero.

$$\lim N/V \to 0: \qquad\qquad Z = N/V \qquad\qquad (13.207)$$

It is necessary to translate Eq. (12.121) into a form suitable for the generalizations we are about to study. The ratio N_{En}/X is the probability in the ensemble that an assembly may have energy E and population n. The energy is specified by position in the classical phase space, and the probability is proportional to the extension in phase space around the position of interest. We separate kinetic from potential energy and in general will be interested only in the probabilities of given potential energies, so that all kinetic energies will be associated with every potential energy. The expression N_{En} is then to be integrated over all kinetic energies to give the probability of any potential energy. Using Eq. (13.201) in Eq. (12.121) and integrating only over the momenta, we obtain the probability that an assembly have n particles at the specified positions $q(n)$ per unit extension in co-ordinate space:

$$P\{q(n)\} = (1/\mathbf{Q})(Z^n/n!)e^{-U_n(\mathbf{q})/kT} \qquad (13.210)$$

$$= \exp (-pV/kT)(Z^n/n!)e^{-U_n(\mathbf{q})/kT} \qquad (13.211)$$

Note that this probability refers to having a specified particle at each of the n positions; if we were to be less specific and allow permutations of the particles, the probability would be multiplied by $n!$

We now find the probability in the ensemble that n particles have the configuration $q(n)$, regardless of whether the n particles form a whole assembly or whether they form part of a larger assembly having altogether $n + m$ particles. This is found by writing down the probability that the $n + m$ particles have a configuration that includes $q(n)$ and integrating over all possible configurations of the other m particles: $\int \cdots \int P\{q(n + m)\} \overset{m}{\Pi} \, dq \cdot (m + n)!/m!n!$—where the factorials represent the number of ways the $n + m$ particles can be subdivided into two parts n and m. The total probability of the configuration $q(n)$ is then found by adding expressions like this for every value of m:

$$\sum_{m=0} \int \cdots \int P\{q(n+m)\} \overset{m}{\Pi} dq \cdot (n+m)!/m!n! \tag{13.212}$$

If this expression is multiplied by $n!$ we have the probability in the ensemble of finding n unspecified particles at the positions $q(n)$. The distribution function $F\{Z,q(n)\}$ is defined as the ratio of this probability divided by $(N/V)^n$, where N is the average in the ensemble of the total population of an assembly. Thus

$$F\{Z,q(n)\} = (V/N)^n \sum_{m=0} \{(n+m)!/m!\} \int \cdots \int P\{q(n+m)\} \overset{m}{\Pi} dq \tag{13.213}$$

The notation is intended to imply that the distribution function depends on the fugacity Z. From Eq. (13.211) written out for the number $n+m$, it is easy to prove that

$$\lim N/V \to 0: \qquad (1/V)^n \int \cdots \int F\{Z,q(n)\} \overset{n}{\Pi} dq = 1 \tag{13.214}$$

recalling Eq. (13.207). This may be regarded as a normalizing condition on the distribution function. A modified distribution function is sometimes more convenient, defined by

$$G\{Z,q(n)\} = (N/VZ)^n F\{Z,q(n)\} \tag{13.215}$$

Evidently G has the same normalizing condition as F. Rewriting Eq. (13.211) for $n+m$ particles and using the result in Eqs. (13.213) and (13.215), we find

$$\exp(pV/kT)G\{Z,q(n)\} = \sum_m (Z^m/m!) \int \cdots \int \exp\{-U_{n+m}(\mathbf{q})/kT\} \overset{m}{\Pi} dq \tag{13.216}$$

Write this out again for $G\{Z,q(n+m)\}$, multiply by $(-Z)^s/s!$, sum over all integers s from zero up, integrate over $q(s)$ co-ordinates, and obtain

$$\exp(pV/kT) \sum_s \{(-Z)^s/s!\} \int \cdots \int G\{Z,q(n+s)\} \overset{s}{\Pi} dq$$

$$= \sum_s \sum_m \{(-Z)^s Z^m/s!m!\} \int \cdots \int \exp\{-U_{n+m+s}(\mathbf{q})/kT\} \overset{s+m}{\Pi} dq$$

$$= \sum_s \sum_r \{(-1)^s Z^r/s!(r-s)!\} \int \cdots \int \exp\{-U_{n+r}(\mathbf{q})/kT\} \overset{r}{\Pi} dq \tag{13.217}$$

where $r = m + s$.

If we now sum over all s, keeping r constant, we see that the coefficients form a particular example of the binomial series:

$$r! \sum_s (-1)^s/s!(r-s)! = (1-1)^r = 0 \quad \text{if } r \text{ is not zero}$$

The only surviving term in the r-sum is therefore the first with $r = 0$, and so

$$\exp(pV/kT) \sum_s \{(-Z)^s/s!\} \int \cdots \int G\{Z,q(n+s)\} \stackrel{s}{\Pi} dq = \exp\{-U_n(\mathbf{q})/kT\} \tag{13.218}$$

Now rewrite Eq. (13.216) for a different pressure p', and hence a different fugacity Z'; also rewrite Eq. (13.218) with $n+m$ in place of n. Then we can use the new form of Eq. (13.218) to transform the right side of the new form of Eq. (13.216), deriving:

$$\exp(p'V/kT)G\{Z',q(n)\}$$

$$= \sum_m \{(Z')^m/m!\} \sum_s \{(-Z)^s/s!\} \exp(pV/kT)$$

$$\times \int \cdots \int G\{Z,q(n+m+s)\} \stackrel{m+s}{\Pi} dq$$

$$= \sum_m \sum_r \{(Z')^m(-Z)^{r-m}/m!(r-m)!\}$$

$$\times \int \cdots \int G\{Z,q(n+r)\} \stackrel{r}{\Pi} dq \cdot \exp(pV/kT) \tag{13.219}$$

where again $r = m + s$.

The coefficients here, summed for any given r, become

$$\sum_m (Z')^m(-Z)^{r-m}/m!(r-m)! = (Z'-Z)^r/r!$$

so that we can finally write Eq. (13.219) in the form:

$$\exp\{(p'-p)V/kT\}G\{Z',q(n)\}$$

$$= \sum_r \{(Z'-Z)^r/r!\} \int \cdots \int G\{Z,q(n+r)\} \stackrel{r}{\Pi} dq \tag{13.220}$$

This formula connects the properties of the assembly at one fugacity with those at another fugacity and can be regarded as a generalization of the grand partition function theorem of Eq. (13.206) which connects any fugacity with zero fugacity only. Equation (13.220) is the theorem of Mayer that we set out to derive. The present derivation started from the quasi-classical weighting of Eq. (13.201); however, the original proof * was perfectly general, and Eq.

---

* J. E. Mayer, *J. Chem. Phys.*, **10** (1942), p. 629.

(13.220) is actually valid for any quantum degenerate assembly, with the properly defined weights and fugacity.

13.3   Formal equation of state of condensed assemblies.   Mayer's generalization of the grand partition function leads almost at once to a formal expression for the equation of state of the condensed assembly. If we multiply Eq. (13.220) by $(-Z')^n/n!$, integrate over the co-ordinate space of the n particles, and then sum over all values of n, we find

$$\exp\{(p'-p)V/kT\} \sum_n \int \cdots \int G\{Z',q(n)\}(-Z')^n/n! \overset{n}{\Pi} dq$$

$$= \sum_n \sum_r \{(-Z')^n(Z'-Z)^r/n!r!\} \int \cdots \int G\{Z,q(n+r)\} \overset{n+r}{\Pi} dq$$

$$= \sum_s \sum_r \{(Z'-Z)^r(-Z')^{s-r}/r!(s-r)!\} \int \cdots \int G\{Z,q(s)\} \overset{s}{\Pi} dq \quad (13.301)$$

where $s = n + r$. The sum over r yields $(Z'-Z-Z')^s/s! = (-Z)^s/s!$, so the right side of the equation becomes exactly the same function as the left side, the one of Z, the other of Z'. Since Z' is any arbitrary fugacity we have

$$\exp(pV/kT) \sum_n \{(-Z)^n/n!\} \int \cdots \int G\{Z,q(n)\} \overset{n}{\Pi} dq = \text{constant} \quad (13.302)$$

This constant over the ensemble means that the expression is independent of the variables that can differ from assembly to assembly in the ensemble, i.e., pressure, density, and fugacity, but could depend perhaps on variables that are fixed throughout the ensemble and only vary if we make another ensemble, like V or T. Actually we can prove the constant to be unity for any ensemble. To do this we compare Eqs. (13.215) and (13.302) to write

$$\exp(pV/kT) \sum_n \{(-N/V)^n/n!\} \int \cdots \int F\{Z,q(n)\} \overset{n}{\Pi} dq = C \quad (13.303)$$

Then letting the density go to zero—which does not change C—we have

$$\lim N/V \to 0: \quad C = \exp(pV/kT) \sum_n (-N)^n/n! = \exp(pV/kT - N)$$

and because in this limit $pV = NkT$, this proves

$$C = 1 \quad (13.304)$$

This limiting process is permissible even if we are initially in the liquid phase, because, as we saw in § 13.1, there is no mathematical discontinuity in $\ln \mathbf{Q}$ at the condensation point.

Taking the logarithm of Eq. (13.303) we now have

$$pV/kT = -\ln\left[\sum_n \{(-N/V)^n/n!\} \int \cdots \int F\{Z,q(n)\} \prod^n dq\right] \quad (13.305)$$

since $\ln C = 0$. Unfortunately, the series converges too slowly to be of use in any numerical discussion of the equation of state. To approach such a discussion, it is necessary to factorize the integrals in somewhat the same way as was used in the work of Chapter VII.

We omit the proof that the distribution functions for any number n of particles can be expressed as a sum of products, the factors of which involve clustered parts of the total number.* The equation of state is expressed in terms of integrals over these partial clusters, and a formal similarity is obtained with the equations of § 7.5. Two forms of the equation of state were derived by Mayer:

$$pV/kT = -\sum_{s=1} (-N/V)^s V b^*_s(Z) \quad (13.306)$$

$$pV/kT = \sum_{s=1} Z^s V b^*_s(0) \quad (13.307)$$

In the first of these the cluster integrals are determined at the fugacity of the actual assembly; this form of equation is suitable for the liquid phase. In the second form, the power development is in terms of the fugacity, but the cluster integrals are evaluated in the limit of zero fugacity. These equations reduce to the equation of state of the nonideal gas derived in § 7.5, although not obviously so, because the cluster integrals are defined differently; Eq. (13.306) may be compared with Eq. (7.527), and again note that the cluster integrals b^* are not the same as the b's of § 7.5.

To give these equations of state a physical meaning, we have to be able to calculate the cluster integrals and the fugacity. The fugacity is in fact derivable from the chemical potential, through Eqs. (13.106) and (13.204), and these equations are equivalent to

$$N = Z\partial \ln Q/\partial Z \quad (13.308)$$

The cluster integrals are defined in terms of the distribution functions. We quote here only the first two:

$$b^*_1(Z) = (1/V)\int \cdots \int F\{Z,q(1)\}dq \quad (13.309)$$

$$b^*_2(Z) = (1/2V)\left\{\int \cdots \int F\{Z,q(2)\} \prod^2 dq - \left[\int F\{Z,q(1)\}dq\right]^2\right\} \quad (13.310)$$

From Eqs. (13.213), (13.210), and (13.205), we can show that these result in the

* W. G. McMillan, Jr., and J. E. Mayer, *J. Chem. Phys.*, **13** (1945), p. 276.

following expressions in terms of potential energy functions; we have

$$(N/V)F\{Z,q(1)\} = (1/\mathbf{Q}) \sum_m (Z^{m+1}/m!) \int \cdots \int \exp(-U_{m+1}/kT) \overset{m}{\Pi} dq$$

(13.311)

But the right-hand side of this, when integrated over another particle, is nothing but the average number N in the assemblies of the ensemble. Thus we derive exactly

$$b^*_1(Z) = 1$$

(13.312)

Using the same sequence of equations, we also derive

$$b^*_2(Z) = \tfrac{1}{2}V\{(1/N^2\mathbf{Q}) \sum_{m=0} (Z^{m+2}/m!) \int \cdots \int \exp(-U_{m+2}/kT) \overset{m+2}{\Pi} dq - 1\}$$

(13.313)

The first expression inside the bracket is almost $(1/N^2)$ times the mean value of the square of the population, so that b^*_2/V is very small, and methods of successive approximation become feasible.

A much simpler form of the equation of state can be derived,* viz.,

$$kT(\partial\rho/\partial p)_T = 1 + 2\rho b^*_2(Z)$$

(13.314)

where $\rho = N/V$ is the numerical density. This equation gives the isothermal compressibility in terms of the second cluster integral alone.

The mathematical problem is now to evaluate the integrals appearing in Eq. (13.313). A glance at Eq. (7.406) will remind the reader that we have already studied exactly these same integrals before. In Chapter VII we were able to find the equation of state of an imperfect gas to some considerable accuracy merely by making a rough approximation to $Q(\mathbf{q})$, it being sufficient to know only the logarithms with sufficient accuracy. If we try the same approximations here, we can prove that $b^*_2(Z) = b_2$ of the imperfect gas theory. Thus from Eq. (7.416), we write

$$\int \cdots \int \exp(-U_m/kT) \overset{m}{\Pi} dq = V^m(1 + m^2 b_2/V)$$

(13.315)

Using this in Eq. (13.308) and Eq. (13.205), it is not difficult to show that

$$N/VZ = (1 + 2b_2Z + b_2/V)$$

(13.316)

and then that Eq. (13.313) yields

$$b^*_2(Z) = \tfrac{1}{2}V\{(1 + 4Zb_2 + 4b_2/V)/(1 + 2Zb_2 + b_2/V)^2 - 1\}$$

(13.317)

To terms linear in b_2 this reduces to the theorem to be proved:

$$b^*_2(Z) = b_2$$

(13.318)

* W. Band, "Statistical Mechanics of the Liquid Phase," O.N.R. 010–603, 1952.

To derive an equation of state for the liquid phase, a much better approximation is needed.

This theory has been generalized to cover the properties of multicomponent liquid mixtures and also of ionic solutions. The full power of the grand ensemble formalism is required to handle both these applications. It leads to a useful expression for departures from van't Hoff's law of osmotic pressure in mixtures, and to a modified law of mass action and the Debye-Huckel formula in ionic solutions. (References to this work will be found at the end of the chapter.)

13.4 Quantum degeneracy in the liquid phase. As mentioned at the end of § 13.2, Mayer's generalized grand partition function theorem is true even when quantum degeneracy is present. The same is true of the immediate consequences of this theorem, in particular, the equations of state discussed in the last section. To be able to apply these equations to quantum degenerate assemblies, we have to know how to evaluate the cluster integrals for such assemblies. To do this we have to reject Eq. (13.210) and go back to the generally valid expression, Eq. (12.121), for the probabilities in the ensemble and evaluate this by means of the Slater-sum of § 11.2.

In place of the previous expression for the grand partition function, Eq. (12.111) and Eq. (13.205), we now write it in terms of the Slater-sum in Eq. (11.202), as follows:

$$Q = \sum_{n=0}^{\infty} (Z^n/n!)g^{3n} \int \cdots \int Q_n(\mathbf{q}) \overset{n}{\Pi} dq \qquad (13.401)$$

where g is the same as in Eq. (11.135), and $Q_n(\mathbf{q})$ is the integrand in Eq. (11.202):

$$Q_n(\mathbf{q}) = G(\mathbf{q})e^{-U_n(\mathbf{q})/kT} \qquad (13.402)$$

In place of Eq. (13.210), we now have

$$P\{q(m)\} = (1/Q)(Z^m/m!)g^{3m}Q_m(\mathbf{q}) \qquad (13.403)$$

for the probability of finding m particles in the positions $q(m)$. In place of Eq. (13.216), we now have

$$\exp(pV/kT)G\{Z,q(n)\} = g^{3n}\sum_{m=0}^{\infty}(Z^m/m!)g^{3m}\int \cdots \int Q_{m+n}(\mathbf{q}) \overset{m}{\Pi} dq \qquad (13.404)$$

Eq. (13.308) is true here, of course, and it leads, through Eq. (13.401), to the relation:

$$Q = \sum_{m=0}^{\infty}(Z^m/m!)g^{3m}\int \cdots \int Q_m(\mathbf{q}) \overset{m}{\Pi} dq$$

$$= (1/N)\sum_{m=0}^{\infty}(Z^{m+1}/m!)g^{3(m+1)}\int \cdots \int Q_{m+1}(\mathbf{q}) \overset{m+1}{\Pi} dq \qquad (13.405)$$

Using this $m+1$ order integral for Q in the generalization of Eq. (13.313) for the second cluster integral, we find

$$2(N/V)b^*{}_2(Z) + N = \sum_{m=0} (Z^{m+2}/m!)g^{3(m+2)} \int \cdots \int Q_{m+2}(\mathbf{q}) \overset{m+2}{\text{II}} dq$$

$$\div \sum_{m=0} (Z^{m+1}/m!)g^{3(m+1)} \int \cdots \int Q_{m+1}(\mathbf{q}) \overset{m+1}{\text{II}} dq \quad (13.406)$$

The numerator in this expression is $Z^2(\partial/\partial Z)$ of $(1/Z)$ times the denominator, while the denominator is $Z(\partial/\partial Z)\mathbf{Q}$. Then using Eq. (13.308) for the N on the left of Eq. (13.406), we find this equation can be expressed in the very concise form:

$$2(N/V)b^*{}_2(Z) = Z(\partial/\partial Z)\{\ln (\partial \ln \mathbf{Q}/\partial Z)\} \quad (13.407)$$

The equation of state, Eq. (13.314), is true here also, and may be written now in the form:

$$kT(\partial\rho/\partial p)_T = 1 + Z(\partial/\partial Z)\{\ln (\partial \ln \mathbf{Q}/\partial Z)\} \quad (13.408)$$

where the fugacity Z is determined by Eq. (13.308):

$$N = Z(\partial/\partial Z) \ln \mathbf{Q} \quad (13.409)$$

While it seems impracticable to use these equations for a quantitative study of the liquid phase, some qualitative remarks may be in order. It is quite possible to set up some simple models in terms of which the grand partition function could be evaluated—for example, the free volume model in its simplest form, with an ideal gas free to fill the free volume V_f. The grand partition function for an ideal, quantum degenerate gas is easily constructed from Eqs. (13.401) and (13.402) and Eqs. (11.126) and (11.134), with the result:

$$\mathbf{Q} = \sum_{n} (1/n!) \sum_{\{m_s\}n} n! \prod_{s=1} (1/m_s!)\{(\pm 1)^{s-1}V_f g^{3(s-1)}s^{-\frac{5}{2}}Z^s\}^{m_s} \quad (13.410)$$

where the sum is over all sets m_s restricted by $\sum_{s} sm_s = n$. Inspection of this expression shows that it reduces to

$$\mathbf{Q} = \sum_{n} (1/n!) \left\{ \sum_{s=1} (\pm 1)^{s-1}V_f Z^s g^{3(s-1)}s^{-\frac{5}{2}} \right\}^n \quad (13.411)$$

and therefore that

$$\ln \mathbf{Q} = V_f g^{-3} \sum_{s=1} (\pm 1)^{s-1}Z^s g^{3s}/s^{\frac{5}{2}} \quad (13.412)$$

Eq. (13.409) then yields

$$N/V_f = g^{-3} \sum_{s=1} (\pm 1)^{s-1}Z^s g^{3s}/s^{\frac{3}{2}} \quad (13.413)$$

and the pressure from Eq. (12.130) is

$$p = kTg^{-3} \sum_{s=1} (\pm 1)^{s-1}Z^s g^{3s}/s^{\frac{5}{2}} \quad (13.414)$$

If we had started out to consider an ideal gas, instead of the free-volume liquid, we would get these same results with V_f interpreted as the whole volume, and it is then simple to check that Eq. (13.413) coincides with the familiar results for quantum degenerate gases, Eqs. (8.305) and (8.409), while Eq. (13.414) coincides with Eq. (8.337) for Bose-Einstein, and the corresponding result, for Fermi-Dirac statistics.

We can discuss the possibility of an Einstein condensation in the quantum degenerate liquid in quite general terms, before resorting to any simplified model. It will be recalled that the condensation at T_0 occurs in the Bose-Einstein gas when the series of Eq. (13.413) reaches its radius of convergence; the series has a finite sum at the radius of convergence, and is infinite beyond. The finite sum is a function of T and cannot be made equal to N/V below the transition temperature, and a proportion of the particles then condense into the zeroth state, only the "normal" ones being counted in the N of Eq. (13.413). Incidentally, for the ideal gas, $b^*_2(Z)$ becomes infinite below the transition, and the isothermal elasticity $(\partial p / \partial \rho)_T$ vanishes.

By analogy, we may state a sufficient condition for a similar behavior in the liquid. Thus if we express the right-hand side of Eq. (13.409) as a series in powers of Z, this series must have a finite sum at its radius of convergence which decreases as T is decreased; T_0 is then the temperature at which this finite (maximum possible) sum reduces to N. For T less than T_0, particles must condense out of the normal energy spectrum into the zeroth state, whose population is neglected by the integration approximation used in evaluating the Slater-sum. More specifically, it will be sufficient for the modified cluster integrals $b^*_s(Z)$ to behave asymptotically for large s-values in the same way as, or more strongly than, the cluster integrals in the ideal gas, as given in Eq. (11.134). Thus we could state that if

$$\lim s \to \infty: \qquad b^*_s(Z) = \gamma g^{3s} / s^c \qquad (13.415)$$

where γ decreases with decreasing T, and where $c > 2$; then the typical *lambda*-transition must occur in the liquid. The outstanding mathematical problem is therefore to determine the asymptotic dependence of the quantum mechanical cluster integrals on cluster size.

EXERCISES AND PROBLEMS

1. Provide the details in the proofs of Eqs. (13.214), (13.217), and (13.219).

2. Verify from Eq. (13.214) that Eq. (13.305) reduces to the ideal gas law.

3. Prove Eqs. (13.316) and (13.317).

4. Assume that $U_{m+1} = U_m - \phi$ and $U_{m+2} = U_m - 2\phi + U_2$ are valid approximations when m is very large. Evaluate the grand partition function assuming that the terms of large populations dominate the series. Show that Eq. (13.308) becomes

$$N = VZe^{\phi/kT}; \text{ show that } 2b^*_2(Z)/V = (1/V^2) \int \cdots \int \exp (-U_2/kT) dq^2 - 1:$$

compare this with the second cluster integral of § 7.4.

5. Show that Eq. (13.313) is consistent with the following assumption: the average value N of the population is equal to the value of m that marks the maximum term in any of the series, the ratio of the two series being equated to the ratio between their maximum terms.

6. Discuss the *lambda*-transition for a free-volume model liquid.

7. Discuss the Einstein condensation in terms similar to the reasoning outlined in § 13.1 concerning the condensation into the liquid phase.

REFERENCES FOR FURTHER STUDY

"Molecular Distribution," J. E. Mayer and E. W. Montroll, *J. Chem. Phys.*, **9** (1941), p. 2.

"Atomic Distribution Functions of Liquids," Akira Harasima, *J. Phys. Soc.* (Japan), **8** (1953), p. 590.

"Contribution to Statistical Mechanics," J. E. Mayer, *J. Chem. Phys.*, **10** (1942), p. 629.

"Statistical Thermodynamics of Multicomponent Systems," W. G. McMillan and J. E. Mayer, *J. Chem. Phys.*, **13** (1945), p. 276.

"Statistical Mechanical Theory of Solutions," J. G. Kirkwood and F. P. Buff, *J. Chem. Phys.*, **19** (1951), p. 774.

"Theory of Ionic Solutions," J. E. Mayer, *J. Chem. Phys.*, **18** (1950), p. 1426.

"Thermodynamic Functions from Mayer's Theory of Ionic Solutions," J. C. Poirier, *J. Chem. Phys.*, **21** (1953), pp. 965; 972.

"Statistical Mechanics of Mixtures of B. E. and F. D. Systems," W. Band, *J. Chem. Phys.*, **16** (1948), p. 343.

Chapter XIV

SOME SOLID STATE PROBLEMS

14.1 Ferromagnetism. In recent years the physics of the solid state has become a science of its own, and a number of excellent treatises now exist dealing with this subject. We therefore make no attempt here to summarize the field as a whole but discuss briefly several specific problems, to the solution of which statistical mechanics has made a major contribution. The theory of the heat capacity of crystals has already been discussed, § 7.2 and § 7.3. In this chapter we discuss briefly the contribution of statistical mechanics to the understanding of ferromagnetism, order-disorder in binary alloys, lattice imperfections, etc.; the behavior of electrons in metals and the problem of superconductivity.

It is assumed that the student is already familiar with the general nature of ferromagnetism. In statistical theory, ferromagnetism may be treated as a co-operative phenomenon in the sense of § 12.4. In § 4.7 we obtained the partition function of an atom due to the energy of its spin in a magnetic field [Eq. (4.702)]:

$$\epsilon_{mj} = -gm_j\mu_0 H \tag{14.101}$$

where μ_0 is the Bohr magneton, g the Landé factor, H the magnetic field, and m_j the magnetic quantum number—taking values from $-j$ to $+j$ at integer intervals, where j is a half-integer or an integer depending on the angular momentum of the ground state of the atom. In the co-operative theory of ferromagnetism, it is supposed that the energy of Eq. (14.101) has to be corrected by a term depending on the magnetization of the material as a whole:

$$\epsilon_{mj} = -gm_j\mu_0(H + \alpha\bar{\mu}N/V) \tag{14.102}$$

where $\bar{\mu}$ is the mean magnetic moment per particle, N/V the number of atoms per unit volume, and α a parameter that determines the co-operative effect. The energy of n_{mj} atoms in the state m_j is $E_{mj} = n_{mj}\epsilon_{mj}$, and this compares with the co-operative expression in Eq. (12.401) if we set

$$y_{mj}\{n\} = -gm_j\mu_0\alpha\bar{\mu}N/V \tag{14.103}$$

Since $N = \sum_{mj} n_{mj}$, differentiating y_{mj} with respect to $n_{mj'}$ yields

$$d(y_{mj})/dn_{mj'} = y_{mj,mj'} = -gm_j\mu_0\alpha\bar{\mu}/V \tag{14.104}$$

283

Using this in Eq. (12.407) for the mean populations, going to the classical limit, and eliminating the free energy μ from Eq. (12.407) by summing over all states, one easily finds that

$$\bar{n}_{mj} = N \exp\{gm_j\mu_0(H + 2\alpha\bar{\mu}N/V)/kT\} / \sum_{mj'} \exp\{gm_{j'}\mu_0(H + 2\alpha\bar{\mu}N/V)/kT\} \tag{14.105}$$

In some presentations of this formula, the factor 2 is omitted from the co-operative term, because the energy Eq. (14.102) is usually substituted directly into the Boltzmann expression for the distribution numbers. Actually the co-operative analysis of § 12.4 shows this direct substitution to be erroneous.

Now we have for the total magnetic moment of the assembly:

$$N\bar{\mu} = \sum_{mj} \bar{n}_{mj}gm_j\mu_0 \tag{14.106}$$

so with Eq. (14.105), we have an equation for the mean magnetic moment:

$$\bar{\mu} = \frac{\sum\limits_{mj} gm_j\mu_0 \exp\{gm_j\mu_0(H + 2\alpha\bar{\mu}N/V)/kT\}}{\sum\limits_{mj} \exp\{gm_j\mu_0(H + 2\alpha\bar{\mu}N/V)/kT\}} \tag{14.107}$$

Write

$$x = e^\theta = \exp\{g\mu_0(H + 2\alpha\bar{\mu}N/V)/kT\} \tag{14.108}$$

then Eq. (14.107) is equivalent to

$$\bar{\mu} = g\mu_0 \sum_{m=-j}^{+j} mx^m \div \sum_{m=-j}^{+j} x^m \tag{14.109}$$

Expand x in powers of θ as far as θ^2, perform the summations indicated in Eq. (14.109), and finally neglect all terms cubic in θ, or higher powers; we find the terms in θ^2 disappear identically, leaving only the single term:

$$\bar{\mu} = \tfrac{1}{3}g\mu_0 j(j + 1)\theta \tag{14.110}$$

From the meaning of θ implied in Eq. (14.108), we can solve for $\bar{\mu}$ to find:

$$N\bar{\mu}/V = (HT_c/2\alpha)/(T - T_c) \tag{14.111}$$

where

$$kT_c = \tfrac{2}{3}j(j + 1)\alpha g^2\mu_0^2 N/V \tag{14.112}$$

This result is exactly Curie's law for the susceptibility of a ferromagnetic material at temperatures T above the Curie point T_c. The various approximations used between Eq. (14.109) and this final result are valid only so long as θ is smaller than unity, which means that $\mu_0 H\{1 + 1/(T/T_c - 1)\} < kT$, or

$$H < (kT/\mu_0)(1 - T_c/T) \tag{14.113}$$

Now $\mu_0 \sim 10^{-20}$, so this result limits H to less than about $(1 - T_c/T)T \times 10^4$; if for H we use ordinary laboratory fields of a few hundred oersteds, and assume T_c is about 1000 °K, our formula is restricted only to temperatures not less than about one-tenth of a degree above T_c. Closer to T_c than this, the formula breaks down, and an avalanche of magnetization is to be expected. A check on the magnitude of α, the co-operative term, can be obtained from the equation for the Curie temperature, Eq. (14.112). Taking orders of magnitude only, we may write $T_c \sim 500$ °K, $\mu_0 \sim 10^{-20}$, $N/V \sim 10^{23}$, $g = 2$, and $j = 3$; these lead to $\alpha = 200$.

To study the problem at lower temperatures than T_c, a different approach is required. First consider the limit when $T \ll T_c$. In this limit we can approximate to Eq. (14.109) with $x \gg 1$; retaining only the two largest terms in each of the sums, one finds easily that, to terms linear in $1/x$:

$$\bar{\mu} = jg\mu_0(1 - 2/jx) \qquad (14.114)$$

The saturation moment at $T = 0$ is evidently $jg\mu_0$, and the spontaneous magnetization under zero H depends on T, dropping as T increases. To follow this spontaneous magnetization as T increases towards T_c, it is necessary to consider the exact expression, Eq. (14.107) or Eq. (14.109). This can be written in terms of the Brillouin functions defined by

$$B_j(Y) = \{(j + \tfrac{1}{2})/j)\} \coth \{(j + \tfrac{1}{2})Y/j\} - (1/2j) \coth (Y/2j) \qquad (14.115)$$

It can in fact be shown * that Eq. (14.107) is equivalent to

where
$$\left. \begin{array}{l} \bar{\mu} = jg\mu_0 B_j(Y) \\[4pt] Y = jg\mu_0(H + 2\alpha\bar{\mu}N/V)/kT \end{array} \right\} \qquad (14.116)$$

Then for the spontaneous magnetization, we merely set $H = 0$ in Y and seek a solution of Eq. (14.116) for $\bar{\mu}$. The curve of $\bar{\mu}$ against Y is given by the Brillouin function, Eq. (14.115). Then the second of Eqs. (14.116) gives $\bar{\mu}$ plotted against Y as a straight line with a gradient proportional to T. The curve of $B_j(Y)$ v. Y has a finite gradient at the origin, and there exists a temperature—which turns out to be T_c—at which the straight line is tangent to the $B_j(Y)$ curve at the origin. For temperatures below this, there exists a spontaneous nonzero value of $\bar{\mu}$, which decreases with increasing temperature towards zero at $T = T_c$. For $T > T_c$, the spontaneous magnetization remains zero.

The energy of the assembly is given by Eq. (14.102) as

$$E = - \sum_{mj} n_{mj}gm_j\mu_0(H + \alpha\bar{\mu}N/V) \qquad (14.117)$$

In zero field there remains a negative energy due to the spontaneous magnetization, provided $T < T_c$:

$H = 0:$ $\qquad\qquad\qquad E/V = -\alpha(\bar{\mu}N/V)^2 \qquad (14.118)$

* Mayer and Mayer, *Statistical Mechanics*, Wiley, 1940; p. 346.

where we have used Eq. (14.106). This energy rises towards zero as T increases towards T_c and therefore gives rise to an anomalous heat capacity below T_c. Because there is no spontaneous magnetization above T_c, there is a discontinuity in the heat capacity at T_c. By differentiating the Brillouin function, it can be shown that the peak heat capacity due to the spontaneous magnetization at T_c is

$$\Delta C = 5Nkj(j + 1)/\{j^2 + (1 + j)^2\} \tag{14.119}$$

This discontinuity does not depend on the co-operative parameter α, which cancels from the formula. The theory agrees qualitatively with observation: the heat capacity curve does indeed show an anomalous increase with T increasing towards T_c and a sudden drop just above T_c, of the right order of magnitude. Detailed comparison with the data is not immediate, because there are other terms than the magnetic one in the heat capacity.

It is noteworthy that the foregoing theory treats the molecular spins as a co-operative lattice gas; each spin is localized on a lattice point and free to take any one of a set of states specified by the magnetic quantum number m_j, and neighboring spins do not interact except in the aggregate through the co-operative term. The general feeling is that this form of co-operative theory, while pragmatically very useful, is not as realistic as one in which the nearest neighbor interaction between spins is explicitly taken into account. Such a model was first proposed by E. Ising in 1925, and is usually known by his name. While certainly more satisfactory from a physical point of view, the Ising model runs into so many mathematical difficulties that it can be worked out only by a process of successive approximations. Even for the highly artificial case of a two-dimensional crystal, it has been solved exactly only in the simplest case where $j = \frac{1}{2}$, and there are only two spin states per lattice point. A great deal of recent work has been directed towards the accurate solution of the Ising problem, and there is of course always the hope that an exact solution may eventually be obtained.

14.2   Order-disorder in binary alloys. Briefly the phenomenon under discussion is the following: at high temperatures, X-ray analysis indicates that certain binary alloys, e.g., CuZn, have their atoms arranged at random on a single (body-centered) lattice. As the crystal is cooled, a discontinuous jump in heat capacity is observed at a transition temperature (742 °K), the jump being at least 8k. The heat capacity drops rapidly again from this sharp peak with further cooling; the peak is so sharp that it could be theoretically infinite without actually contradicting the data. Below the transition, X-ray analysis shows that the two kinds of atom progressively sort themselves out on two separate interpenetrating cubic lattices as T is reduced. If T is brought far enough below the transition, complete long range order exists, X-ray pictures showing the existence of a superlattice having double the basic spacing compared with that observed above T_c.

Evidently the superlattice or ordered state is of lower configurational energy than the disordered state, and the transition can be discussed statistically if we assess the interaction energies and count possible configurations properly. Many good discussions of the various existing theories of the order-disorder transition are readily available, and we shall not describe them here, beyond outlining the generally accepted method of attack. Instead, we shall use this section to develop a novel form of approximate theory as an illustration of the general treatment of co-operative effects.

We may describe the low-temperature, completely ordered state of the crystal as having N_A A-type atoms on an a-lattice, and N_B B-type atoms on a b-lattice. The a- and b-lattices are identical in structure, the b-lattice forming the body-centers of the a-lattice. The nearest neighbor of every a-lattice point is a b-lattice point, and vice-versa, and such a pair of nearest neighbor lattice points may be called a "couple," because the interaction between two atoms occupying the couple would constitute a coupling between the a-lattice and the b-lattice. There are four ways in which such a couple could be occupied, namely (A,A), (A,B), (B,A), and (B,B), the first-named atom being on the a-lattice point in each case. In distinguishing between the states (A,B) and (B,A), we are distinguishing between lattice points; but in counting complexions of the configuration, we shall count atoms of a kind as indistinguishable, so that the four symbols enumerated completes the list of possible ways in which any couple of lattice points can be occupied. Let us abbreviate the notation and use numeral suffixes for the four states of a couple; hence the number of couples having the state (A,A) is N_1, the number of couples in the state (A,B) is N_2, in the state (B,A), N_3, and in state (B,B), N_4. Consider only 50 per cent alloys, so that the total number of each kind of atom $N_A = N_B = \frac{1}{2}N_L$, where N_L is the number of lattice points in the whole crystal. Let there be z nearest neighbors to each lattice point (in the particular case CuZn, $z = 8$), so that z couples terminate at each lattice point, the total number of couples in the crystal being $X = \frac{1}{2}zN_L$. There are two necessary relations among the four numbers N_t, $t = 1, 2, 3, 4$:

$$2N_1 + N_2 + N_3 = zN_A \quad \text{and} \quad 2N_4 + N_3 + N_2 = zN_B \quad (14.201)$$

If we keep to the 50 per cent lattice, $N_A = N_B$; then we also have $N_1 = N_4$.

On the Ising model, with nothing but nearest neighbor interactions, the energy of the crystal, i.e., the configurational energy alone, is specified by the four numbers N_t. Let zW_t be the interaction energy of the two atoms occupying a couple in the state t; then the configurational energy of the crystal is

$$E = \sum_t N_t W_t \quad (14.202)$$

The factor z disappears, because in counting all the couples Eq. (14.202) actually includes every atom z times, and we have to correct for this. The configurational state of the lattice is therefore to be specified by the four numbers N_t, and we can in principle set up the assembly partition function for the configuration of the crystal. Thus, if there are $\Omega\{N\}$ configurations with the same given set of numbers N_t, the assembly partition function is

$$Q = \sum_{\{N\}X} \Omega\{N\}e^{-\sum_t N_t W_t/kT} \tag{14.203}$$

where the summation is over all sets N_t, restricted only by the relations (14.201), where we may note that, for the 50 per cent lattice, $zN_A = zN_B = X$. The central problem which all present theories attempt to solve is the exact counting of the weight $\Omega\{N\}$.

In the present section we shall accept a very crude approximation to $\Omega\{N\}$, called the quasi-chemical approximation, and develop a co-operative modification of the theory, more as an illustration of various useful methods, than as a serious contribution to the problem. On this approximation we treat all the couples as independent, therefore we can count complexions in the familiar Boltzmann ideal-gas fashion:

$$\Omega\{N\} = X!/\prod_t N_t! \tag{14.204}$$

This is actually quite a bad approximation, because of course the couples are not only not independent, but they actually connect with each other; thus the a-lattice point of any given couple is also the a-lattice point of $z - 1$ other couples, so that, having decided on the state of the first couple, we have already restricted our choice of the states of all the $z - 1$ other couples. Nevertheless, the expression Eq. (14.204) is so convenient, and leads to a form of assembly partition function that is so easily handled, that it is at least acceptable as the basis of a phenomenological theory. Thus we now write

$$Q = \sum_{\{N\}X} (X!/\prod_t N_t!)e^{-\sum_t W_t N_t/kT} \tag{14.205}$$

We can now find the most probable, or average in the ensemble, values of N_t, say $\bar{N}_t$, by selecting those values of N_t that maximize the logarithm of the typical term in the series of Eq. (14.205), and making the variations of the N_t's subject to the restrictions of Eq. (14.201). The results are easily found to be

$$\left. \begin{array}{ll} \bar{N}_1/X = e^{-2\alpha - W_1/kT}, & \bar{N}_2/X = e^{-\alpha - \beta - W_2/kT} \\ \bar{N}_4/X = e^{-2\beta - W_4/kT}, & \bar{N}_3/X = e^{-\alpha - \beta - W_3/kT} \end{array} \right\} \tag{14.206}$$

where α and β are the Lagrangian parameters corresponding to the two restrictions of Eq. (14.201). We can eliminate these parameters very easily and derive the "law of mass action":

$$\bar{N}_1\bar{N}_4/\bar{N}_2\bar{N}_3 = e^{2W_0/kT} \tag{14.207}$$

where

$$W_0 = W_2 - \tfrac{1}{2}(W_1 + W_4) \tag{14.208}$$

We have assumed here that $W_2 = W_3$, a necessary consequence of the Ising model of nearest neighbor interactions. In some accounts of the quasi-chemical model, Eq. (14.207) is simply written down as the basic postulate, and used as part of other considerations to deduce the order-disorder transition. Here we shall stay with the Eqs. (14.206) from which the law of mass action is derived. We note first that with $W_2 = W_3$, the mean values of N_2 and N_3 are necessarily equal, which means physically that no long-range order can ever exist on the pure quasi-chemical model: there are always just as many AB pairs in the right direction as there are BA pairs in the wrong direction. We shall solve the Eqs. (14.206) exactly for all four populations. Thus with a 50 per cent alloy, as we saw, $\bar{N}_1 = \bar{N}_4$, which leads at once to $\beta = \alpha + \frac{1}{2}(W_1 - W_4)/kT$, and, when this is substituted into the equation for $\bar{N}_2$ (or $\bar{N}_3$, which is the same), we have $\bar{N}_2 = X e^{-2\alpha - W_0/kT}$. Because $\bar{N}_1 + \bar{N}_2 = \frac{1}{2}X$, we now can eliminate α and find, after some elementary manipulations, that

$$\bar{N}_1/\tfrac{1}{2}X = 1/(1 + e^{-W_0/kT}) \quad \text{and} \quad \bar{N}_2/\tfrac{1}{2}X = 1/(1 + e^{W_0/kT}) \quad (14.209)$$

with, of course, $\bar{N}_4 = \bar{N}_1$ and $\bar{N}_3 = \bar{N}_2$. These are smooth functions of temperature, and in the limit $T \to 0$, $\bar{N}_1 \to 0$, $\bar{N}_2 \to \frac{1}{2}X$, if W_0 is negative; in the limit $T \to \infty$, $\bar{N}_1$ and $\bar{N}_2$ both approach the value $\frac{1}{4}X$. Thus the crystal goes gradually over from a half-ordered state at absolute zero to a completely random state at sufficiently high temperatures. On this model, to achieve a sudden transition starting at a definite temperature, it is necessary to include a co-operative term in the energy, not allowed for on the Ising model.

The most obvious co-operative form of energy for this problem is

$$E = \sum_t N_t W_t + \tfrac{1}{2}G(N_2 - N_3)^2 \quad (14.210)$$

If G is negative, this new term will have the tendency to push the crystal over into an excess of N_2 over N_3 if a slight excess exists, or vice versa if N_3 is greater than N_2. The solution $\bar{N}_2 = \bar{N}_3$ will be unstable under suitable conditions, and complete long range order may be possible. Comparing this energy with the general form of Eq. (12.401), we can read off almost by inspection of Eq. (12.407) the proper modifications of Eqs. (14.206), due to the co-operative term. The solutions can also be derived the hard way by the same method outlined to derive Eqs. (14.206). The results are easily obtained: $\bar{N}_1$ and $\bar{N}_4$ are the same as before, in Eq. (14.206), but $\bar{N}_2$ and $\bar{N}_3$ are not now identical:

$$\left. \begin{array}{l} \bar{N}_2/X = \exp\{-\alpha - \beta - W_2/kT - G(\bar{N}_2 - \bar{N}_3)/kT\} \\ \bar{N}_3/X = \exp\{-\alpha - \beta - W_2/kT - G(\bar{N}_3 - \bar{N}_2)/kT\} \end{array} \right\} \quad (14.211)$$

The parameters α and β are related as before, because $\bar{N}_1 = \bar{N}_4$, and so we can eliminate β from the equations (14.211), leading to the following results:

$$\left. \begin{array}{l} \bar{N}_2/X = \exp\{-2\alpha - (W_0 + W_1)/kT - G(\bar{N}_2 - \bar{N}_3)/kT\} \\ \bar{N}_3/X = \exp\{-2\alpha - (W_0 + W_1)/kT - G(\bar{N}_3 - \bar{N}_2)/kT\} \\ \bar{N}_1/X = \bar{N}_4/X = \exp\{-2\alpha - W_1/kT\} \end{array} \right\} \quad (14.212)$$

Adding all four of these and equating to unity determines α, and then we have:

$$\begin{aligned}
\overline{N}_1/\tfrac{1}{2}X = \overline{N}_4/\tfrac{1}{2}X &= 1/\{1 + e^{-W_0/kT} \cosh [G(\overline{N}_2 - \overline{N}_3)/kT]\} \\
\overline{N}_2/\tfrac{1}{2}X &= e^{-G(\overline{N}_2-\overline{N}_3)/kT}/\{e^{W_0/kT} + \cosh [G(\overline{N}_2 - \overline{N}_3)/kT]\} \\
\overline{N}_3/\tfrac{1}{2}X &= e^{G(\overline{N}_2-\overline{N}_3)/kT}/\{e^{W_0/kT} + \cosh [G(\overline{N}_2 - \overline{N}_3)/kT]\}
\end{aligned} \qquad (14.213)$$

The significant relation is obtained by subtracting the last two equations:

$$\theta = \sinh (-GX\theta/kT)/\{e^{W_0/kT} + \cosh (-GX\theta/kT)\} \qquad (14.214)$$

where $\theta = (\overline{N}_2 - \overline{N}_3)/X$. This quantity is a valid measure of the degree of order in the lattice, although it does not coincide with the parameter ordinarily used; we shall adopt it here because it comes out so naturally from the analysis. Inspection of Eq. (14.214) shows that at $T = 0$, the degree of order θ may be either plus or minus unity, or zero. The zero solution is unstable; the other two solutions correspond to the crystal being lined up one way or the other on the two lattices. At very high temperatures the limiting value of θ is zero, and incidentally all four of the ratios in Eq. (14.213) are equal to one-half, corresponding to complete randomness. The solution of Eq. (14.214) is easiest by graphical methods. Draw two curves, $Y = \theta$ and $Y = \sinh (-GX\theta/kT)/\{e^{W_0/kT} + \cosh (-GX\theta/kT)\}$. Change to the variable $\phi = -GX\theta/kT$, so the two curves are $Y = -kT\phi/GX$ and $Y = \sinh \phi/(A + \cosh \phi)$, where $A = e^{W_0/kT}$. The gradient of the second curve is monotonic, decreasing with increasing ϕ, from a maximum value at $\phi = 0$ of $(dY/d\phi)_0 = 1/(1 + A)$. The straight line has a gradient greater than this, and there is only one solution, viz., $\phi = 0$ if $-kT/GX > 1/(1 + A)$. For temperatures below the value given by

$$kT_c = -GX/(1 + A) \qquad (14.215)$$

there are two solutions. The solution $\phi = 0$ is now unstable, and the second solution is nonzero, yielding a value of θ that increases with decreasing T. The degree of order thus remains zero for all $T > T_c$ but starts to increase when T goes below T_c.

To find the heat capacity effect at the transition, we note that the co-operative term in the energy, Eq. (14.210), is $\tfrac{1}{2}GX^2\theta^2$, so the anomalous heat capacity depends on $d\theta^2/dT$. This can be evaluated at the transition temperature as $\theta \to 0$ from Eq. (14.214), and it is not difficult to show that

$$\tfrac{1}{2}T_c(d\theta^2/dT)_{T=T_c} = -1/\{(1 + e^{W_0/kT_c})(1 - \tfrac{1}{2}e^{W_0/kT_c})\} \qquad (14.216)$$

when T approaches T_c from below. There is no such term for $T > T_c$. The heat capacity discontinuity due to this term is thus

$$\Delta C = Xk/(1 - \tfrac{1}{2}e^{W_0/kT_c}) \qquad (14.217)$$

where we have used Eq. (14.215) to eliminate G. The total heat involved in the co-operative energy term is $-\tfrac{1}{2}GX^2 = \tfrac{1}{2}(1 + e^{W_0/kT})XkT_c$. It is clear from Eq. (14.217) that the heat capacity peak at T_c can become infinite in this model only if we choose $W_0 = kT_c \ln 2$. Actually such an assumption that W_0 be positive would be quite dangerous; physically, it would mean that two separate pure crystals of A and B would have less energy than an alloy, so that a phase separation might occur—see § 14.3—instead of a disordered alloy. A stable alloy can exist if W_0 is negative, and in this case the order-disorder transition will occur, having a heat capacity jump given by Eq. (14.217) rather less than $2Xk$ or zR per mole. The total heat involved in such a transition would be rather more than $\frac{1}{2}XkT_c$ or $\frac{1}{4}zRT_c$ per mole. These results are only qualitatively satisfactory; for example, the transition in Cu-Zn at 742 °K shows a heat capacity jump certainly more than $6R$ per mole, and a total heat somewhat less than $\frac{1}{2}RT_c$ per mole. From experiment it is suspected that the more precisely the heat capacity jump could be measured, the greater it would be found, and that a theory giving ΔC infinite would be the most satisfactory. In the exact solution of the Ising problem, one does in fact get an infinite heat capacity jump for the two-dimensional problem, and successive approximations to the cubic lattice appear to give increasing value to ΔC with increasing accuracy. There is definite hope that if an exact solution can be found, it will lead to a sufficiently sharp capacity peak at T_c, without the need to call upon an *ad hoc* co-operative term like that introduced in Eq. (14.210).

14.3 Ideal lattice imperfections in substitutional alloys. There are many types of lattice imperfections of great interest and practical importance: for example, dislocations caused by internal strains, impurity atoms located in "wrong" positions at interstitial positions between the lattice points, atoms of the material itself located at interstitial positions, and vacant lattice points. These last two are directly amenable to statistical treatment, and we shall discuss an idealized problem in which the crystal has no other type of imperfection than these two.

We consider a substitutional alloy composed of N_A atoms of type A and N_B atoms of type B, so alike that they all lie on the points of a single lattice and can substitute for each other at random. This is the same as that we considered in the last section, but we consider here only the completely disordered phase. Suppose there are two types of interstitial sites where a misfit atom would find a potential minimum—though of course a shallower minimum than at a proper lattice point; and suppose that the number of each of these types of sites is equal to the number of lattice points. Given the energies of these sites, we are to find the most probable assignment of atoms to the lattice, together with its interstitial sites.

In any arbitrary assignment of atoms to the lattice, let N_{aj} be the numbers of A-atoms in the two types of interstitial sites, $j = 1, 2$; and let N_{bj} be the corresponding numbers of B-atoms. Let N_h be the number of lattice points remaining unoccupied, i.e., the number of "holes." The total number of lattice points N_L is then

$$N_L = N_A + N_B - \sum_j (N_{aj} + N_{bj}) + N_h \qquad (14.301)$$

The total number of different configurations all having this same numerical assignment, remembering that all the sites and lattice points are mutually distinguishable, is given as

$$\Omega\{N\} = \frac{N_L!}{N_h!(N_A - \sum_j N_{aj})!(N_B - \sum_j N_{bj})!} \prod_j \frac{N_L!}{N_{aj}!N_{bj}!(N_L - N_{aj} - N_{bj})!}$$

(14.302)

The first factor here represents the number of configurations of the lattice points in the following three states: empty, occupied by A-atoms, and occupied by B-a oms; the second factor, $j = 1$, is the number of configurations among the first-type interstitial sites, considering that they may also be occupied either by A-atoms, or by B-atoms, or remain empty; and the third factor $j = 2$, is the same for the second-type of interstitial site.

The energy of the crystal in any of these configurations is assumed to be

$$E = E_0 + N_h W_h + \sum_j N_{aj}W_{aj} + \sum_j N_{bj}W_{bj}$$

(14.303)

where E_0 is the energy of a perfect crystal with the same number of atoms and no defects, W_h is the energy required to remove an atom of either type from an interior lattice point of the perfect crystal and place it on the surface, W_{aj} is the energy needed to remove an A-type atom from the surface of a perfect crystal and place it on a j-type interstitial site, and W_{bj} is the same for the B-type atom. These operations are purely conceptual; in an actual crystal, the process of hole-formation would not be likely to be by means of migration to or from the outer surface. The surface here merely forms a convenient energy level with respect to which the other energies may be measured. The statistical problem is to find those values of the five variables, N_{aj}, N_{bj}, and N_h that maximize $\ln \Omega\{N\}$ for a given energy. As in the previous section, we form the assembly partition function:

$$\mathbf{Q} = \sum_{\{N\}} \Omega\{N\}e^{-E/kT}$$

(14.304)

and maximize the logarithm of the typical term of this series. This time there are no restrictions automatically imposed on the five populations; note that Eq. (14.301) is not such a restriction, but a definition of N_L, which is a variable also, but does not appear in the expression for E. Using the Stirling approximation on the factorials, it is not difficult to show that by treating the variations of all five variables as independent, we obtain the following five equations to determine the most probable populations:

$$(N_L - N_{a1} - N_{b1})(N_L - N_{a2} - N_{b2})N_h = N_L^3 e^{-W_h/kT}$$

(14.305)

$$(N_L - N_{a1} - N_{b1})^2(N_L - N_{a2} - N_{b2})(N_A - N_{a1} - N_{a2})$$

$$= N_L^3 N_{a1}e^{W_{a1}/kT}$$

(14.306)

$$(N_L - N_{a2} - N_{b2})^2(N_L - N_{a1} - N_{b1})(N_A - N_{a1} - N_{a2})$$
$$= N_L{}^3 N_{a2} e^{W_{a2}/kT} \quad (14.307)$$

$$(N_L - N_{a1} - N_{b1})^2(N_L - N_{a2} - N_{b2})(N_B - N_{b1} - N_{b2})$$
$$= N_L{}^3 N_{b1} e^{W_{b1}/kT} \quad (14.308)$$

$$(N_L - N_{a2} - N_{b2})^2(N_L - N_{a1} - N_{b1})(N_B - N_{b1} - N_{b2})$$
$$= N_L{}^3 N_{b2} e^{W_{b2}/kT} \quad (14.309)$$

For convenience write

$$x_j = N_{aj}/N_A, \quad y_j = N_{bj}/N_B, \quad z = N_h/(N_A + N_B) \quad (14.310)$$

and

$$c = N_A/(N_A + N_B)$$

$$\theta_j = (N_{aj} + N_{bj})/(N_A + N_B) = cx_j + (1 - c)y_j \quad (14.311)$$

Provided the ratios x_j, y_j, and z all turn out to be very small compared with unity, it becomes apparent from inspection of Eqs. (14.305)–(14.309) that they yield the following first approximations:

$$x_j = e^{-W_{aj}/kT}, \quad y_j = e^{-W_{bj}/kT}, \quad z = e^{-W_h/kT} \quad (14.312)$$

These approximations are satisfactory provided the various energies, W_{aj}, W_{bj}, and W_h are all equal to or greater than about $5kT$. If the temperature is too high for this to be so, it becomes necessary to proceed to a second approximation. For this purpose we can use the first approximations of Eq. (14.312) in the smaller terms on the left side of Eqs. (14.305)–(14.309) and finally get

$$x_1 = (1 + 2\theta_1 + \theta_2 - e^{-W_{a1}/kT} - e^{-W_{a2}/kT})e^{-W_{a1}/kT} \quad (14.313)$$

$$x_2 = (1 + \theta_1 + 2\theta_2 - e^{-W_{a1}/kT} - e^{-W_{a2}/kT})e^{-W_{a2}/kT} \quad (14.314)$$

$$y_1 = (1 + 2\theta_1 + \theta_2 - e^{-W_{b1}/kT} - e^{-W_{b2}/kT})e^{-W_{b1}/kT} \quad (14.315)$$

$$y_2 = (1 + \theta_1 + 2\theta_2 - e^{-W_{b1}/kT} - e^{-W_{b2}/kT})e^{-W_{b2}/kT} \quad (14.316)$$

$$z = (1 + \theta_1 + \theta_2)e^{-W_h/kT} \quad (14.317)$$

where for θ_j, we have used

$$\theta_j = ce^{-W_{aj}/kT} + (1 - c)e^{-W_{bj}/kT} \quad (14.318)$$

All these ratios increase rapidly with increasing temperature, but the formulae remain valid as long as T is not greater than about $W/2k$, where W is the smallest of the energy parameters. The numbers of interstitial atoms evidently depend linearly on the concentration c, but only significantly at the higher temperatures, where the second approximation formulae are required. At the lower temperatures where Eqs. (14.312) are valid, the relative numbers of each type of atom misplaced on interstitial sites are independent of the relative concentrations of the two types of atom in the crystal. Formulae (14.313)–(14.317) can be written down at once for the special case where only one type of atom exists in the crystal, and $c = 1$:

$$x_1 = (1 + e^{-W_1/kT})e^{-W_1/kT} \qquad (14.319)$$

$$x_2 = (1 + e^{-W_2/kT})e^{-W_2/kT} \qquad (14.320)$$

$$z = (1 + e^{-W_1/kT} + e^{-W_2/kT})e^{-W_h/kT} \qquad (14.321)$$

where W_1 and W_2 are the energies needed to place an atom in the two different kinds of interstitial sites.

These results are of interest in connection with nonelastic properties. Any strain of the lattice produced by mechanical stress can be expected to alter the energies, W_1, W_2, W_h, etc., involved in the equilibria. In particular, a high compression of the lattice would almost certainly make it more difficult to produce a hole, by increasing W_h, while a tortional shear may be expected to alter the relative values of the two energies W_1 and W_2, making one type of interstitial site less attractive, and the other type more attractive than under conditions of zero strain. Consider a crystal that has reached equilibrium under zero strain and then suddenly apply a mechanical stress. The resulting strain alters the equilibrium populations N_h, N_{aj}, and N_{bj}, but because there are potential barriers hindering migration of atoms in the lattice, the populations take time to readjust; some work is done by the stress in overcoming the potential barriers and is recovered in the form of heat. If the stress is changed very slowly, the populations can readjust through the effects of equilibrium fluctuations, and no work is used up in the process, which is then effectively reversible. If the stress is caused to oscillate in time with a sufficiently high frequency, there is no time for the populations to readjust between oscillations, and they eventually settle down somewhere between the equilibrium values corresponding to the two extreme states; again no work is used up, and the oscillations are reversible. Only when the frequency of an oscillating stress is near the reciprocal time of relaxation for the population readjustments, does the stress have to do work on the populations against their potential barriers, exhibiting internal friction.

We have discussed this internal friction in terms of lattice imperfections in the disordered lattice; but the same thing occurs in the partially ordered lattice of a binary alloy, due simply to the fact that the degree of order is a function of the energy parameters: any mechanical strain in general can alter the energy parameters and hence alter the equilibrium degree of order. To respond to this altered equilibrium, the atoms of the crystal must migrate against potential barriers, and this takes a time of relaxation. Any oscillation having a period comparable to the relaxation time for the degree of order will exhibit internal friction. In practice, relaxation times are found corresponding to very many different atomic processes in the lattice, and they vary all the way from several seconds down to a fraction of a millisecond.

Lattice imperfections may make a significant contribution to the heat capacity of a crystal at temperatures near the melting point. To see this, it is sufficient to consider a crystal composed of only one kind of atom and with only one kind of interstitial site. The formulae (14.319)–(14.321) then reduce to

$$x = (1 + e^{-W_i/kT})e^{-W_i/kT} \tag{14.322}$$

$$z = (1 + e^{-W_i/kT})e^{-W_h/kT} \tag{14.323}$$

where x is the ratio of the number of interstitial atoms to the total number of atoms, and z is the ratio of empty lattice sites to the total number of atoms; W_i is the energy required to place an atom in the interstitial site from a surface site. The energy of the crystal is then derived from the modification of Eq. (14.303), using Eq. (14.322) and Eq. (14.323) for the populations, and the heat capacity contribution from the configuration energy can be derived directly from this. In general, the actual energy parameters W_i and W_h are large enough compared with kT to make the first approximation good enough, and we shall use simply $x = e^{-W_i/kT}$ and $z = e^{-W_h/kT}$ and find for the heat capacity contribution:

$$C = Nk\{(W_i/kT)^2 e^{-W_i/kT} + (W_h/kT)^2 e^{-W_h/kT}\} \tag{14.324}$$

The order of magnitude of this effect is easily estimated. It is in fact reasonable to suppose that the energies W_i and W_h are several times as great as the heat of fusion, because melting probably requires only a small fraction of the lattice sites to become empty in order to destroy the permanence of the lattice. The atomic heat of fusion is roughly equal to kT_m, where T_m is the melting temperature. As a very rough guess, therefore, we may take both W_i and W_h equal to $6kT_m$. At the melting point the crystal lattice will, from Eq. (14.323), have only about 0.25 per cent holes. Its configurational heat capacity, given by Eq. (14.324), turns out to be about $0.18Nk$. This is of the same order of magnitude as observed discrepancies in the heat capacities of crystals near their melting temperatures. Many elements show a value between $0.1R$ and $0.8R$ higher than the classical $3R$. While this can be explained at least in part by a contribution from the free electrons in the case of metals, the contribution from lattice imperfections may also be significant.

14.4 Phase separation of substitutional alloys. If two metal elements are mixed together in a melt in some arbitrary proportion and allowed to solidify, the mixture generally separates into two or more phases having different concentrations of the two elements. The precise concentrations of the two phases depend only on the final temperature if cooled slowly enough, and the quantity of material in either phase depends on the initial mixing proportions. Typical alloys exhibit a multiplicity of phases depending on temperature; the phase diagrams, giving the equilibrium concentrations of the various phases as functions of T, have been determined experimentally for very many examples, but not all these diagrams have been theoretically explained in any detail. In this section we give the statistical explanation of the simplest form of phase diagram, and indicate how the theory could be extended to give at least a qualitative account of more complicated ones.

The statistical or thermodynamic condition for the equilibrium between two phases, stated in § 6.3 for gases, and in § 12.1 generally, is that the atomic free energy or chemical potential of each component shall be the same in both phases. A hypothetical isothermal free energy curve is shown in the diagram, plotted against the concentration of element B. The "zero" of this curve is of course entirely arbitrary. Obviously this curve for a mixture prepared with equal parts A and B elements would cause the free energy to be higher than if the mixture were separated into two phases of concentrations c_1 and c_2. We show now that these two concentrations would be in equilibrium with each other if

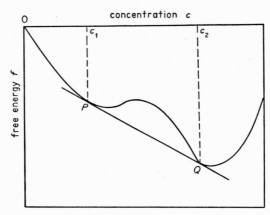

Fig. 14.41. Illustrating equilibrium concentrations of a two-phase alloy.

the points Q and P correspond to these concentrations and lie on a common tangent to the free-energy curve.

Write F_j for the total free energy of the j-phase, and the condition of equilibrium:

$$\partial F_1/\partial N_{1A} = \partial F_2/\partial N_{2A}; \quad \partial F_1/\partial N_{1B} = \partial F_2/\partial N_{2B} \qquad (14.401)$$

where N_{1A}, and N_{2A}, etc., are the numbers of A-atoms, etc., in the two phases. Write

$$F_j = f_j(N_{jA} + N_{jB}) \qquad (14.402)$$

so that f_j is the atomic free energy of the jth phase; it is a function of the concentration of components in the phase, and of temperature. Then the atomic free energy of one component in the phase is related to f_j by

$$\partial F_j/\partial N_{jA} = f_j + (N_{jA} + N_{jB})\partial f_j/\partial N_{jA} \qquad (14.403)$$

Write

$$c_j = N_{jB}/(N_{jA} + N_{jB}) \qquad (14.404)$$

then

$$\partial f_j/\partial N_{jA} = (df_j/dc_j)(\partial c_j/\partial N_{jA}) = -c_j/(N_{jA} + N_{jB})$$

which with Eq. (14.403) yields:

$$\partial F_j/\partial N_{jA} = f_j - c_j df_j/dc_j \tag{14.405}$$

Similarly

$$\partial F_j/\partial N_{jB} = f_j + (1 - c)df_j/dc_j \tag{14.406}$$

The condition of equilibrium, Eq. (14.401), now can be written in the form:

$$\left.\begin{array}{l} f_1 - c_1 df_1/dc_1 = f_2 - c_2 df_2/dc_2 \\ f_1 + (1 - c_1)df_1/dc_1 = f_2 + (1 - c_2)df_2/dc_2 \end{array}\right\} \tag{14.407}$$

Adding these equations yields $df_1/dc_1 = df_2/dc_2$. Rearrange the second of Eqs. (14.407) to give $f_1 - f_2 = (1 - c_2)df_2/dc_2 - (1 - c_1)df_1/dc_1$. Combining these last two results we find the desired form for the condition of equilibrium:

$$(f_1 - f_2)/(c_1 - c_2) = df_1/dc_1 = df_2/dc_2 \tag{14.408}$$

which means that the curve of $f(c)$ against c has a common tangent at the two points corresponding to c_1 and c_2. Clearly a single phase having composition anywhere between c_1 and c_2 will have a higher free energy than the two separated phases at c_1 and c_2. Instability is present whenever the free energy curve has a negative curvature; the existence of a minimum or maximum in the curve is not essential for the separation of the phases, so long as the segment of negative curvature lies between two segments having positive curvature. As the diagram makes clear, the total free energy is always reduced by splitting into two phases given by the common tangent. Evidently the curvature changes sign twice, so the second derivative of free energy with respect to concentration must have two zeroes. This can easily be checked for any particular model.

We consider an ideal crystal, neglecting all lattice imperfections such as were discussed in the last section. Later we could investigate qualitatively the complications introduced by interstitial atoms, where the substitutional nature of the alloy is imperfect. We assume for simplicity that the energy of the crystal is, per atom:

$$E = cE_B + (1 - c)E_A + c(1 - c)(E_A - E_B)/(1 - 2c_0) \tag{14.409}$$

where E_A is the energy per atom of pure A-crystal, etc., and c_0 is the concentration at which E has its maximum value:

$$E_m = E_A - c_0{}^2(E_B - E_A)/(1 - 2c_0) \tag{14.410}$$

Alternatively we may express c_0 in terms of the three energy parameters:

$$c_0 = \{(E_m - E_A)/(E_A - E_B)\}\{[(E_m - E_B)/(E_m - E_A)]^{1/2} - 1\} \tag{14.411}$$

Eq. (14.409) can be interpreted as the simplest analytical way to join up two physically acceptable expressions at the two extremes, $c \ll 1$ and $1 - c \ll 1$.

Thus, at $c \ll 1$, it reduces to

$$E = E_A + \alpha c(E_A - E_B) \qquad (14.412)$$

where

$$\alpha = 2c_0/(1 - 2c_0) \quad \text{or} \quad 2c_0 = \alpha/(1 + \alpha)$$

When $1 - c \ll 1$, it reduces to

$$E = E_B - \beta(1 - c)(E_A - E_B) \qquad (14.413)$$

where

$$\beta = -2(1 - c_0)/(1 - 2c_0) \quad \text{or} \quad 2(1 - c_0) = \beta/(1 + \beta)$$

In both these formulae one can think of the dominant element fixing the lattice, and the substitution of the other element causing some local distortion and therefore adding to the energy of the lattice; the energy difference $E_A - E_B$ being accepted as a measure of the distortion, the extra energy must be proportional to this difference, and to the amount of added material, c or $1 - c$ as the case may be. The mechanical explanation of such a behavior in terms of atomic sizes, electron populations, etc., would take us too far afield, and for discussions of this aspect of the problem, the student is referred to texts on solid-state physics or theoretical metallurgy.

Because we are neglecting all lattice imperfections, like holes and interstitial atoms, the total number of counted configurations in the crystal is

$$\Omega\{N\} = (N_A + N_B)!/N_A!N_B! \qquad (14.414)$$

If we attach a suffix j, where $j = 1$ or 2, to each numerical symbol, to represent populations in the two separate phases, we can set up the grand partition function for the two-phase, two-species assembly:

$$\mathbf{Q} = \sum_{\{N\}} \prod_j \Omega_j\{N_j\} \exp\left(-E_j + \mu_a N_{Aj} + \mu_b N_{Bj}\right)/kT \qquad (14.415)$$

where μ_a and μ_b are the chemical potentials of the two species of atoms. The most probable populations are derived by looking for the maximum term in the $\mathbf{Q}$ series. To find this, we maximize the logarithm of the typical term in the series with respect to each of the four population numbers, N_{Aj}, N_{Bj}, independently. This leads at once to

$$\left.\begin{array}{l} \mu_a = (\partial/\partial N_{Aj})[-kT \ln \Omega_j\{N_j\} + E_j] \quad \text{whether } j = 1 \text{ or } 2 \\ \mu_b = (\partial/\partial N_{Bj})[-kT \ln \Omega_j\{N_j\} + E_j] \quad \text{whether } j = 1 \text{ or } 2 \end{array}\right\} \qquad (14.416)$$

The quantities in the [brackets] are evidently the total free energy F_j; see Eq. (3.145). From Eq. (14.414) we have

$$\ln \Omega\{N\} = (N_A + N_B)\{-c \ln c - (1 - c) \ln (1 - c)\} \qquad (14.417)$$

where $c = N_B/(N_A + N_B)$. Remembering that E_j is the total energy of the phase, $(N_A + N_B)$ times the energy written in Eq. (14.409), we see now that the free energy per atom in any phase, f, is given by

$$f = kT\{c \ln c + (1 - c) \ln (1 - c)\} + cE_B + (1 - c)E_A$$
$$+ c(1 - c)(E_A - E_B)/(1 - 2c_0) \quad (14.418)$$

As discussed earlier, a region of instability exists if the curve $f(c)$ has two points of inflexion. These points are given by the roots of the equation $d^2f/dc^2 = 0$, which, from Eq. (14.418), is

$$1/c + 1/(1 - c) - 2(E_A - E_B)/(1 - 2c_0)kT = 0$$

which solves for c:

$$2c = 1 \pm (1 - 4\phi)^{\frac{1}{2}} \quad (14.419)$$

where

$$\phi = \tfrac{1}{2}(1 - 2c_0)kT/(E_A - E_B) = c_0{}^2 kT/(E_m - E_A)$$

As an example we may suppose $\phi = 0.09$, which gives the two concentrations at which $f(c)$ has inflexions at $c = 0.1$ and 0.9; the range of instability is quite wide, being generally wider than the c-gap between the two points of inflexion. The width of the gap is temperature-dependent both through the T factor in ϕ and because the energy parameters are probably temperature-sensitive. The gap decreases with increasing T, and no phase separation can occur if $\phi \geq \tfrac{1}{4}$. In the most familiar example of a substitutional alloy, copper-silver, the insolubility gap is still wide at the melting point.

Very few solid-phase diagrams are as simple as this theory indicates. Instead, there are numerous low-temperature phases, indicating a multiplicity of inflexion points in the free-energy curve. The most obvious way to match this observed behavior in our simple model would be to include lattice imperfections, like holes or interstitial atoms. The latter may be expected to play a very important part, especially if the low concentration element in an alloy does not fit very well into the lattice.

14.5 The energy of the free electrons in metals. In § 8.4 we discussed the Fermi-Dirac statistics of an electron gas and mentioned the part played by this theory in explaining the properties of metals. In first approximation, we consider any metal at ordinary laboratory temperatures to contain a gas of free electrons in the lowest possible states permitted by the Pauli exclusion principle. This gas has a considerable zero-point energy given by Eq. (8.406): $E_0 = N_e\mu_0$. The effective number of free electrons, N_e, can be estimated from a comparison between the electron theory of dispersion and the observed optical properties of the metal. In copper the number turns out to be 0.69 times the number of atoms, and in gold it is 1.01 per atom.* The zero-point energies are 57,500 calories per mole in copper and 93,400 calories per mole in gold.

Differentiating Eq. (8.406) with respect to volume gives the pressure exerted by the electron gas, and we find in copper, 2.2×10^{11} dynes/cm^2, and in gold,

* L. G. Schulz, *J. Opt. Soc. Am.*, **44** (1950), p. 540.

2.55×10^{11} dynes/cm^2. These pressures compare with those exerted by the phonon gas discussed in § 8.2; the sum of the electron and phonon pressures has to be balanced by the intrinsic pressure. Although these electron energies are large compared with the energy of the phonons, they vary so slightly with temperature that the electrons make hardly any contribution to the heat capacity. At $T = 500$ °K for instance, $kT/\mu_0 = 0.018$ in copper, and 0.010 in gold. Remembering that it is N_e that should be used in Eq. (8.428) for the heat capacity, we find 0.066 cal/mole deg for copper, and 0.073 cal/mole deg for gold. These may be contrasted with about 3 cal/mole deg for the phonons.

It is worthwhile to review the theory of order-disorder in binary alloys given in § 14.2 in the light of these figures. There can be little doubt that the electronic energies depend slightly at least on the degree of order in the lattice. The value of μ_0 depends directly on the effective mass of the electron; this is determined by the lattice potential, and this in turn depends on the degree of order in the lattice. The configurational energies involved in the order-disorder transition are found to be of the order 1500 cal/mole; it is clear, therefore, that only a very small fractional jump in the zero-point energy of the electrons would suffice to swamp the effect of the configurational energy itself. If, however, we can assume that the effective mass of the electron is a continuous and monotonic function of the degree of order, it may have no serious effect on the transition, and the theory as presented can be allowed to stand.

On the other hand, these large electronic energies are believed to have a decisive effect on the phase diagram of binary alloys. The electrons are held inside the metal by electrical forces—essentially image forces. We can sketch the electrical potential of an electron as follows: At the top of the diagram is the potential of an electron on the outside of the surface of the metal. At a distance W_0 below this is the Fermi level: W_0 is the work function. And μ_0 below the Fermi level is the lowest state of a free electron in the metal. Both W_0 and μ_0 can conceivably vary with composition of the alloy. The sum $W_0 + \mu_0$ essentially represents the work done against image forces and is probably less sensitive to changes in composition than either W_0 or μ_0 separately. Small changes in μ_0 then directly result in changes in free energy with composition and are to be included in the discussion of phase equilibria. In particular, there is very decidedly a sudden jump in μ_0 on melting, and this is responsible for part of the latent heat of fusion. Changes in this latent heat of fusion with composition provide a direct indication of the dependence of μ_0 on composition of the alloy.

In all this discussion, we have considered a single piece of metal and taken the electron at rest outside its surface as the energy reference point. Consider next two different metals A and B in electrical contact with each other. The free electrons in these metals may now be considered a single assembly with two separate phases A and B, and we can discuss the statistical problem: How are the electrons distributed between the two phases? (The theory of phase equilibria in quantum degenerate gases was given in Chapter IX, and the general theory of Chapter XII is applicable also to quantum degenerate systems.) Here we recall the major theorem, that the free energy of the two phases must be the same in equilibrium. In the case under consideration, however, electrical effects are important, and the theorem must not be applied without thought.

Suppose the two metals are at first separate, so that an exterior free electron defines the energy reference level. The two electron gases are then essentially independent and in separate containers. The two metals are now placed in contact, so that electrons can flow freely between them; the two containers are now connected. According to the theorem, electrons flow over from the metal with the higher Fermi level, i.e., the higher free energy, until the two levels are equalized. Equation (8.406) gives the Fermi level as measured from the lowest

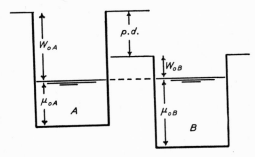

FIG. 14.51. Equilibrium between electrons in two metals in contact. The two Fermi levels match; the contact potential equals the difference between their work functions.

state, in terms of the number of free electrons in the metal, but this formula is valid only for an electrically neutral metal. As soon as electrons spill over from the other metal, neither metal is electrically neutral. In fact the lower Fermi level is raised, not through the operation of Eq. (8.604), but simply by charging up the metal to a higher electrical potential as a whole. As is well known, unbalanced charges reside at the surface of a conductor; therefore we may picture the process as the transfer of charge from just inside the surface of conductor B to just inside the surface of conductor A: Fig. 14.51. The area of contact between the two metals is a condenser whose electrical capacity is inversely proportional to the distance between the two charged layers. Under ordinary conditions of electrical contact, this distance is probably not less than about 10^{-6} cm, and therefore has a capacity of 10^6 cm per square centimeter of area. The potential difference required to equalize the two Fermi levels is equal to the difference between the two work functions, and may be of the order of a few volts; for the sake of argument, let us take it as 0.005 esu. The charge needed for this is 5×10^3 esu or about 10^{13} electrons per square centimeter. Since there are about 10^{21} electrons per cubic centimeter in the metals, this surface charge distribution makes a negligible difference to the Fermi energy μ_0, so that the energy picture simply shifts bodily until the two Fermi levels match. The exterior surfaces of the two metals now differ by the contact potential, which, on this model, should be exactly equal to the difference between the two work functions, and this is actually found to be true.

If the temperature is increased, we may assume that the sum $W_0 + \mu_0$ remains practically constant, although some change may be expected due to thermal expansion of the lattice. Neglecting this in first approximation, we have from Eq. (8.425), $W - W_0 = \mu_0 - \mu = \pi^2 k^2 T^2 / 12\mu_0$, so the contact potential changes with temperature according to this model:

$$W_A - W_B = W_{0A} - W_{0B} + (\pi^2/12)k^2 T^2 (1/\mu_{0A} - 1/\mu_{0B}) \quad (14.501)$$

The degeneracy temperature for copper, calculated from Eq. (8.410), turns out to be about 8000 °K, so that Eq. (14.501) is good for any temperature at which the metal is still solid. In Cu, μ_0 is about 2.5 ev, and at T about 100 °K, kT is about 0.3 ev, so the temperature-dependent term comes to only about 0.03 ev and is therefore usually quite negligible.

The evaporation of electrons from a metal by thermionic emission is a familiar phenomenon, and this can be investigated theoretically, by considering the equilibrium between the electrons in the metal and an ideal electron gas outside the metal. The latter will be expected to have a numerical density so small that its degeneracy temperature is very much lower than the temperature of the metal, so that it obeys classical statistics, and has a negative free energy μ_{0g}. Equilibrium exists if the two free energy levels coincide: $\mu_{0g} = -W_0$. To avoid any complicated electrical effects, we may suppose the electrons required for the gas outside the metal are fed in from outside, and the space potential is kept at ground along with the surface of the metal. The numerical density of the electron atmosphere is then given by the first term in the series of Eq. (8.409): $N_g/V = 2(2\pi mkT/h^2)^{3/2} e^{-W_0/kT}$. From kinetic theory, we know that the number of particles hitting a square centimeter of surface of a classical gas per second is $(kT/2\pi m)^{1/2}(N_g/V)$. Let a fraction r of these be reflected; then $(1 - r)$ times the number incident goes into the metal. Since equilibrium is maintained, the same number must be coming out of the metal per second. If the gas is drawn off in the form of an electric current, and the metal kept supplied with charge, the current can be maintained at the rate given by the number coming out per second at equilibrium. Therefore, we find for the thermionic emission current:

$$I = (4\pi em/h^3)(kT)^2 (1 - r)e^{-W_0/kT}$$

or, numerically,

$$I = (1 - r)120T^2 e^{-W_0/kT} \text{ amp/cm}^2 \quad (14.502)$$

This is the Richardson formula for thermionic emission and can be used to obtain a direct measure of the work function W:

$$W/kT = 2 \ln T + \ln (120) - \ln I_{\text{amp}} + \ln (1 - r)$$

The thermionic current is surprisingly large. For Cu, with W about 4 ev, the current is no less than $(1 - r)$ times 700 amp/cm² at 1000 °K.

14.6 Thermal and electrical conductivity. Neither thermionic emission nor thermal and electrical conductivity questions are strictly part of equilibrium statistical mechanics, being amenable only to kinetic theory. They are briefly discussed here only because the Fermi-Dirac statistics of electrons have been so fundamental to the success of kinetic theory in dealing with them.

The most obvious experimental fact calling for theoretical interpretation is that the thermal conductivity of good electrical conductors like copper, with 1 cal/sec cm, is much greater than that of electrical insulators, like porcelain with 0.0025 cal/sec cm. The thermal current is transmitted by lattice vibrations in an electrical insulator, and roughly the same current must be carried by lattice vibrations in a conductor; the high thermal current in electrical conductors must be due to the free electrons. First consider the thermal current carried by the lattice vibrations. We can regard these vibrations as a gas of phonons, more-or-less localized packets of elastic energy, as in § 8.3. These packets are shooting about the lattice at the speed of sound, and at first sight, there seems to be nothing to stop them from transmitting heat right through the lattice with the speed of sound, and so providing the lattice with an infinite thermal conductivity. In the classical kinetic theory of gases, collisions between the particles are responsible for the resistance; in the phonon gas, collisions between phonons are responsible for the finite thermal conductivity. It may seem at first strange to talk about collisions between phonons, but in fact there is an efficient mechanism for them. In the first place, phonons are not normally localized very sharply but spread over considerable distances in the lattice, so that at any one time many phonons interpenetrate each other—are in fact in collision. Unlike photons, which can pass through each other with practically no interference, phonons do in fact perturb each other. This perturbation arises from the presence of relatively small anharmonic terms in the elastic forces, which cause acoustical energy to pass readily from one mode of vibration to another. It is in fact the same mechanism that establishes and maintains thermal equilibrium among the modes of vibration. The rate at which such transitions occur may be such that the life-time of a given phonon may be a large number of wave periods of the mode, but most of the thermal energy is carried by very high-frequency phonons, from one-tenth of the maximum frequency of the Debye model and up, perhaps around 10^{12} per sec. Therefore we may allow a phonon to persist without collisions for perhaps a hundred wave periods, and still come out with life-times of no more than 10^{-10} sec. Neglecting dispersion, the speed of a phonon equals the speed of propagation of sound, of the order 10^5 cm/sec, so the mean free path of a phonon may be around 10^{-5} cm. The classical formula from kinetic theory for thermal conductivity reads

$$K = lvC/3V \qquad (14.601)$$

where l is the mean free path, v the speed of the particles, and C their contribution to heat capacity at constant volume V. At sufficiently high temperatures, the heat capacity of the phonon gas is of course $3Nk$, where N is the number of atoms (not phonons); hence the thermal conductivity would be

$$K = lvkN/V \tag{14.602}$$

With the above estimates of the numerical values, and $N/V = 10^{22}$, this K comes to about 10^{-3} cal/sec cm, about the same as that mentioned above for porcelain. At very high temperatures, l appears to become proportional to $1/T$, and the conductivity gets smaller as T increases. At very low temperatures, the heat capacity goes over to the T^3 law, and it is found instead that

$$T \ll \theta: \qquad\qquad K = (4\pi^4/5)lv(T/\theta)^3kN/V \tag{14.603}$$

This appears to go to very small values at low T, but actually, a moment's reflection will show that the mean free path may increase almost without limit at low enough temperatures. With lattice energies dropping towards the zero-point, the anharmonic terms become less and less significant, and this mechanism for transfer of energy from one mode to another becomes progressively less effective. At sufficiently low temperatures the mean free path in fact becomes effectively comparable with the linear dimensions of the whole crystal, and heat transfer is found to be sensitive to the geometry of the specimen.

At ordinary temperatures, we have to explain the good thermal conductivity of the metals in terms of their free electrons, kinetic energy being carried by those electrons with energy near the Fermi level. Electrons may be pictured as making collisions with the lattice atoms, and so to have a mean free path l proportional to the lattice spacing. Their mean speeds would be the speed v_f corresponding to the Fermi energy. Using Eq. (8.428) for the heat capacity, one then finds that

$$K = (\pi^2/3)(N/V)lk^2T/mv_f \tag{14.604}$$

where $v_f = (2\mu_0/m)^{1/2}$ is the speed corresponding to the Fermi level. In an actual metal, v_f may be of the order of 10^8 cm/sec, $N/V \sim 10^{22}$, and so very roughly $K = 10^6$ cal/sec cm. To account for the observed conductivities of about 1 cal, l must be of the order 10^{-6} cm, or about 100 lattice spacings. The contribution of the phonons to the heat current appears to be completely negligible compared with that of the electrons, at least at ordinary temperatures. However, at very low temperatures, as remarked in a previous paragraph, it is possible for the resistance mechanism of the phonons to break down, so that the lattice conductivity might actually become appreciable. In fact it is believed that in single-metal crystals the thermal conductivity of the lattice at very low (liquid helium) temperatures, may not be limited by the phonon-phonon interaction at all, but by phonon-electron interaction instead.

The classical kinetic theory of electrical conductivity yields the result

$$\sigma = (N/V)e^2l/2m\bar{v} \tag{14.605}$$

where N/V is the number of free electrons, charge e; l their mean free path; and $\bar{v}$ their mean speed. Perturbation theory applied instead to the Fermi-Dirac statistics gives the same result, if we interpret $\bar{v}$ as one-half the speed corresponding to the Fermi level:

$$\sigma = (N/V)e^2 l/mv_f \qquad (14.606)$$

The ratio of electrical and thermal conductivities is then independent of everything but universal constants and the temperature:

$$K/\sigma = (\pi k/e)^2 T/3 \qquad (14.607)$$

The Lorentz number is $L = K/\sigma T = 2.45 \times 10^{-8}$ v^2/deg^2. Experimental values of this ratio agree remarkably well with the theory.

The quantum mechanical problem is evidently to calculate the mean free path l or the mean relaxation time $\tau = l/v_f$. The ideal rigid lattice has no electrical resistance; a periodic potential field has steady state solutions for the electron wave function, with any desired momentum, and energy dissipation does not prevent maintaining the momentum of an electron in such a crystal. Thermal motion upsets the simplicity of this situation. On the Einstein model of a crystal one can regard each atom as an individual oscillator, having motion not correlated with the motion of its neighbors. Each atom then becomes a scattering center, and resistance results. However, Einstein's model does not work too well at low temperature in explaining heat capacity, and we use Debye's model instead. This model analyzes the motion of the crystal as a whole into its normal modes. Here the motions of different atoms are coherent, and one has to consider the motion of the whole crystal lattice as causing perturbations of the lattice potential. The theory of resistance has been developed on the basis of treating the Debye modes as time dependent perturbations of the lattice potential. Qualitatively it gives a resistance—reciprocal conductivity—proportional to the amplitude of the lattice vibrations at higher temperatures, i.e., proportional to $T/M\theta^2$, where M is the atomic mass and θ the characteristic Debye temperature of the lattice. At very low temperatures the resistance becomes proportional to $T^5/M\theta^6$; comparison with experiment can in fact yield a rough measure of the Debye temperature.

In addition to these temperature dependent terms, there is also a resistance due to lattice imperfections; foreign atoms or misfits in interstitial sites cause a random lack of periodicity in the lattice potential, on a much larger scale (in distance) than the random motion of the lattice points. This resistance is practically independent of the temperature, and is called "residual" resistance, because it remains effective down to the lowest temperatures where the thermal resistance approaches zero. Theory (due to Nordheim) predicts that this residual resistance is proportional to $x(1 - x)$, where x is the atomic concentration of the imperfections, and this has been very well verified by comparison with the residual resistance observed in deliberately prepared disordered solid solutions having known concentrations.

14.7 Theory of superconductivity. Since the superconducting transition was first discovered, in 1911, by Kamerlingh Onnes at Leiden (Hg, 4.2 °K), it has been discovered in twenty elements and a very large number of alloys. The problem of superconductivity has become one of the most extensively and intensively prosecuted fields of research. The relevant literature is extremely voluminous, and the experimental data, enormously rich and stimulating; yet there is still no completely satisfactory explanation of the basic phenomenon.

Briefly the basic phenomenon consists of two effects: 1) at the transition temperature T_s, the metal loses all its d-c resistance quite suddenly, and currents once set up can persist in a closed superconducting ring with no emf literally for days, indeed just so long as the cryostat can be maintained in operation; 2) in the presence of a magnetic field, the transition temperature is lowered, and at the transition, all the magnetic field is expelled from the specimen; and this effect is reversible—absence of magnetic field in the specimen is necessary for it to be superconducting. The critical magnetic field increases from zero at the normal transition temperature T_s to a finite limit at 0 °K.

In seeking to understand this basic phenomenon, there are a number of side effects to be borne in mind, and we list these here: a) There is a *lambda*-type jump in the heat capacity at T_s; a latent heat of transition exists when a magnetic field is used to restore the resistance at temperatures below T_s.   b) There are rather sudden changes in thermal conductivity of the metal at the transition, and the Wiedemann-Franz law no longer holds for superconductors. The thermoelectric power of superconductors is zero.   c) There is no observable change in any of the more obvious properties of a crystal at the superconducting transition: crystal structure, density, optical properties, elastic constants, etc.—all are identical on either side of the transition.   d) There appears to be no systematic correlation between the crystal symmetries of those metals in which superconductivity has been observed. There does, however, seem to be a fairly narrow range of atomic volumes among these metals. It has recently been discovered that high pressure up to 20,000 atm has the effect of lowering the transition temperature in Sn from 3.72 °K to 2.9 °K, while stretching under tension has been observed to raise the transition from 3.7° to as high as 9 °K.   e) Comparing the transition temperatures of isotopes of the same element, it has been discovered that $T_s W^n$ is a constant for the element, where W is the isotopic mass number, and n is almost exactly one-half. Both Hg and Sn have been thoroughly examined for this effect, which is really the only piece of evidence existing that the superconducting transition is not a purely electronic phenomenon.

Even without understanding the basic phenomenon, we can use a thermodynamic type of reasoning to correlate some of the effects. Thus it is believed that the expulsion of the magnetic field necessarily produces a latent heat of the transition below T_s; because no change in crystal structure occurs, we can say that the *lambda*-type heat capacity is due to an increase in order, or decrease in entropy, of the conduction electrons below the transition; the difference in heat capacity of the superconducting phase and normal phase (in the magnetic field) at any one temperature below the transition T_s is thermodynamically related with the shape of the critical field versus temperature curve. It is reassuring that there is no conflict between experiment and these findings of thermodynamics in spite of the admittedly baffling nature of the phenomenon.

Progress towards understanding the basic problem has been made in terms of a phenomenological theory, the so-called two-fluid model. The point of departure of this model is the above remark that there must exist an increase in order among the conduction electrons below the transition. On this model the assembly of conduction electrons breaks up into two phases at the transition, one remaining completely normal, and the other consisting of supercurrent electrons that can travel throughout the crystal without resistance; the population of the supercurrent phase is a function of T, starting from zero at T_s, and increasing in some way as T decreases. Because of the superelectrons it is evidently impossible to maintain a steady field intensity E inside a superconductor; if, however, one were temporarily imposed, the superelectrons would be subjected to a steady acceleration, such that $d(\lambda \mathbf{j}_s)/dt = \mathbf{E}$, where $\lambda = m/e^2 n_s$; $\mathbf{j}_s = n_s e \mathbf{v}$ is the current density; n_s, the number of superelectrons per unit volume; m, their mass; and e their charge. Take the curl of this equation and integrate over time starting from rest, and we have:

$$\operatorname{curl}(\lambda \mathbf{j}_s) = \int_0^t \operatorname{curl} \mathbf{E}\, dt = -\mathbf{H}/c$$

the last step using one of Maxwell's equations. This gives the final current density in terms of final magnetic field produced by the current. F. London suggested that we may drop the doubtful argument leading to this result, and just accept the resulting relation:

$$\operatorname{curl}(\lambda \mathbf{j}_s) = -\mathbf{H}/c \qquad (14.701)$$

as the basic equation for the supercurrent, to be added to the other Maxwell equations for the electromagnetic field. In terms of this hypothesis, all the peculiar properties of superconductors can be understood, including the superdiamagnetism (repulsion of magnetic fields), and many other phenomena—high-frequency effects, penetration depths, etc.—into which we shall not inquire in the present discussion.

It is not difficult to give this two-fluid model a very reasonable basis in terms of the Fermi-Dirac statistics, and we shall devote this section to such a discussion; later we shall also discuss briefly various attempts to understand the basic problem more fundamentally.

From the assumption that the energy of the excluded magnetic field is the only difference in free energy between the normal and superconducting phases, it can be proved by elementary thermodynamics that the difference between the heat capacities of the two phases, $C_n - C_s$, at any given temperature below the transition is related to the temperature dependence of the critical magnetic field according to the relation:

$$(C_n - C_s)/T = -V\{(dH_c/dT)^2 + H_c d^2 H_c/dT^2\} \qquad (14.702)$$

where H_c is the critical (excluded) magnetic field at the temperature T. The observed dependence of H_c on T is approximately

$$H_c = H_0\{1 - (T/T_c)^2\} \tag{14.703}$$

and H_0 is the (extrapolated) critical field at absolute zero. Therefore

$$(C_n - C_s)/T = 2VH_0^2(1 - 3T^2/T_c^2)/T_c^2 \tag{14.704}$$

If this equation, which has been directly verified by experiment, is integrated over T and the constant adjusted to make it vanish at $T = T_c$, we find

$$\begin{aligned}
E_n - E_s &= \tfrac{1}{2}VH_0^2\{1 + 2(T/T_c)^2 - 3(T/T_c)^4\} \\
&= 2VH_0^2(T/T_c)^2\{1 - (T/T_c)^2\} + \tfrac{1}{2}VH_0^2\{1 - (T/T_c)^2\}^2 \quad (14.705)
\end{aligned}$$

In the two-fluid picture, this energy difference ought to be given in a form derivable from

$$E_n = N\epsilon_n, \quad E_s = N_n\epsilon_n + N_s(\epsilon - \alpha N_s/N) \tag{14.706}$$

where ϵ_n is the average energy of the normal states in the normal phase, ϵ, the average energy per supercurrent electron at zero population, and $\alpha N_s/N$ a cooperative term of the type discussed in § 12.4. Writing $N = N_n + N_s$, we then have to compare Eq. (14.705) with

$$E_n - E_s = N_s(\epsilon_n - \epsilon) + \alpha N_s^2/N \tag{14.707}$$

Evidently this comparison yields

$$N_s/N = H_0(V/2\alpha N)^{1/2}\{1 - (T/T_c)^2\} \tag{14.708}$$

and

$$\epsilon_n - \epsilon = 2H_0(2V\alpha/N)^{1/2}(T/T_c)^2 \tag{14.709}$$

We know from the theory of Fermi-Dirac assemblies that for free electrons,

$$\epsilon_n = (3\mu_0/5)\{1 + 5(\pi kT/\mu_0)^2/12\}$$

so if we make the simplest possible assumption about the average energy,

$$\epsilon = 3\mu_0/5 \tag{14.710}$$

Eq. (14.709) leads to the following expression of the co-operative term:

$$H_0(2V\alpha/N)^{1/2} = (\pi kT_c/\mu_0)^2/8 \tag{14.711}$$

At the absolute zero of temperature, the excluded field energy is $\tfrac{1}{2}VH_0^2$, and this must be equal to the co-operative term at the absolute zero, since the difference between ϵ_n and ϵ vanishes there: this is a direct consequence of Eq. (14.708), whatever value may be assumed for the factor $H_0(V/2\alpha N)^{1/2}$. However, in its simplest form, the model assumes this factor to be unity, so that

$$\alpha N = \tfrac{1}{2}VH_0^2 \quad \text{and} \quad N_s/N = 1 - (T/T_c)^2 \tag{14.712}$$

The last equation means that all the free electrons go over into the supercurrent states at absolute zero. This feature is not a necessary part of the model but is made for simplicity. Combining Eqs. (14.712) and (14.711) to eliminate α, we find

$$VH_0{}^2 = N(\pi k T_c)^2/8\mu_0 \tag{14.713}$$

and using Eq. (8.406) to express μ_0 in terms of N/V, we have a relation between H_0, T_c, and the effective number of free electrons per unit volume:

$$H_0/kT_c = (\pi^4/3)^{1/3} m^2 (N/V)^{1/6}/h$$

If the universal constants are put in numerically, one has in cgs units,

$$H_0/T_c = 2 \times 10^{-3}(N/V)^{1/6} = 18.4 N_e(\rho/W)^{1/6} \tag{14.714}$$

where N_e is the effective number of free electrons per atom, and ρ is the density and W the atomic weight of the material. We tabulate some of the values of N_e derived in this way from the observed values of T_c and extrapolated values of H_0, compared in a few cases with values of N_e derived from other properties of the same metals.

TABLE OF SOME SUPERCONDUCTORS

Element	$T_c{}^\circ K$	H_0 gauss	ρ g/cm³	W	N_e	N_e(opt)
Pb	7.2	900	11.35	207	4.2	5.1
Sn	3.7	300	6	119	2.68	4.1
Hg	4.2	410	13.5	200	3.38	2.1
In	3.4	275	7.28	115	2.8	
Ta	4.4	1100	16.6	181	9.1	
Nb	9.2	2600	8.4	93	10.3	
Th	1.4	600	11.3	232	14.0	
Zr	0.7	200	6.4	91	10.0	

The numbers obtained for the "soft" superconductors, H_0/T_c less than 200, are reasonable enough, but those for the hard superconductors seem unduly large; evidently the simple model is qualitatively satisfactory, but it needs improving before a quantitative validity is secured. The most obvious way to do this would be to replace Eq. (14.710) by

$$\epsilon = 3\mu_0/5 - \sigma(\pi k T)^2/\mu_0 \tag{14.715}$$

where σ is an adjustable parameter. Equation (14.713) gets multiplied by a factor $(1 + \sigma)$. A large value of σ will then accompany the hard superconductors to reduce the number N_e. Physically, this would mean that in the hard superconductors the supercurrent states at the transition are more stable energetically than the soft superconductors, quite apart from the co-operative term in the energy.

The value of this kind of phenomenological model is that it focuses attention on two or three points of attack in developing a more fundamental theory: What is the origin of the co-operative energy? Why does the number of superelectrons depend on T, according to Eq. (14.712)? What is the nature of the supercurrent state?

Recent theories of Fröhlich have attempted to explain the stability of the supercurrent in terms of resonance between electron wave functions and the elastic waves of the lattice. While there are serious objections to his theory in some details, it did in fact lead Fröhlich to predict correctly the isotope effect before its discovery. Bardeen has also developed similar ideas and derived plausible criteria to explain why certain elements become superconductors and others do not.

There is one feature of the Bardeen-Fröhlich theories that has not been sufficiently emphasized in the literature; the lattice vibrations are treated quantum mechanically, and the classical motion of the atoms in the lattice is replaced by harmonic oscillator eigenfunctions. Because of this, the periodic lattice potential "seen" by the electrons and perturbed by the lattice vibrations is not time-dependent, as it was classically. Automatically, therefore, there exist steady current-carrying states of an electron in such a lattice that suffer no random scattering—these are essentially the steady states of the Fröhlich theory. Now the basic assumption of extant theories of the electrical resistance of a metal is that the thermal (elastic) vibrations of the lattice cause random scattering of the electron wave functions, due to their time-dependent perturbation of the lattice potential. But if there are no time-dependent perturbations of the lattice, we can find scattering only if we set up the wrong wave functions; if we set up the true wave functions, there is no scattering.

Consequently insofar as the Fröhlich-Bardeen theories succeed in explaining the supercurrent states, they implicitly conflict with the generally credited theory of resistance. It must be agreed that the quantum mechanical representation of the lattice vibrations, as steady harmonic oscillator eigenfunctions without a time factor, is essentially correct. The proper way to explain normal resistance is to generalize the theory of the vibrational states of a lattice in such a way as to include transitions between these states. Thus a crystal must be regarded as a member of an ensemble, the most probable vibrational state found statistically, and fluctuations among states near the most probable must be provided for in the theory. These fluctuations, being random, will give rise to random scattering of electrons in resonance with the vibrational states, and so cause resistance. This is a project for quantum statistics that will involve the von Neumann matrix method of Eq. (11.414). (See also Problem 7 of Chapter XV.)

To understand the superconducting transition in terms of this picture, it is necessary to discover some mechanism whereby some of the modes of vibration can be locked into pure states so permanently that an electron in resonance with them can stay indefinitely in one current-carrying state without scattering. This mechanism is evidently a property of the lattice, not only of the electrons, and must tie in with the isotope effect in some way.

EXERCISES AND PROBLEMS

1. Verify the steps leading to each of the following equations: (14.105), (14.110), (14.114), (14.115), and (14.116).

2. Plot a curve of $B_j(Y)$ for $j = \frac{1}{2}$, $j = 1$, and $j = $ infinity.

3. Find a simple asymptotic expression for the mean magnetic moment as a function of T as T approaches zero.

4. Verify Eq. (14.119) for the discontinuity in heat capacity. The fact that the parameter α does not appear in this expression might suggest that the discontinuity would exist even in the absence of any co-operative term; discuss this point in detail.

5. Derive Eq. (14.206).

6. Derive Eq. (14.209).

7. Express Eq. (14.210) in the form of Eq. (12.401) and so derive Eq. (14.211).

8. Derive Eqs. (14.212) and (14.213).

9. Prove that the solution $\theta = 0$ corresponds to a physically unstable solution of Eq. (14.214) when T is near zero.

10. Derive Eq. (14.216).

11. Try to derive Eqs. (14.305)–(14.309) both in the way outlined in the text, and also as follows: include N_L as another independent variable, and treat Eq. (14.301) as a numerical restriction; introduce a Lagrangian parameter, and proceed to maximize the typical term by variation of all six variables.

12. Derive Eqs. (14.313)–(14.317).

13. Derive Eq. (14.324) for the heat capacity.

14. In Eq. (14.324) let $W_i = W_h$ and find the maximum heat capacity by adjusting the value of W/kT.

15. Give a simple thermodynamic argument to prove Eq. (14.418) without using the grand-partition-function method described in the text.

16. Develop a simple theory for the possible effects of interstitial atoms on the phase equilibrium of a substitutional alloy.

REFERENCES FOR FURTHER STUDY

Ferromagnetism, R. M. Bozorth, Van Nostrand, 1951.

Theory of Metals, A. H. Wilson, Cambridge, 1953.

Elasticity and Anelasticity of Metals, C. M. Zener, Chicago, 1948.

The Modern Theory of Solids, F. Seitz, McGraw-Hill, 1940.

Superfluids, I: Macroscopic Theory of Superconductivity, F. London, Wiley, 1950.

Theory of Superconductivity, M. von Laue, Academic Press, 1952.

"Statistics of the Simple Cubic Lattice," A. J. Wakefield, *Proc. Cambridge Phil. Soc.*, **47** (1951), pp. 419; 799.

"Methods of Approximation in the Theory of Regular Mixtures," J. A. Barker, *Proc. Roy. Soc.* (London), **A216** (1953), p. 45.

"A Statistical Theory of Order-Disorder Equilibrium at High Temperatures," P. Schwed and G. Groetzinger, *J. Chem. Phys.*, **21** (1953), p. 963.

"The Thermal Conductivity of Metals," R. E. B. Makinson, *Proc. Cambridge Phil. Soc.*, **34** (1938), p. 473.

ɪ The Thermal Conductivity of a Copper-Nickel Alloy at Low Temperatures," J. K. Hulm, *Proc. Phys. Soc.* (London), **B64** (1951), p. 207.

"Superconductivity of the Isotopes of Tin," E. Maxwell, *Phys. Rev.*, **86** (1952), p. 235.

"The Isotope Effect in Superconductivity, II. Tin and Lead," Serin, Reynolds, and Lohman, *Phys. Rev.*, **86** (1952), p. 162.

"Relation between Lattice Vibrations and London Theories of Superconductivity," J. Bardeen, *Phys. Rev.*, **81** (1951), p. 829.

"Debye Modes and Superconductivity," W. Band, *Phys. Rev.*, **79** (1950), pp. 739; 1005.

"Interaction of Lattice Vibrations with Electrons in a Metal," G. Wentzel, *Phys. Rev.*, **83** (1951), p. 168.

Chapter XV

FLUCTUATIONS AND NONEQUILIBRIUM PHENOMENA

15.1 The concept of fluctuations in equilibrium. By a fluctuation is meant a spontaneous departure or deviation of some property of an assembly from the mean value of that property in an ensemble. Thermodynamic equilibrium is usually specified only by the mean values of the various state variables, like p, T, V, etc., and fluctuations are ignored. In discussing statistical equilibrium, not only do we have to specify the mean values, but have also to become aware of the fact that, in equilibrium, fluctuations from these mean values occur—in fact that these fluctuations are an essential characteristic of the statistical equilibrium state rather than departures from that state. We have already discussed briefly the significance of this in connection with reversible processes, § 3.7, but in general we have so far neglected the existence of fluctuations. In this chapter we shall examine the technique of calculating fluctuations, using the method of the grand partition function, investigate the conditions under which fluctuations are small enough to constitute a generally negligible disturbance, and note certain peculiar circumstances under which fluctuations become so violent that the equilibrium state becomes highly agitated.

The mean square deviation of any function F is defined by the average of the square of the difference between an individual measure of F and its average measure $\langle F \rangle$: $\langle (\langle F \rangle - F)^2 \rangle$. This is equal to $\langle \langle F \rangle^2 \rangle - 2\langle \langle F \rangle F \rangle + \langle F^2 \rangle = \langle F^2 \rangle - \langle F \rangle^2$. Since the grand partition function gives a technique for calculating averages, we can find both these terms, and so compute the mean square relative fluctuation, defined by

$$\langle F^2 \rangle / \langle F \rangle^2 - 1 \qquad (15.101)$$

These fluctuations are calculated in terms of an ensemble of assemblies. We may now appeal once again to the ergodic hypothesis, mentioned briefly in § 7.1: what goes for the average in an ensemble at any one time, goes also for the average behavior of a single assembly over a long enough period of time. Where the ensemble indicates only minute fluctuations, any particular assembly under test may be expected to show only minute fluctuations; where the ensemble indicates violent fluctuations, any particular test assembly should also in the course of time exhibit wide variations in its equilibrium state variables. The time element is something that our technique as so far developed is quite inadequate to handle quantitatively. We can calculate the mean amplitude of deviations from mean values, but not how rapidly in time these deviations can occur. This time question is evidently closely related to nonequilibrium or dynamical problems. For example the rapidity with which a wide deviation in density will smooth itself out again may be expected to depend on such normally irreversible effects as self-diffusion, viscosity, etc. In the last sections of this chapter we shall discuss briefly the most significant recent work on the relation between fluctuations and irreversible processes, and show how statistical mechanics is linked up with the new field of irreversible thermodynamics.

15.2   Fluctuations in phase population and density. In Chapter XII we used the notation $\bar{F}$ to represent the ensemble average of F; here it is more convenient to use the notation $\langle F \rangle$, introduced in the last section and also in § 1.2. This is not intended to imply that the ensemble average is the same thing as a quantum mechanical expectation value—it is not. The mean square population fluctuation is then, for any one phase,

$$\langle (\langle n \rangle - n)^2 \rangle = \langle n^2 \rangle - \langle n \rangle^2 \tag{15.201}$$

From Eq. (12.123) we have

$$\langle n \rangle = (1/Q)(kT\partial Q/\partial \nu) \tag{15.202}$$

where the partial derivative is taken with respect to the chemical potential of the one phase of interest only. Putting n^2 for F in Eq. (12.133) yields essentially

$$\langle n^2 \rangle = (1/Q) \sum_{En} n^2 \Omega_{En} \exp (n\nu - E)/kT$$

$$= (1/Q)(k^2 T^2 \partial^2 Q/\partial \nu^2)$$

$$= kT(\partial/\partial \nu)\{(1/Q)(kT\partial Q/\partial \nu)\} + (1/Q)^2(kT\partial Q/\partial \nu)^2$$

$$= kT\partial \langle n \rangle/\partial \nu + \langle n \rangle^2$$

Hence

$$\langle (\langle n \rangle - n)^2 \rangle = kT\partial \langle n \rangle/\partial \nu \tag{15.203}$$

To translate this result into more familiar terms, we note first that all assemblies in the ensemble have the same volume, and therefore populations are proportional to densities; hence a convenient abbreviation for the relative square fluctuations would be

$$\langle (\langle n \rangle - n)^2 \rangle / \langle n \rangle^2 = \langle \Delta\rho/\rho \rangle^2 \tag{15.204}$$

where ρ is the density of the phase. From Eq. (3.142) the isothermal variation of a phase gives

$$dF = Vdp + \nu d\langle n \rangle \tag{15.205}$$

while [see Eqs. (4.103) and (4.104)] we also have $F = \nu\langle n\rangle$ and hence

$$dF = \langle n\rangle d\nu + \nu d\langle n\rangle \tag{15.206}$$

Comparison of the last two equations therefore yields

$$\langle n\rangle d\nu = V dp \tag{15.207}$$

Divide this by $d\langle n\rangle$ to obtain the isothermal $\partial\langle n\rangle/\partial\nu$, and use the result in Eqs. (15.203) and (15.204) to find

$$\langle\Delta\rho/\rho\rangle^2 = -kT/[V^2(\partial p/\partial V)_T] \tag{15.208}$$

In an ideal gas phase, where $pV = \langle n\rangle kT$, we evidently have

$$\langle\Delta\rho/\rho\rangle^2 = 1/\langle n\rangle \tag{15.209}$$

The mean square fluctuations in density are exceedingly small when the assembly has no more than a few hundred atoms; for any macroscopic gas with as many as 10^{18} atoms per cubic centimeter, the fluctuations in density are normally completely negligible.

15.3 Fluctuations in energy and pressure. Write the energy E for F in Eq. (12.133) and recall then that

$$E = (1/Q)\partial Q/\partial\beta \tag{15.301}$$

where β is $1/kT$. Write E^2 for F in the same expression and therefore

$$\langle E^2\rangle = (1/Q)\sum_{En} E^2\Omega_{En}\exp(\nu n/kT - \beta E) \tag{15.302}$$

In taking partial derivatives with respect to β, it is understood that the parameter ν/kT does not vary. Then we have from (15.302):

$$\langle E^2\rangle = (1/Q)(\partial^2/\partial\beta^2)\sum_{En}\Omega_{En}\exp(\nu n/kT - E)$$

$$= (\partial/\partial\beta)\{(1/Q)(\partial Q/\partial\beta)\} + (1/Q)^2(\partial Q/\partial\beta)^2$$

$$= -\partial\langle E\rangle/\partial\beta + \langle E\rangle^2$$

Therefore the mean square energy fluctuation is

$$\langle(\langle E\rangle - E)^2\rangle = \langle E^2\rangle - \langle E\rangle^2 = -\partial\langle E\rangle/\partial\beta = -\partial^2(\ln Q)/\partial\beta^2 \tag{15.303}$$

The differentiations in these formulae are purely formal: in the actual ensemble β is not subject to variation. What we have to do in effect, is to compare two different ensembles having different values of β in order to give a physical meaning to the variation with respect to β. Mathematically, the formal process is straightforward. In general when we compare two different ensembles the same phase may have different populations in each—this is the population fluctuation of the last section; this population fluctuation will contribute a term to the energy fluctuation. If we confine our attention to a single phase assembly, and so rule out the population fluctuations completely, the energy fluctuations are reduced. In such a case Eq. (15.303) can be written:

isolated phase $\qquad\qquad \langle((\langle E\rangle - E)^2\rangle = kT^2C_v \qquad\qquad\qquad$ (15.304)

where C_v is the heat capacity at constant volume. The relative fluctuations may then be written symbolically

$$\langle \Delta E/E\rangle^2 = kT^2C_v/\langle E\rangle^2 \qquad\qquad (15.305)$$

For an ideal classical gas, $\langle E\rangle = 3\langle n\rangle kT/2$, $C_v = 3\langle n\rangle k/2$, and so:

classical gas $\qquad\qquad \langle \Delta E/E\rangle^2 = 2/(3\langle n\rangle) \qquad\qquad\qquad$ (15.306)

illustrating again the exceedingly small fluctuations to be expected normally in macroscopic assemblies. It is of interest to compare this last result with the fluctuations in an isolated phase of quantum degenerate Bose-Einstein gas, using Eq. (8.321) and Eq. (8.322) for the energy and heat capacity in Eq. (15.305):

Bose-Einstein gas $\qquad \langle \Delta E/E\rangle^2 = (3.22/\langle n\rangle)(T_0/T)^{3/2} \qquad\qquad$ (15.307)

This increases with decreasing temperature, and is appreciably greater than in the classical gas at the same temperature.

We may apply the general formula Eq. (15.305) to liquid helium, where we have approximately

$$C_v = \langle n\rangle C_\lambda (T/T_\lambda)^6 \qquad\qquad (15.308)$$

where C_λ is the atomic heat at the *lambda*-point, 2.19 °K. Integration of this gives $\langle E\rangle$, and using this, one finds from Eq. (15.305) that for

liquid helium: $\qquad\qquad \langle \Delta E/E\rangle^2 = (7k/C_\lambda\langle n\rangle)(T_\lambda/T)^6 \qquad\qquad$ (15.309)

Experimentally C_λ is roughly $60k$, so that these fluctuations are smaller than those of an ideal Bose-Einstein gas at the *lambda*-temperature; but because of the high power of T, the fluctuations increase rapidly below T_λ; for example at $T = \frac{1}{4}T_\lambda$, or about 0.5 °K, they would be roughly four hundred times as big as those of a classical gas. Indeed appreciable fluctuations are to be expected in volumes as small only as a thousand atoms of liquid helium at this temperature.

Consider next a crystalline assembly at very low temperature, and using the Debye expression for mean energy and heat capacity, Eq. (7.218), we find

$$\langle \Delta E/E\rangle^2 = (20/3\pi^4)(\theta/T)^3/\langle n\rangle \qquad\qquad (15.310)$$

This again becomes anomalously large at low temperatures compared with θ. For solid helium, with a Debye θ roughly 30° at 2 °K, the factor $(\theta/T)^3$ is so great that fluctuations in energy would be appreciable even with $\langle n\rangle$ as large as one thousand.

Of course these large relative fluctuations in energy are in fact due to the very small mean values of energy $\langle E\rangle$ in the denominators, rather than to any absolute increase in mean deviations. So far as the equilibrium characteristics are concerned, however, the relative fluctuations are the significant quantities. Conventionally it is agreed that equilibrium is difficult to approach at very low temperatures, simply because the rates of change become very small at low temperatures. Here we can point out a further difficulty, namely, that the equilibrium state is itself ill-defined at the very lowest temperatures because of the very large relative fluctuations.

Returning to Eq. (12.128), we see that the mean pressure of any phase is

$$\langle p \rangle = (kT/\mathbf{Q})(\partial \mathbf{Q}/\partial V) \tag{15.311}$$

The general formula Eq. (12.133) states that the mean square pressure is

$$\langle p^2 \rangle = (1/\mathbf{Q}) \sum_{En} (\partial E/\partial V)^2 \Omega_{En} \exp{(\nu n - E)/kT} \tag{15.312}$$

To reduce this we note that

$$(kT)^2 \partial^2 \mathbf{Q}/\partial V^2 = -kT(\partial/\partial V) \sum_{En} (\partial E/\partial V)\Omega_{En} \exp{(\nu n - E)/kT}$$

$$= -kT \sum_{En} (\partial^2 E/\partial V^2)\Omega_{En} \exp{(\nu n - E)/kT}$$

$$+ \sum_{En} (\partial E/\partial V)^2 \Omega_{En} \exp{(\nu n - E)/kT} \tag{15.313}$$

It follows that

$$\langle p^2 \rangle = (kT)^2(1/\mathbf{Q})\partial^2 \mathbf{Q}/\partial V^2 + (1/\mathbf{Q})kT \sum_{En} (\partial^2 E/\partial V^2)\Omega_{En} \exp{(\nu n - E)/kT}$$

therefore

$$\langle p^2 \rangle = kT(\partial/\partial V)\{(1/\mathbf{Q})kT\partial \mathbf{Q}/\partial V)\} + (1/\mathbf{Q})^2(kT\partial \mathbf{Q}/\partial V)^2 + \langle kT(\partial^2 E/\partial V^2)\rangle$$

so

$$\langle p^2 \rangle = kT\partial\langle p \rangle/\partial V + \langle p \rangle^2 - kT\langle \partial p/\partial V \rangle \tag{15.314}$$

Finally, therefore, the mean square pressure fluctuation is

$$\langle (\langle p \rangle - p)^2 \rangle = kT\{\partial\langle p \rangle/\partial V - \langle(\partial p/\partial V)\rangle\} \tag{15.315}$$

The first expression on the right, $\partial\langle p \rangle/\partial V$, is the familiar thermodynamic quantity, the variation of the mean pressure with isothermal changes in volume. The other expression is not the familiar one, because it entails measuring the ratio directly and averaging afterwards. However, the ratio $\partial p/\partial V$ does enter directly in the propagation of a sound wave, and its mean value could therefore be found by dynamical measurements. In other words the pressure fluctuations depend on the difference between static and dynamic elasticity, the latter being defined ideally in terms of equilibrium assemblies. It is apparently not easy to give a general proof that these fluctuations are small for large assemblies, but Fowler estimated its value for an ideal gas to be of the order $\langle n \rangle^{-2/3}$, which is indeed small for all ordinary quantities of matter.

15.4   Fluctuations near the critical point.   At the critical point of a gas, the compressibility becomes infinite, and the pressure coefficient $\partial p/\partial V$ vanishes. Formally, Eq. (15.208) then gives the spurious result that density fluctuations should become infinite.   This is spurious because Eq. (15.207), from which it was derived, becomes the meaningless relation $0 = 0$ for isothermal changes at the critical point.   To get around this difficulty and obtain an exact estimate of the density fluctuations at the critical point, we proceed as follows:

Consider an assembly of one phase only, but divide this phase into a large number of equal (imaginary) cells, each containing a large number of atoms. Every assembly in the ensemble is provided with exactly the same geometrical pattern of cells.   The formalism of the grand partition function carries over without change to this arrangement if, for the word "phase," one now substitutes the word "cell."   Equation (15.208) now reads to give the mean relative square fluctuations in density of one particular cell averaged over the ensemble, and the pressure derivative on the right is the average over the ensemble of the pressure derivative for a particular cell.   To obtain a relation dealing directly with observed quantities for the phase as a whole, it is necessary to average once again over all the cells in the assembly.   We may write this formally as

$$\langle\langle\Delta\rho/\rho\rangle^2\rangle = -kT/(V^2\langle\partial\langle p\rangle/\partial V\rangle) \tag{15.401}$$

This is the average over the assembly of the mean square fluctuations in the density of any one cell; but the average over the assembly of the pressure derivative in a cell is on the right side, and this is not what one would measure for the pressure derivative that vanishes at the critical point.   To repeat, the derivative that vanishes at the critical point is the derivative of the mean (over the ensemble) of the pressure of the assembly, which on the present model would be written $\partial\langle\langle p\rangle\rangle/\partial V$.

Next let us reinterpret Eq. (15.315) for the cell assembly.   To do this we first average the cell pressures over the whole assembly, writing the result $\langle p\rangle$, and then we apply the formula to $\langle p\rangle$, thus:

$$\langle((\langle\langle p\rangle\rangle - \langle p\rangle)^2\rangle = kT\{\partial\langle\langle p\rangle\rangle/\partial V - \langle(\partial\langle p\rangle/\partial V)\rangle\} \tag{15.402}$$

The left side is then exactly what one would measure for the mean square fluctuations of the assembly pressure, and the right side contains both the observed pressure coefficient and the pressure coefficient that appears in the density fluctuation relation Eq. (15.401).   Putting the observed pressure coefficient equal to zero for the critical point condition, and then using Eq. (15.402) in Eq. (15.401), we find for the critical point the following reciprocal relation between the density and pressure fluctuations:

$$T = T_c: \qquad\qquad (\Delta\rho/\rho)^2(\Delta p/p)^2 = (kT/pV)^2 \tag{15.403}$$

The pressure here refers to the mean value for the assembly, while the density refers to the cells, and the volume V is the volume of a cell.   The density fluctuations cannot become infinite unless the pressure fluctuations vanish.   In general, the quantity on the right of Eq. (15.403) has a value approximately equal to $10/N^2$, where N is the mean number of atoms in the cell. Thus the density fluctuations may be said to have an order of magnitude at the critical point equal to the normal density fluctuations divided by the pressure fluctuations.

For an order-of-magnitude check on this relation, we may assume that the pressure and density variations are related by the van der Waals equation in the neighborhood of the critical point:

$$\partial^3 p/\partial V^3 = -9p_c/V_c{}^3 \quad \text{and} \quad \Delta p = (1/3!)(\partial^3 p/\partial V^3)\Delta V^3 \quad \cdots$$

so that

$$\Delta p/p_c = \tfrac{3}{2}(\Delta\rho/\rho_c)^3 \tag{15.404}$$

If, quite formally of course, we equate these quantities $\Delta p/p_c$ and $\Delta\rho/\rho_c$ to the fluctuations, to get an order-of-magnitude check, we find that Eq. (15.403) becomes

$$(\Delta\rho/\rho_c)^2 = (128/27)^{1/4}N^{-1/2} \tag{15.405}$$

where N is the mean number in the cell. The critical density of CO_2 is 0.460 g/cm^3. The interatomic distance is about 14.4 A, and a cell containing 10^6 molecules would have linear dimensions about half a wavelength of blue light. From Eq. (15.405), the density of such a cell would fluctuate by about 4 per cent, possibly enough to account for critical opalescence—the observed scattering of light from density fluctuations at the critical point.

The conventional treatment of density fluctuations can be extended to temperatures very close to the critical point without error. Thus at T_c we have $\partial p/\partial V = 0$, so that near T_c we can expand in a Taylor's series to one term: $\partial p/\partial V = (T - T_c)(\partial/\partial T)(\partial p/\partial V)$. Therefore if we put this into Eq. (15.208) we get

$$(\Delta\rho/\rho)^2 = -(kT/V^2)/\{(\partial^2 p/\partial T\partial V)(T - T_c)\} \tag{15.406}$$

indicating that the mean square fluctuations should be roughly inversely proportional to the temperature difference, $T - T_c$. This still leads to the aforementioned spurious infinity at $T = T_c$, and for the same reasons as before.

15.5 Fluctuations in quantum degenerate gases. The general formulae obtained above, viz., Eqs. (15.203), (15.303), and (15.315), are true whether the assembly is quantum degenerate or not. We shall consider the application of these general formulae to an ideal Bose-Einstein gas in considerable detail, and later rather briefly to a Fermi-Dirac gas.

To apply Eq. (15.203) for the population fluctuations, we need Eq. (8.305) for the mean population as a function of the chemical potential, and we find

$$kT\partial\langle n\rangle/\partial\nu = V(2\pi mkT/h^2)^{3/2} \sum_j (1/j^{1/2})e^{j\nu/kT} \tag{15.501}$$

or, in terms of the degeneracy temperature T_0 defined in Eq. (8.308):

$$kT\partial\langle n\rangle/\partial\nu = \langle n\rangle(1/2.612)(T/T_0)^{3/2} \sum (1/j^{1/2})e^{j\nu/kT}$$

The mean relative square density fluctuations are therefore

$$(\Delta\rho/\rho)^2 = (1/2.612\langle n\rangle)(T/T_0)^{3/2} \sum_j (1/j^{1/2})e^{j\nu/kT} \qquad (15.502)$$

This is valid for $T > T_c$ and formally approaches infinity when $T \to T_c$, because there $\nu \to 0$ and the series in the numerator diverges to infinity. This situation is quite similar to the violent fluctuations occurring at the critical point in a classical gas. In fact we may recall that, in the last paragraph of § 8.3, we noted that the pressure becomes independent of density below the degeneracy temperature, so that the denominator of Eq. (15.208) would vanish, just as it did at T_c in the van der Waals classical gas. This unrealistic infinity can be avoided just as it was in § 15.4 by considering the assembly divided into a large number of equal cells, applying the equation (15.208) to each cell individually, averaging over all the cells in the assembly, and finally appealing to the concept of pressure fluctuations. The general formula for the pressure fluctuations, Eq. (15.305), is valid, and below T_0 we have $\partial\langle\langle p\rangle\rangle/\partial V = 0$; hence the same argument goes through as for Eq. (15.403), which is valid here also. Therefore we have for the Bose-Einstein gas below the transition:

$$T < T_0: \qquad (\Delta\rho/\rho)^2(\Delta p/p)^2 = (kT/pV)^2 = (3.8/N^2)(T_0/T)^3 \qquad (15.503)$$

where the density fluctuations refer to cells containing N particles. (We have used Eq. (8.342) for the equation of state in the last step.) The magnitude of these fluctuations increases with decreasing T, approaching infinity only when T approaches absolute zero; they are already comparable with those producing critical opalescence in a van der Waals gas when $T = 0.7T_0$.

It would be highly satisfying if these large fluctuations could be observed in some experiment; the nearest thing to a quantum degenerate Bose-Einstein gas is liquid helium, and unfortunately we cannot expect liquid helium to exhibit the fluctuations, even below the *lambda*-transition, because the pressure coefficient $\partial\langle\langle p\rangle\rangle/\partial V$ does not vanish in liquid helium at the *lambda*-temperature.

It is interesting to discuss the fluctuations in the population of the lowest energy state of a Bose-Einstein gas below the transition temperature, where the population in question is comparable with that of the whole gas, and can be treated as a separate phase—or "semiphase" as it has been called. A true phase would be separated in space from the rest of the assembly, whereas the low-energy semiphase coexists with the rest of the gas in the same space. This does not invalidate any of the arguments employed in the method of the grand ensemble and grand partition function, and we may still use Eq. (15.203) to find the fluctuations in $\langle n_0\rangle$, the mean population of the low-energy semiphase. From Eq. (8.301) we have

$$\langle n_0\rangle = w_0/(e^{-\nu/kT} - 1) \qquad (15.504)$$

and therefore $\partial\langle n_0\rangle/\partial\nu = (1/kT)w_0e^{-\nu/kT}/(e^{-\nu/kT} - 1)^2$. Using Eq. (15.504) again to express $e^{-\nu/kT}$ in terms of $\langle n_0 \rangle$, we can then write

$$\partial \langle n_0 \rangle / \partial \nu = (1/kT)(\langle n_0 \rangle^2 / w_0 + \langle n_0 \rangle) \qquad (15.505)$$

and therefore from Eq. (15.203) we have

$$\langle ((\langle n \rangle - n)^2 \rangle = 1/\langle n_0 \rangle + 1/w_0 \qquad (15.506)$$

Expressed in terms of the partial density of the low-energy semiphase ρ_0, this fluctuation can be written as

$$\langle \Delta \rho_0 / \rho_0 \rangle^2 = 1/\langle n_0 \rangle + 1/w_0 \qquad (15.507)$$

Comparing this with Eq. (15.209), we see that $1/w_0$ is an anomalous term. The normal term $1/\langle n_0 \rangle$ would be appreciable near enough to the transition temperature where $\langle n_0 \rangle$ starts from small values, but it is extremely small for all temperatures appreciably below T_0. The term $1/w_0$ is, however, ideally unity throughout the whole temperature range where the semiphase exists, and we may therefore drop the normal term and write for the fluctuations of the low-energy semiphase population density:

$$\langle \Delta \rho_0 / \rho_0 \rangle^2 \sim 1 \qquad (15.508)$$

a result that indicates the low-energy semiphase to be in a state of extreme unrest. These results suggest some very interesting speculations about the behavior of liquid helium. If as suggested in § 8.6 liquid helium behaves like a Bose-Einstein gas, with atoms having an effective mass $m^* = 1.43 m_{\text{He}}$, we may look for violent fluctuations in the concentration of the superfluid part of liquid helium below the *lambda*-temperature. From the discussion of § 8.8, we believe that the superfluid has zero entropy because the uncertainty principle is unable to blur the energy levels into a continuous spectrum, leaving each energy state distinct and nondegenerate. Consider then a small region in the liquid having linear dimensions L cm; the liquid in this region may fluctuate into the lowest state for a finite time, but the result would not be counted as superfluid unless the time τ were long enough for the energy levels to sharpen into nondegenerate states and the entropy to be zero. For a given life-time of the fluctuation, this sets an upper limit on the size of the fluctuating region. The spacing between the energy levels in such a region is $h^2/8\pi m^* L^2$, and the uncertainty principle will blur these levels if L is not less than the value given by

$$\tau h^2 / 8\pi m^* L^2 > h \qquad (15.509)$$

The experimental data on thermal currents in liquid helium have suggested the following relation between relaxation life-time τ and the speed of flow of the superfluid motion: *

$$\tau u_s^2 = J(T) \qquad (15.510)$$

* L. Meyer and W. Band, *Phys. Rev.*, **74** (1948), pp. 386, 394.

where $J(T)$ is of the order $5 \times 10^{-2} \mathrm{cm}^2/\mathrm{sec}$ near the *lambda*-temperature, and u_s is the speed of flow of the superfluid. Substitution of these equations yields

$$(Lu_s)^2 < Jh/8\pi m^* \sim 10^{-6} \tag{15.511}$$

This result can be interpreted as setting a limit on the speed of transport for given size of fluctuations. One can for instance fill a capillary of diameter 3×10^{-5} cm with superfluid flowing at a speed of 30 cm/sec, but any higher speed would result in incomplete filtering out of the entropy and a return to normal liquid inside the capillary. Experimentally, this is just about what actually happens.

The fluctuations in a Fermi-Dirac gas are in marked contrast with those in a Bose-Einstein gas, and we shall illustrate this point only by giving the density fluctuations below the degeneracy temperature, using Eq. (15.208) and the equation of state Eq. (8.427). From the latter we have

$$\partial p/\partial V = -\tfrac{2}{3}(N\mu_0/V^2)\{1 + (\pi^2/12)(kT/\mu_0)^2 + \cdots\}$$

and so the density fluctuations are

$$\langle \Delta\rho/\rho \rangle^2 = (1/N)(3kT/2\mu_0)/\{1 + (\pi^2/12)(kT/\mu_0)^2 + \cdots\} \tag{15.512}$$

where N is the mean number of particles in the fluctuating region. Compared with the classical result of Eq. (15.209), we see that the Fermi-Dirac gas is even less fluctuating at very low temperature.

15.6 Fluctuations in microstates. Up to this point we have studied fluctuations only in entire phases—macroscopic quantities of substance—but the work of the last section on the fluctuations of the low-energy semiphase suggests that we should apply the same methods to study fluctuations in the populations of individual atomic energy states. This can indeed be done; as we have already seen several times, the formalism of the grand ensemble can be rewritten with a different physical interpretation without invalidating any step in the reasoning —one merely has to substitute the words "energy state" for "phase." The student will in fact find it a rewarding exercise to work through the restatement of § 12.1 in detail and to verify that the general probability formula Eq. (12.133) takes the following forms:

Boltzmann statistics:

$$\langle F \rangle = \frac{\sum_n F\{n\} \prod_i (1/n_i!)e^{(\nu-\epsilon_i)n_i/kT}}{\sum_n \prod_i (1/n_i!)e^{(\nu-\epsilon_i)n_i/kT}} \tag{15.601}$$

Bose-Einstein or Fermi-Dirac statistics:

$$\langle F \rangle = \frac{\sum_n F\{n\} \prod_i e^{(\nu-\epsilon_i)n_i/kT}}{\sum_n \prod_i e^{(\nu-\epsilon_i)n_i/kT}} \tag{15.602}$$

The Fermi-Dirac case differs from the Bose-Einstein only in the fact that the sets of numbers $\{n\}$ are restricted to $n_i = 0$ or 1. In the above formulae we have considered each energy state nondegenerate. To find the mean population of the jth state, we simply write $F\{n\} = n_j$ and go through the indicated summations, verifying that the three processes lead to the same results obtained before, Eqs. (3.510)–(3.512); some of the details of this work will make the student grateful for the simpler method of Chapter II.

To find the mean fluctuation, we now have to write $F\{n\} = n_j{}^2$ and proceed with the summations. For the classical Boltzmann case, we use the following algebraic lemma that is easily proved:

$$\sum_n (n^2/n!)e^{An} = (e^{2A} + e^A) \sum_n (1/n!)e^{An} \tag{15.603}$$

We find then that $\langle n_j{}^2 \rangle = \langle n_j \rangle^2 + \langle n_j \rangle$ so that

$$\langle \Delta n_j/n_j \rangle^2 = 1/\langle n_j \rangle = e^{(\epsilon_j - \nu)/kT} \tag{15.604}$$

For the Bose-Einstein case we need another algebraic lemma, also easy to prove:

$$\sum_n n^2 e^{An} = \{(e^A - 1)^{-1} + 2(e^A - 1)^{-2}\} \sum_n e^{An} \tag{15.605}$$

and find that $\langle n_j{}^2 \rangle = \langle n_j \rangle + 2\langle n_j \rangle^2$ and hence:

B.E.: $$\langle \Delta n_j/n_j \rangle^2 = 1/\langle n_j \rangle + 1 = e^{(\epsilon_j - \nu)/kT} \tag{15.606}$$

The Fermi-Dirac calculation goes through more easily because there are only two terms in the sums, and one finds almost at once $\langle n_j{}^2 \rangle = \langle n_j \rangle$, which leads to

F.D.: $$\langle \Delta n_j/n_j \rangle^2 = 1/\langle n_j \rangle - 1 = e^{(\epsilon_j - \nu)/kT} \tag{15.607}$$

We note first that when expressed in terms of the appropriate potential, all three fluctuations are formally identical. Note also that the result for the Bose-Einstein gas is the same as that found for the low-energy semiphase, Eq. (15.507), with $w_0 = 1$ and 0 for j. Superficially the Fermi-Dirac result is the more remarkable: if the mean population $\langle n_j \rangle = 1$, the fluctuation is zero, and if the mean population is zero, the fluctuation is infinite. However, neither of these extremes should surprise us. If the mean population is unity it cannot change; any possible change is to reduce the population, and this would lower the mean value; whereas if the mean were zero, any finite change would be an infinite relative change. The anomalies of the Bose-Einstein case are much more impressive, and we have already discussed them.

15.7 The fluctuation-dissipation theorem. As emphasized in § 15.1, the time scale of fluctuations remains an open question as far as our present theory has been developed. We now describe the approach to this question in terms of the fluctuation-dissipation theorem. Historically, the first example of this type of theorem was discovered in 1928 by Nyquist, and reads as follows:

$$\langle V^2 \rangle = (2/\pi)kT \int_0^\infty R(w)\,dw \qquad (15.701)$$

where $\langle V^2 \rangle$ is the mean square voltage of an equipotential conductor carrying zero current, and $R(w)$ is the electrical resistance of the conductor for currents of frequency $w/2\pi$. Since the conductor is equipotential, the mean voltage is zero, and the mean square voltage is exactly the same thing as the fluctuation; one cannot, incidentally, define a relative fluctuation here. Thinking of the free electrons in the conductor as a gas, the voltage fluctuations are a manifestation of the pressure fluctuations discussed § 15.4, the electron pressure fluctuating independently at the two ends of the conductor. To get a relative fluctuation, one would have to take the zero-point pressure of the Fermi electron gas as the mean pressure, instead of the mean voltage.

In the statistical theory developed so far, there is no hint of any reason for such a relationship as that of Eq. (15.701). It has, however, been used experimentally as a device for measuring high temperatures, the voltage fluctuations being detected by a suitable electronic amplifier. The generalization of the theorem has been developed quite recently by Callen and Greene, using quantum statistics. While the mathematical details of this work are somewhat cumbersome, an outline is presented here in order to bring out the essentially new ideas involved.

Since the theorem involves currents and resistance, the element missing so far from statistics is the response of an assembly to nonconservative forces. To discuss this, a general Hamiltonian dynamics of assemblies—i.e., of thermodynamic systems—is necessary. Most presentations of classical statistical mechanics begin with a discussion of the classical Hamiltonian dynamics and Liouville's theorem on the relative probabilities of different regions in phase space; the Hamiltonian is naturally expressed as a function of the microscopic co-ordinates of the individual atoms, and the forces are all considered to be conservative. Here we have in mind something quite different. We are not going to use atomic co-ordinates, but will accept the thermodynamic state variables as generalized co-ordinates, or generalized forces, i.e., the actual empirical quantities that one uses to describe a thermodynamic system. We seek a suitable Hamiltonian in terms of these generalized co-ordinates, remembering that the system is to be nonconservative, and we are going to be interested in irreversible processes.

In classical mechanics, the Hamiltonian equals the total energy of a conservative system; in a nonconservative system, the essential property of the Hamiltonian is that it plays the part of a potential in the canonical equations of motion, and this suggests that we accept the appropriate thermodynamic potential as the Hamiltonian of the thermodynamic system. If the state variables are entropy S and pressure p, the proper potential turns out to be the enthalpy H, where [see Eq. (3.131)] $dH = TdS + Vdp$. If temperature T and pressure p are chosen for state variables, we may use the Gibbs free energy F where $dF = Vdp - SdT$, as in Eq. (3.111). Both these equations may be written in the form:

$$dH_0 = \sum_j Q_j dX_j \qquad (15.702)$$

where X_j are generalized forces, Q_j generalized co-ordinates, and H_0 now stands for the Hamiltonian. The justification for calling Q_j co-ordinates comes from the expression of the work involved in the process. In both cases this is $dW = pdV$, so if p is a force, V is a co-ordinate. If we restrict ourselves to adiabatic (isentropic) processes and use Eq. (3.131), we do not need to give any thought to the interpretation of entropy as a force, because $dS = 0$ and it drops from the formula; similarly, if we are interested instead in isothermal processes and use Eq. (3.111), we can avoid having to interpret T as a force, because $dT = 0$ and it drops from the formula. Generally, however, S and T are to be regarded as generalized forces along with p; if S is a force, T is a co-ordinate, and vice-versa. We consider only adiabatic processes and accept $dH = Vdp$ for the variation of enthalpy, and

$$H_0 = E + pV \qquad (15.703)$$

for the Hamiltonian of the thermodynamic system; compare Eq. (4.140). To keep the work perfectly general we rewrite this in the form:

$$H_0 = E + \sum_j Q_j X_j \qquad (15.704)$$

where Q_j and X_j are the generalized co-ordinates and forces, leaving open the question of their physical interpretation. If the forces are varied, a perturbation is induced in this Hamiltonian according to Eq. (15.702), and we have for the perturbed Hamiltonian:

$$H = H_0 + \sum_j Q_j dX_j \qquad (15.705)$$

where we interpret H_0 as the unperturbed Hamiltonian of Eq. (15.704). If the forces dX_j are time-dependent, they can in general be expressed as Fourier integrals over frequency w:

$$dX_j(t) = \int X_j(w)e^{iwt}dw \quad \text{or} \quad \sum_w X_j(w) \sin wt \qquad (15.706)$$

where the summation form is used if a discrete spectrum suffices; $X_j(w)$ is the amplitude of the w-harmonic component of the spectral analysis of the behavior of X_j as a function of time. If the changes are small enough, there exists a linear relationship between the increments dX and the corresponding rates of change $\dot{Q}$, for every harmonic component, which can be expressed in the form:

$$\dot{Q}_j(w) = - \sum_j Y_{ji}(w)X_i(w) \qquad (15.707)$$

the total response being a Fourier integral over all frequencies:

$$\dot{Q}_j(t) = \int \dot{Q}_j(w)e^{iwt}dw \qquad (15.708)$$

The dynamical problem is to determine the coefficients $Y_{ji}(w)$ from the Hamiltonian of Eq. (15.705). The relations of Eq. (15.707) are exactly analogous to the relations between currents and emf's in an electrical circuit, and we can call the quantities Y_{ji} the complex admittance matrix for the thermodynamic system.

Consider a monochromatic perturbation, frequency w, such that

$$H = H_0 + \sum_j Q_j(w)X_j(w) \sin wt \qquad (15.709)$$

The unperturbed Hamiltonian H_0 formally defines a set of eigenfunctions $u_n(Q)$, such that $H_0 u_n(Q) = E_n u_n(Q)$, and time-dependent perturbation theory expresses the perturbed eigenfunctions for the Hamiltonian H in the form:

$$\phi_n = \sum_m b_{nm}(t)u_m(Q)e^{-iE_m t/\hbar} \qquad (15.710)$$

The coefficients $b_{nm}(t)$ are easily found in terms of the Heisenberg matrix for the co-ordinates [see § 1.6]:

$$(Q_j)_{mn} = \int \bar{u}_n(Q)Q_j u_m(Q) \prod_i dQ_i \qquad (15.711)$$

These perturbed eigenfunctions are used to compute the expectation values of the co-ordinate rates:

$$\langle \dot{Q}_j \rangle_n = \int \bar{\phi}_n \dot{Q}_j \phi_n \prod_i dQ_i \qquad (15.712)$$

the time derivatives being found in the integrand, from the quantum mechanical relation Eq. (1.606);

$$\hbar \dot{Q}_j = Q_j H - H Q_j \qquad (15.713)$$

The expression $\langle \dot{Q}_j \rangle_n$ is the expectation value for the nth quantum state. To find the average expectation value, these have to be averaged over an ensemble in which the number of assemblies in the nth state is proportional to the Boltzmann factor $e^{-E_n/kT}$, and it is assumed further that the states are close enough together to permit an integration approximation in the averaging process. The result turns out to have the following form:

$$\dot{Q}_j(w) = -\sin wt \sum_i g_{ji}X_i(w) + \cos wt \sum_i b_{ji}X_i(w) \qquad (15.714)$$

which is indeed identical in form with Eq. (15.707). Evidently $g_{ji}(w)$ is the real part of $Y_{ji}(w)$, and so is the conductance; $b_{ji}(w)$ is the imaginary part of $Y_{ji}(w)$ and is the susceptance of the system. Both sets of quantities are given explicitly by the theory in terms of the matrix $(Q_j)_{mn}$ of Eq. (15.711).

We are now ready to examine the fluctuations of the co-ordinates Q_j in an unperturbed system—spontaneous fluctuations in the absence of any perturbing forces. Since the equilibrium values of Q_j are not in general zero, the direct study of these fluctuations is clumsy; instead the mean square values of the velocities are found, and since these average to zero in the unperturbed system, their mean squares equal their fluctuations. It is a simple matter to go over from these to the co-ordinate fluctuations through the Fourier transform. The quantities to be found are the expectation values of the products $\dot{Q}_j\dot{Q}_i$, in terms of the unperturbed eigenfunctions—absence of perturbing force. When $j \neq i$, the quantity $\langle \dot{Q}_j\dot{Q}_i \rangle$ is the correlation moment, and when $j = i$, it becomes the mean square deviation, or the fluctuation. The result of this work is to prove that

$$\langle \dot{Q}_j\dot{Q}_i \rangle = (1/\pi) \int E(w,T) \{g_{ij}(w) + g_{ji}(w)\} dw \tag{15.715}$$

where

$$E(w,T) = \tfrac{1}{2}\hbar w + \hbar w/(e^{\hbar w/kT} - 1)$$

is the mean energy of an oscillator of frequency $w/2\pi$ at temperature T. This is the general fluctuation-dissipation theorem relating the spontaneous fluctuations of a system in equilibrium to the conductance matrix of the system in response to nonconservative perturbations.

To show that the Nyquist relation is a special consequence of this general theorem, we reduce it to a single variable:

$$\langle \dot{Q}^2 \rangle = (2/\pi) \int E(w,T) g(w) dw \tag{15.716}$$

The linear relation of Eq. (15.707) can be inverted to read:

$$X(w) = -Z(w)\dot{Q}(w) \tag{15.717}$$

where $Z(w)$ is the impedance, so that from Eq. (15.716), we have

$$\langle X(w)^2 \rangle = (2/\pi) \int |Z(w)|^2 g(w) E(w,T) dw$$

Since g is the real part of the reciprocal of Z, this reduces to the relation:

$$\langle X(w)^2 \rangle = (2/\pi) \int R(w) E(w,T) dw \tag{15.718}$$

At sufficiently high temperature, the energy $E(w,T)$ becomes the classical kT, so Eq. (15.718) is then equivalent to the Nyquist theorem, Eq. (15.701).

Other examples have been given by Callen and co-workers. In particular, the pressure fluctuations of a gas can be expressed in terms of the radiation resistance experienced by an oscillating piston emitting sound waves into the gas. But perhaps the most impressive application is to the theory of the Brownian motion. Any particle suspended in a fluid is subject to fluctuating forces due to the incoherence between hydrostatic pressure fluctuations on different parts of the particle's surface. If the particle is small enough to respond to this fluctuating force, and at the same time large enough for the hydrostatic pressure to have a meaning, it exhibits the Brownian motion. A steady force on such a particle will produce a constant velocity proportional to the viscosity, η, which is therefore identified with the resistance term in Eq. (15.718). The fluctuation-dissipation theorem now takes the form:

$$\langle X^2 \rangle = (2/\pi) \int \eta E(w,T)dw \qquad (15.719)$$

and again at ordinary temperatures $E(w,T) = kT$, and this equation reduces to the classical theorem of the Brownian motion:

$$\langle X^2 \rangle = (2/\pi)\eta kT \int dw \qquad (15.720)$$

the integral meaning the width of the frequency range of the Fourier analysis of the fluctuations.

15.8 Irreversible steady-flow processes. In this section we stray briefly beyond the logical boundaries of our subject in order to make direct contact with the new field of irreversible thermodynamics and so take full advantage of the discussion of the last section. There we considered fluctuations in terms of oscillatory perturbations and oscillatory responses, coupled through the linear relation of Eq. (15.707) defining the complex admittance, or its reciprocal, the impedance, of the thermodynamic system in response to oscillatory perturbations. In practice one is more often interested in the steady response to a nonoscillatory perturbation, e.g., the diffusion of matter under a concentration gradient, viscous flow under a pressure gradient, heat flow under a temperature gradient; here the perturbations are steady rather than oscillatory, and a Fourier transform becomes unnatural. To handle the steady perturbation problem, one is forced once again to introduce *ad hoc* the concept of a relaxation time τ for the regression of a fluctuation, admitting that our theory is still unable to predict this time. From the point of view of kinetic theory, the existence of this relaxation time is logical enough. Under the action of a constant perturbing force, a perturbation is built up continually, and would increase indefinitely, except that a mechanism of relaxation continually operates to break it down. The steady condition is achieved by a balance between the two opposing mechanisms— perturbing force and relaxing mechanism. We assume that this balance can be computed as follows: The constant perturbation existing in practice is equal to that perturbation which the constant perturbing force would produce in time τ if the relaxation mechanism were inhibited. If the relaxation mechanism were then switched on at this time, during the next interval τ, it would destroy the perturbation, but the continuing constant force would at the same time be rebuilding the perturbation; hence the net result is constant.

This device enables us to apply the Fourier transform theorem to the perturbation, because now we have a finite time τ during which the force acts to build up the perturbation. Thus if the constant force is X_j, its Fourier integral expression is

$$X_j = \int X_j(w)e^{iwt}dw \quad 0 \le t \le \tau,$$

where

$$X_j(w) = X_j\int_0^\tau e^{-iwt}dt = (X_j/iw)(1 - e^{-i\tau w}) \tag{15.801}$$

If this is used in the admittance relation of Eq. (15.707), we find for the response at time τ:

$$\dot{Q}_i = \int Q_i(w)e^{iw\tau}dw = \sum_j \int Y_{ji}(w)X_j(w)e^{iw\tau}dw$$

and therefore

$$\dot{Q}_i = \sum_j L_{ji}(\tau)X_j \tag{15.802}$$

being the steady response, according to our agreed assumption. Here the matrix L is defined by

$$L_{ji}(\tau) = \int \{Y_{ji}(w)/iw\}(e^{iw\tau} - 1)dw \tag{15.803}$$

which are the ordinary conductivities appearing in steady flow processes. Equation (15.803) gives the relation between these conductivities and the admittance matrix and the relaxation time τ. If the relaxation time is very short compared with the reciprocal frequencies for which the admittance is appreciable, we may put in first approximation $e^{iw\tau} - 1 = iw\tau$, and then we find

$$L_{ij}(\tau) = \tau \int Y_{ij}(w)dw \tag{15.804}$$

showing that the conductivities are proportional to the relaxation time, a familiar theorem in kinetic theory. If there exist frequencies with appreciable admittance coefficients such that $w\tau > 1$, this approximation breaks down, and the conductivities become anomalous. For example, this is just what seems to happen in liquid helium: here the thermal conductivity below the *lambda*-transition is some ten million times as great as it is just above the transition, indicating a tremendous increase in the time of relaxation of thermal perturbations. It is practically certain that Eq. (15.804) cannot be applied below the transition, and in fact, experiment shows that even the linear form of the relation of Eq. (15.802) breaks down. Although speculative explanations of this have been offered in terms of the two-fluid model—see § 8.7—there is as yet no generally accepted explanation.

The simplest and most familiar physical example where the linear relations do hold nicely is the thermoelectric circuit. Here the temperature T and voltage

dE are the generalized forces, so we use the Gibbs free energy as the Hamiltonian potential function, charge Q, and negative entropy $-S$, as the generalized co-ordinates, and replace Vdp in Eq. (3.111) by QdE. The linear relation is now

$$\left.\begin{aligned} \dot{Q} &= L_{11}dE + L_{12}dT \\ -\dot{S} &= L_{21}dE + L_{22}dT \end{aligned}\right\} \tag{15.805}$$

Here L_{11} is the electrical conductivity, and L_{22}/T is the thermal conductivity; the cross-coefficients are the specific thermoelectric coefficients leading to the Peltier heat and thermo-emf. Onsager was the first to prove on the basis of the principle of detailed balancing in quantum mechanics that this matrix L_{ij} is symmetrical, thereby giving for the first time a logically acceptable proof of the Kelvin relations between Peltier heat and thermo-emf. The Equation (15.803) yields a much more general proof of the same symmetry, and Callen has given a general proof that such reciprocal relations exist between the cross-connections in all cases of coupled steady flow processes. This is the point of departure of the completely new and highly significant development of irreversible thermodynamics.

15.9   Nonequilibrium phenomena in liquid helium. Helium was first liquefied in 1908 by Kamerlingh-Onnes at Leiden; its boiling point is 4.2 °K, and its density there is only 0.125 g/cm³. By evaporating liquid helium under reduced pressure, temperatures down to below 2 °K were produced, and in 1928, Keesom and Wolfe described the *lambda*-anomaly in the heat capacity at 2.19 °K. In 1929 it was noticed that at the specific heat peak, 2.18°K, ebullition seemed to have ceased, evaporation proceeding only from the surface for all temperatures below the transition. In 1935 this was explained by Keesom's discovery that the heat conductivity of liquid helium increased suddenly by about a millionfold at the transition. At about the same time Misener discovered that the viscosity of liquid helium suddenly started to drop at the *lambda*-temperature, until at about 1.5 °K, it had only about 5 per cent of the normal viscosity. Rollin noticed in 1936 that all surfaces in contact with the liquid suddenly become covered with a film of helium at the transition—a film that can climb up over the top of the container and spill over to drip off underneath. The film is sometimes as thick as a hundred or more atomic spacings, or about 3×10^{-6} cm. Mass can transfer in this Rollin film with complete absence of friction, the normal viscosity being somehow inhibited, at least as long as the flow rate is kept below a critical value corresponding roughly to 30 cm/sec motion of the center of mass. In 1938 the fountain effect was discovered, a spectacular thermomechanical effect in which the Rollin film, isolated inside a narrow capillary, is caused to flow violently by a minute temperature difference between the ends of the capillary; fountains as high as 20 or 30 cm have been produced inside the cryostat. This effect could be understood thermodynamically only by assuming that the film carried practically no thermal energy at all, it being in a sense already in the state of zero entropy ordinarily expected only at 0 °K.

To understand these anomalous properties of liquid helium the two-fluid model of Tisza has been the most fruitful; see § 8.6 and § 8.7. As we have seen, according to this model, some of the atoms of the liquid begin to go down to the zero-point energy state at the *lambda*-transition temperature; the fraction of atoms doing so increases rapidly as temperature falls below T_λ. Here the liquid behaves like a mixture of two fluids, one of which is superfluid and has only the zero-point energy corresponding to 0 °K, the other remaining normal. Both fluids are occupying the whole volume of the liquid and interpenetrate each other—the one being dissolved, as it were, in the other. An energy gap between the lowest state and the normal states might account for the superfluid character of the former, the two fluids finding it very difficult to exchange momentum across the gap. The model explains the specific heat anomaly very nicely: the extra heat needed to excite the superfluid into the normal states with increasing temperature equals the area under the C_v-T curve. It also explains the Rollin film, if one assumes that the normal fluid sticks at the entrance to the film, only the superfluid being slippery enough to proceed. The thickness of the film and its ability to climb up over considerable distances against gravity can be understood in terms of normal van der Waals forces of attraction with the walls and the absence of viscous drag.

In 1939 Tisza pointed out that if we take his two-fluid model seriously, picturing the two components as able to move independently of each other, an extra degree of freedom is present. Density oscillations (sound waves) are transmitted in the ordinary way; but it is also possible for the two components to oscillate in exactly the opposite phase, so that no net density variations occur. One can picture this process as that of two sound waves, one in each fluid, fitting exactly into each other, and the motions of their particles at all times being opposite. To excite such a wave one should, ideally, have a source of acoustical vibrations operated through a filter that allows only the superfluid to move. The resulting waves would be appropriately called "second sound." One can also picture this same process as a heat wave, because the peak concentrations of normal fluid contain an anomalously large quantity of heat, while the peak concentrations of superfluid contain an anomalously low quantity of heat. Second sound was in fact discovered experimentally by Peshkov in 1946 as transmitted waves of heat excited by an alternating current heat source. The speed of transmission of these waves rises rapidly from zero at the *lambda*-temperature to about 20 m/sec below 2 °K, and the attenuation is exceedingly small under favorable circumstances.

It has become customary in many cryogenic laboratories to refer to second sound as "temperature waves," but the term is rather unfortunate. Temperature waves are familiar phenomena, but they are necessarily diffusive and not oscillatory. The explanation of second sound is still a controversial question, but the following interpretation is suggested. The superfluid is to be pictured as effectively at absolute zero, with zero entropy and zero heat capacity in agreement with the Nernst theorem. The normal fluid has normal heat capacity, so high concentration of normal fluid in the mixture causes the latter to have an anomalously high heat capacity. Oscillations of the relative concentration of the two fluids in second sound therefore produce oscillations in the heat capacity of the liquid, so one may well have an oscillation of heat content without any temperature oscillations at all. Of course even on this picture there may be second-order temperature variations associated with the second sound wave, just as there are with ordinary sound, and related with the ratio between the heat capacities at constant pressure and at constant volume. One can arbitrarily assign an oscillating temperature to a second sound wave in the following way: in isothermal equilibrium the concentration of the normal fluid, ρ_n/ρ, is a definite function of temperature, given approximately by $\rho_n/\rho = (T/T_\lambda)^6$, and one can take $(\rho_n/\rho)^{1/6}T_\lambda$ as a measure of the temperature, even when ρ_n/ρ is oscillating in a second sound wave. This temperature is not necessarily consistent with kinetic theory; it would be quite accidental if the mean random kinetic energy per particle of the normal fluid were to keep step exactly with such a temperature in the second sound wave. Most simplified versions of the theory of second sound propagation are not satisfactory because they neglect this question.

If for the sake of argument we return to the isothermal oscillating heat-capacity picture of second sound, it is clear that the liquid is not in internal equilibrium; at the concentration peaks of normal fluid there is too much heat, and at the concentration peaks of superfluid there is not enough heat, to correspond with the temperature. There will always be a tendency then for the mixture to return towards equilibrium: at the peaks of normal fluid, a tendency must exist for particles to drop into the zero state, leaving the mean kinetic energy of the remaining normal particles higher; the mixture, if given time, will settle down at a temperature lower than that given by the fictitious oscillating temperature, but higher than the initial isothermal temperature. The essential feature of liquid helium is that such a transfer of atoms between the normal and superfluid states is very difficult—it has a long relaxation time, and the period of these second sound waves is so short that there is no time for such a transfer to take place. If the frequency of second sound could be made very low, transfer would occur and attenuation result. Unfortunately there are many other causes of attenuation in the practicable experimental arrangements for observing second sound, and this particular cause is not likely to be separated unequivocally.

It was observed in 1940 by Keesom, Saris, and Meyer that, for steady heat currents along a wide capillary containing liquid helium below the *lambda*-temperature, the heat flow is roughly proportional to the cube root of the temperature gradient. In other words the effective thermal resistance increases with increasing heat current, and decreases toward zero for very small heat currents. In these experiments the heat current was interpreted as a mass flow of normal fluid down the temperature gradient, counterbalanced by a mass flow of superfluid up the temperature gradient. The existence of thermal resistance in this arrangement means that some transfer of momentum—internal friction—occurs between the two fluids during their relative motion. In fact a transfer of mass

has to occur as the normal fluid flows down the temperature gradient and maintains (a) a constant heat flow, and (b) a concentration in equilibrium with the
decreasing temperature; however, the rate of transfer seems to be much faster
than necessitated by these simple requirements. To understand the cube-root
dependence on temperature gradient, it is necessary to have the mass transfer
proportional to the square of the heat flow; but the essential physical reason for
this is still not yet generally understood. Considering heat flow as the zero-
frequency limit of a second sound or heat wave, there is clearly a connection
between the relaxation problems in the two cases. Band and Meyer, in 1948,
predicted that a steady heat current superposed on a second sound wave should
cause appreciable attenuation of the latter, proportional to the square of the
steady heat current. This effect was observed in 1953 by D. W. Osborne *
and may be taken as a verification of this point of view. However, the whole
question is still quite controversial.

Although the two-fluid model promises to be a highly useful hypothesis, the
details of its applications are obviously far from completely worked out. The
two-fluid hydrodynamics required have been studied by several workers, but full
agreement has not yet been reached. More seriously, the theoretical basis of the
model is not yet secured. Modern improvements in the production of low temperatures have extended the range of investigations down well below 1 °K. In
this region, the two-fluid model apparently ceases to be a satisfactory picture.
This is no doubt because the normal fluid becomes so scarce that it should be
treated more like a gas dissolved in superfluid. It has been found more profitable
to consider the various modes of excitation of an ideal quantum liquid at or near
absolute zero. This theory is due chiefly to Landau, and it leads apparently to
correct predictions regarding the limiting velocity of propagation of second sound
at absolute zero. However, the quantum hydrodynamics of liquid motion is
still not very well developed, and considerable controversy surrounds this part
of the theory also. In particular it is not at all clear how one is to pass from the
excitation-perturbation theory of Landau, in the lowest temperature region, to
the Tisza two-fluid model, more useful near the *lambda*-point. A complete quantum statistical theory of the liquid phase should include an explanation of both
models.

EXERCISES AND PROBLEMS

1. Prove from Eq. (15.303) that in an ideal classical gas the relative square fluctuations
of energy are $5/3\langle n\rangle$. Explain the difference between this and Eq. (15.306).

2. Estimate the corrections required on Eq. (15.307) for the energy fluctuations in a
Bose-Einstein gas if population fluctuations are present.

3. Derive Eqs. (15.601) and (15.602) from first principles.

4. Verify that Eqs. (15.601) and (15.602) yield the familiar results already given in
Eqs. (3.510)–(3.512).

5. Prove Eqs. (15.603) and (15.605).

* *Proceedings of the Third International Conference on Low Temperatures*, Rice Institute
(Houston, Texas), December, 1953.

6. Discuss the application of the fluctuation-dissipation theorem to liquid helium below the *lambda*-temperature where the viscosity tends to vanish. Distinguish carefully between the fluctuations in driving force, Eq. (15.718), and the fluctuations in response, Eq. (15.716).

7. Use the method of Problem 10 of Chapter VII to find the average of the square of the number of quanta in the *j*th mode of vibration of a Debye crystal and show that

$$\langle n_j{}^2 \rangle - \langle n_j \rangle^2 = (kT/h)^2 \partial^2 \ln Q/\partial \nu_j{}^2$$

Hence show that the mean square relative fluctuations are equal to $e^{h\nu_j/kT}$. Note that this approaches infinity as $T \to 0$, and prove that the absolute value of the mean square fluctuations vanish when $T \to 0$.

REFERENCES FOR FURTHER STUDY

Statistical Mechanics, R. H. Fowler, Cambridge, 1936.
Principles of Statistical Mechanics, R. C. Tolman, Oxford, 1938.
Thermodynamics of Irreversible Processes, S. R. de Groot, Amsterdam, 1951.
Low Temperature Physics, C. F. Squire, McGraw-Hill, 1953.

"Reciprocal Relations in Irreversible Processes," L. Onsager, *Phys. Rev.*, **37** (1931), p. 405; **38** (1931), p. 2265.
"On Onsager's Principle of Microscopic Reversibility," H. B. G. Casimir, *Revs. Modern Phys.*, **17** (1945), p. 343.
"A Theorem of Irreversible Thermodynamics," H. B. Callen and R. F. Greene, *Phys. Rev.*, **86** (1952), p. 702.
"Statistical Mechanics of Irreversibility," Callen, Barasch, and Jackson, *Phys. Rev.*, **88** (1952), p. 1382.
"Fluctuations and Irreversible Processes," L. Onsager and S. Machlup, *Phys. Rev.*, **91** (1953), pp. 1505; 1512.
"Density Fluctuations at Low Temperatures," P. J. Price, *Phys. Rev.*, **94** (1954), p. 257.
"Relaxation Theory of Thermal Conduction in Helium II," L. Meyer and W. Band, *Phys. Rev.*, **74** (1948), p. 394.
"The Influence of Relaxation on the Two-Velocity Field Model of Helium II," W. Band and L. Meyer, *Phys. Rev.*, **74** (1948), p. 386.
"Non-Equilibrium States in Helium II," W. Band and L. Meyer, *Phys. Rev.*, **76** (1949), p. 417.
"Irreversible Processes with Application to Helium II and Knudsen Effect in Gases," O. K. Rice, *Phys. Rev.*, **89** (1953), p. 793.
"Statistical Fluctuations at Very Low Temperatures," W. Band, *Am. J. Phys.*, **23** (1955), p. 46.
"Atomic Theory of the Lambda Transition in Helium," R. P. Feynman, *Phys. Rev.*, **91** (1953), p. 1291.
"Atomic Theory of Liquid Helium near Absolute Zero," R. P. Feynman, *Phys. Rev.*, **91** (1953), p. 1301.
"Atomic Theory of the Two-Fluid Model of Liquid Helium," R. P. Feynman, *Phys. Rev.*, **94** (1954), p. 262.
"The Theory of Liquid Helium," G. V. Chester, *Phys. Rev.*, **94** (1954), p. 246.
"Superfluidity and Dissipative Processes in Liquid He II," J. G. Dash, *Phys. Rev.*, **94** (1954), p. 825.
"Superfluid Dynamics of Liquid Helium II," J. G. Dash, *Phys. Rev.*, **94** (1954), p. 1091.
"The Problem of Liquid Helium—Some Recent Aspects," J. G. Daunt and R. S. Smith, *Revs. Modern Phys.*, **26** (1954), p. 172.

APPENDIX

TABLE OF THE DEBYE FUNCTION $D(\theta/T)$

θ/T	0.0	0.1	0.2	0.3	0.4	0.5	0.6	0.7	0.8	0.9
0	1.00000	0.96280	0.92699	0.89191	0.85798	0.82493	0.79292	0.76181	0.73174	0.70260
1	0.67442	.64715	.62083	.59535	.57079	.54709	.52424	.50227	.48111	.46073
2	.44116	.42234	.40440	.38687	.37022	.35415	.33879	.32444	.31002	.29649
3	.28355	.27118	.25936	.24808	.23727	.22689	.21660	.20757	.19859	.18993
4	.18170	.17390	.16639	.15924	.15238	.14591	.13984	.13376	.12817	.12283
5	.11763	.11271	.10802	.10352	.09928	.09528	.09137	.08766	.08414	.08073
6	.07739	.07453	.07161	.06884	.06617	.06362	.06117	.05887	.05664	.05454
7	.05253	.05058	.04873	.04697	.04529	.04366	.04210	.04064	.03923	.03785
8	.03658	.03534	.03419	.03305	.03189	.03085	.02985	.02887	.02795	.02706
9	.02619	.02542	.02459	.02382	.02310	.02241	.02174	.02110	.02046	.01988
10	01929	.01873	.01818	.01766	.01719	01676	.01626	.01581	.01538	.01497
11	.01460	.01419	.01381	.01348	.01311	.01277	.01245	.01213	.01183	.01153
12	.01128	.01101	.01076	.01051	.01026	.00999	.00974	.00948	.00927	.00906
13	.00883	.00863	.00843	.00824	.00807	.00791	.00774	.00757	.00740	.00724
14	.00705	.00690	.00676	.00663	.00651	.00638	.00626	.00613	.00601	.00588
15	.00576	.00562	.00551	.00537	.00525	.00517	.00509	.00500	.00492	.00483

TABLE OF SOME INCOMPLETE ZETA FUNCTIONS

$$Z(n,\theta) = \sum_{j=1} (1/j^n)e^{-i\theta}$$

θ	$Z(\frac{1}{2},\theta)$	$Z(1,\theta)$	$Z(\frac{3}{2},\theta)$	$Z(2,\theta)$	$Z(\frac{5}{2},\theta)$	$Z(3,\theta)$	$Z(\frac{7}{2},\theta)$
0.0	inf.	inf.	2.612	1.645	1.341	1.202	1.127
0.1		2.350	1.659	1.310	1.147	1.056	1.002
0.2	2.540	1.710	1.314	1.110	1.001	0.935	0.895
0.3	1.840	1.340	1.099	0.955	0.881	0.832	0.802
0.4	1.420	1.113	0.985	0.835	0.787	0.743	0.717
0.5	1.157	0.933	0.810	0.737	0.693	0.664	0.645
0.6	0.948	0.796	0.711	0.655	0.615	0.595	0.578
0.7	0.795	0.685	0.623	0.580	0.548	0.533	0.520
0.8	0.679	0.592	0.547	0.515	0.493	0.478	0.468
0.9	0.538	0.513	0.481	0.460	0.442	0.430	0.423
1.0	0.506	0.444	0.428	0.409	0.396	0.387	0.381
1.5	0.266	0.252	0.243	0.237	0.233	0.230	0.228
2.0	0.150	0.145	0.142	0.140	0.139	0.138	0.137
2.5	0.0872	0.0857	0.0845	0.0838	0.0833	0.0830	0.0827
3.0	0.0516	0.0511	0.0507	0.0504	0.0502	0.0501	0.0500
3.5	0.0309	0.0307	0.0305	0.0304	0.0304	0.0303	0.0303
4.0	0.0186	0.0185	0.0184	0.0184	0.0184	0.0184	0.0183
4.5	0.0112	0.0112	0.0112	0.0111	0.0111	0.0111	0.0111
5.0	0.00677	0.00676	0.00675	0.00675	0.00675	0.00674	0.00674

$$\phi_{\pm}(n,m,\theta) = \sum_{s=1} \sum_{j=1} (\pm 1)^{s(j-1)} s^{n/2} j^{-m/2} e^{-js^{2/3}\theta}$$

θ	$\phi_{+}(3,5,\theta)$	$\phi_{-}(3,5,\theta)$	$\phi_{+}(5,3,\theta)$	$\phi_{-}(5,3,\theta)$
2.0	0.476	0.469	1.399	1.382
2.1	.393	.386	1.065	
2.2	.327	.322	0.835	
2.3	.274	.270	.665	
2.4	.231	.228	.533	
2.5	.196	.193	.4313	0.426
2.6	.167			
2.7	.143			
2.8	.123	.1214	.2360	
2.9	.106			
3.0	.0918	.0909	.1636	.1618
3.1	.0798			
3.2	.0695	.0689	.1163	.1160
3.3	.0607			
3.4	.0532			
3.5	.0468	.0463	.0720	.0720
3.6	.0411			
3.7	.0362			
3.8	.0320			
3.9	.0283			
4.0	.0250	.0249	.034	.034
4.1	.0222			
4.2	.01974			
4.3	.01756			
4.4	.01563			
4.5	.01394	.01388	.018	.018
4.6	.01244			
4.7	.01111			
4.8	.00992			
4.9	.00887			
5.0	.00795	.00793	.0094	.0094
5.1	.00712			
5.2	.00638			
5.3	.00572			
5.4	.00514			
5.5	.00461	.00461	.0054	.0054
5.6	.00414			
5.7	.00372			
5.8	.00335			
5.9	.00301			
6.0	.00271	.00271	.0030	.0030

INDEX

Absolute zero, fluctuations near, 315, 316
Abundance of the elements, 220–224
Adsorption, critical, 73–75
Adsorption, critical, in B.E. statistics, 188
Adsorption, localized monolayer, Langmuir's isotherm for, 70–73
Adsorption, localized monolayer, quantum statistics of, 195–197
Adsorption, mobile monolayer, classical statistics of, 69–70
Adsorption, mobile monolayer, B.E. statistics of, 185
Adsorption, mobile monolayer, F.D. statistics of, 188
Adsorption, monolayer, of helium isotopes, 194
Adsorption, monolayer, of isotope mixtures, 84
Adsorption, multilayer, B.E.T. theory of, 75, 84
Adsorption, multilayer, of Bose-Einstein gas, 202–204
Adsorption, multilayer, of helium, 84, 205
Alloys, phase separation of, 295–299
Anelastic effects, 294
Antisymmetric wave functions, 10
Argon, theory of liquid, 257
Argon, inter-atomic potential in, 123
Assembly partition function, 107, 109
Assembly partition function for ideal gas, 111

Bardeen's theory of superconductivity, 310–311
B.E.T. isotherm, 75, 80, 81
B.E.T. isotherm and Einstein solid, 83
Black body radiation, 142–145
Bohr magneton, 59, 283

Boltzmann assembly, 18
Boltzmann distribution, 25–26
Boltzmann statistical count, 20, 21
Born-von Karman theory of crystalline solid, 116–118
Bose-Einstein condensation, 151
Bose-Einstein condensation in thin films, 206
Bose-Einstein distribution, 26, 28
Bose-Einstein gas, ideal, 148–156, 184
Bose-Einstein gas, imperfect, 246
Bose-Einstein gas with prescribed momentum, 177–180
Bose-Einstein statistics, distance correlation in, 184
Bose-Einstein statistics, integral functions of, 184
Brillouin function, 285

Cauchy relation between elastic constants, 118, 164
Chemical constants, 47
Chemical potential, 37
Chemical reactions, free energy of, 91
Chemical reactions in ideal gases, 89
Chemical reactions in imperfect gases, 103
Classical distribution, 27, 38
Classical mechanics, partition function in, 47
Classical statistics, 23–24
Classical statistics, limits to validity of, 27, 38
Closure of eigenfunctions, 5
Cluster integrals, 126, 140, 277
Cluster theory of higher virials, 100, 101
Clusters in classical vapor, 93–98, 106
Clusters in Bose-Einstein gas, 207–211

Clusters in Fermi-Dirac gas, 212
Clusters, negative numbers of, 101, 106
Clusters, numbers of in various vapors, 102, 103
Cohesive energy, 148
Commutation of population operators, 264, 267
Commutation relations, Heisenberg's, 15
Complexions, 18, 20
Complexions, number of in B.E. statistics, 22
Complexions, number of in Boltzmann statistics, 21
Complexions, number of in classical statistics, 23, 24
Complexions, number of in F.D. statistics, 23
Condensation, general theory of, 246, 269–271
Condensation in clustering assembly, 97–100, 106
Conductivity, electrical, 303, 305
Conductivity, thermal, of metals, 303–305, 311
Conductivity, thermal, of liquid helium, 331–332
Contact potential, 301
Cooling, magnetic method of, 60, 61
Cooperative effects, general theory of, 259–262
Cooperative effects in alloys, 289
Cooperative effects in ferromagnetism, 283, 286
Cooperative effects in monolayers, 73
Cooperative effects in superconductors, 308
Corresponding states, law of, 123
Creation operator, 263
Critical magnetic field in superconductors, 306
Critical momentum in liquid helium, 178
Critical phenomena, theory of, 140
Critical point, 269
Critical point, Mayer's theory of, 271
Critical point fluctuations, 317, 318
Critical velocity in liquid helium, 180, 329
Crystalline solid, Born-von Karman theory of, 116
Crystalline solid, Debye's theory of, 112
Crystalline solid, Einstein's theory of, 62
Curie's law for ferromagnetics, 284

Darwin-Fowler statistical method, 27
Debye function, 115, 141, 335
Debye modes, 114, 146
Debye temperature, 115, 118, 146
Debye theory of crystalline solid, 112, 145
Degeneracy, exchange, 8, 10
Degeneracy numbers, 5, 7
Degeneracy temperature in B.E. gas, 150
Degeneracy temperature in F.D. gas, 158
Degeneracy volume in B.E. gas, 153
Density matrix, von Neumann's, 245
Density matrix for grand ensembles, 262
Destruction operator, 263
Diagonalization of matrix, 13, 15
Dissociative cluster theory of vapor pressure, 92–100
Dissociative cluster theory of virial coefficients, 100–102
Dissociative equilibrium, classical theory, 85–89, 106
Dissociative equilibrium in diatomic gases, 85
Dissociative equilibrium in monolayers, 105, 106
Dissociative equilibrium in multilayer films, 81
Dissociative equilibrium with quantum degeneracy, 207–219
Distribution functions, 274
Distribution functions in liquids, 141, 282
Distribution functions, quantum mechanical, 246
Distribution-in-energy, 24
Distribution-in-energy in Boltzmann statistics, 25
Distribution-in-energy in B.E. statistics, 26
Distribution-in-energy in classical statistics, 27
Distribution-in-energy in F.D. statistics, 27
Distribution-in-energy in intermediate statistics, 31
Distribution-in-momentum, 48–49
Duplex films, 106

Effective mass of electron, 164
Effective mass of liquid helium atom, 176
Eigenvalue equations, 4
Eigenvalues in box enclosure, 6
Eigenvalues of oscillator, 7
Eigenvalues of rotator, 7

Electron gas pressure in metals, 164
Electron gas pressure and phases in alloys, 300
Electron theory of metals, 163, 299
Electronic heat capacities, 184
Energy operator, 3
Ensemble of Gibbs, 107
Enthalpy, 33
Entropy, 32
Entropy and Heisenberg's uncertainty principle, 181–182
Entropy and probability, 34
Entropy, communal, of a liquid, 131, 134
Entropy of B.E. gas, 154–155
Entropy of helium superfluid, 180
Entropy of F.D. gas, 162
Entropy of phonon gas, 146–147
Entropy of radiation field, 145
Equations of motion, quantum mechanical, 245
Equation of state of B.E. gas, 155–156
Equation of state of B.E. monolayers, 169
Equation of state of classical gas, 36
Equation of state of condensed assemblies, 276–279
Equation of state of Deuterium, 246
Equation of state of electron gas, 164
Equation of state of F.D. monolayers, 172
Equation of state of He^3, 246
Equation of state of liquids, 141
Equation of state, quantum theory of, 246
Equilibrium, thermodynamic, 32
Ergodic hypothesis, quantum mechanical proof of, 245, 268
Exchange forces, 11
Exchange jumps, 19, 20
Exclusion principle, 10, 24, 299
Expectation values, 4
Exp-six potential function, 123
Exp-six potential in hydrogen isotopes, 241

Fermi-Dirac distribution, 38
Fermi-Dirac ideal gas, 156–163
Fermi energy of electrons in metal, 300
Fermi limit in ideal gas, 157
Ferromagnetism, 283–286, 311
Fluctuation-dissipation theorem, 322–327, 333
Fluctuations and critical speed of superfluid, 320–321
Fluctuations and reversible processes, 39

Fluctuations at absolute zero, 315–316
Fluctuations at critical points, 317–318
Fluctuations at lambda point, 319
Fluctuations, concept of, in equilibrium, 312
Fluctuations in microstates, 321–322
Fluctuations in quantum degenerate gases, 318–320
Fluctuations of density, 313, 314, 333
Fluctuations of energy, 314–316
Fluctuations of population, 313
Fluctuations of pressure, 316
Free energy, Gibbs', 33
Free energy, Helmholtz's, 33
Free energy of a chemical reaction, 92
Free volume model of liquid, 135, 139, 173
Fröhlich's theory of superconductivity, 310
Fugacity, 273

Generating functions, 230
Gibbs free energy, 33
Grand ensembles, 247–267
Grand ensembles, B.E. gas in, 246
Grand partition function, 249
Grand partition function, principal theorem of, 251
Grand partition function, Mayer's generalization of, 272, 275

Hamiltonian matrix, 13
Hamiltonian operator, 3, 4
Heat capacity of B.E. gas, 151
Heat capacity of crystals, 115, 117
Heat capacity of F.D. gas, 162
Heat capacity of disorder in alloys, 290, 291
Heat capacity of ferromagnetics, 286
Heat capacity of imperfect gas, 125
Heat capacity of lattice defects, 295
Heat capacity of lattices, face centered, 140
Heat capacity of lattices, simple cubic, 311
Heat capacity of liquids, free volume model, 175
Heat capacity of liquid helium, 315
Heat capacity of metals, 164, 184
Heat capacity of monolayers, 167, 171, 172
Heat capacity of superconductors, 306, 307

Heisenberg uncertainty relation, 15
Heisenberg uncertainty relation and entropy, 181
Helium, 184
Helium film, unsaturated, 206
Helium, interatomic potential, 123
Helium liquid, see liquid helium, 184, 333
Helium solid, 206
Helmholtz free energy, 33
Hermitian matrix, 14
Hydrocarbons, adsorption of, 73
Hydrogen bomb, 145

Imperfect gas, classical, 119–126
Imperfect gas, quantum degenerate, 233–242, 246
Intrinsic pressure in liquid, 135
Intrinsic pressure in solid, 148
Ionic solutions, 279, 282
Irreversible processes, 327–329
Ising model of ferromagnet, 286
Ising model of order-disorder in alloys, 287, 291
Isotope effect in superconductors, 306, 310, 311

Kahn-Uhlenbeck theory of imperfect gas, 233–237
Kinetic theory, classical, 48, 49
Kinetic theory, Bose-Einstein, 49, 50
Kinetic theory of liquids, 140

Lagrange multipliers, 25
Lambda transition and virial coefficients, 242
Lambda transition in helium isotope mixtures, 184
Lambda transition in helium vapor droplets, 218, 219
Lambda transition in liquid helium, 151, 329
Landau's theory of liquid helium, 332
Langmuir function, 72
Langmuir's isotherm, 70–73
Lattice imperfections, 291–295
Lattice vibrations and superconductivity, 311
Lennard-Jones potential, 122
Liquid helium and B.E. statistics, 148, 201, 202
Liquid helium, nonequilibrium effects, 329–332

Liquid-solid equilibrium, 137, 148
Liquid-vapor equilibrium, 139
Liquids, B.E. theory of, 173–177, 184
Liquids, cage model of, 131, 133, 134
Liquids, cell model of, 132
Liquids, double-life model of, 254–259
Liquids, exact formal theory of, 269–282
Liquids, free volume model of, 135, 139, 141
Liquids, hard sphere model of, 140
Liquids, hole theory of, 140, 141
Liquids, lattice theory of, 140
Liquids, Lennard-Jones and Devonshire theory of, 135, 137, 141
Liquids, oscillator model of, 134, 138, 140
Liquids, quantum degeneracy in, 279–281
London's equation for superconductor, 307

Magnetic cooling, 60, 61
Magnetic fields and partition function, 59
Many-body forces, 130
Mass action, law of, in clustering assembly, 96
Mass action, law of, in ideal gases, 91
Mass action, law of, in imperfect gases, 105
Materialism, 2
Mayer's theory of imperfect gas, 126–131
Mayer's theory of condensation, 269, 271
Meissner effect in superconductors, 306
Melting process, 148
Metals, free electrons in, 164, 299
Mixtures, 106, 282, 311
Modes of vibration of crystal, 113, 116, 119
Modes of vibration of phonon gas, 146
Modes of vibration of radiation field, 144
Momentum, assemblies of prescribed, 63–66, 177–181
Momentum distribution, 48, 65
Momentum operator, 3
Monolayers, see adsorption
Multicomponent systems, 282
Multilayer film, heat capacity of, 84
Multilayers, see adsorption

Neon, interatomic potential, 123
Nernst's law, 40
Nonequilibrium phenomena, 245, 329, 333
Nuclear fluid, 221

Nuclear reactions, 220–223
Number operators, 262–265

Onsager's reciprocal relations, 329, 333
Order-disorder in alloys, 286–291
Orthogonality, 5
Ortho-hydrogen, 56, 57

Para-hydrogen, 56, 57
Partial pressures, law of, 87, 95, 104, 105
Partition function, assembly, 107–109
Partition function of classical systems, 42–45
Partition function of Debye crystal, 113
Partition function of diatomic molecule, 52
Partition function of distinguishable systems, 94
Partition function of imperfect gas, 120
Partition function of indistinguishable systems, 42
Partition function of internal degrees of freedom, 50–52
Partition function of monatomic gas, 45, 46
Partition function in magnetic fields, 58–61
Partition function, quantum mechanical, 246
Partition function theorem invalidated by quantum effects, 142
Phase diagrams of substitutional alloys, 295
Phase diagram of Cu-Ag, 299
Phase diagram, dependence on free electrons, 300
Phase equilibria, classical theory of, 67–84, 137–139
Phase equilibria, grand ensemble theory of, 247–251
Phase equilibria, thermodynamics of, 33, 34
Phase equilibrium and quantum degeneracy, 185–206
Philosophy of quantum mechanics, 1–3
Phonons, 145–148
Phonons and thermal conduction, 303
Photon, 1
Photons and black body radiation, 142–145
Polymer solutions, 140, 141
Probability and entropy, 34

Probability distribution functions, 274
Probability in quantum mechanics, 4

Quantum mechanics, 1–16
Quantum mechanics, Feynman's approach to, 246
Quantum mechanics of wave fields, 16
Quantization of sound waves, 246
Quasi-chemical approximation, 288–289

Radiation pressure in phonon gas, 147
Radiation pressure in photon gas, 145
Reciprocal relations of Onsager, 329
Relativistic statistical mechanics, 223, 224
Relaxation effects in alloys, 294
Relaxation effects in irreversible thermodynamics, 327–329
Relaxation effects in liquid helium, 320, 321, 332
Resistance, classical theory, 304
Resistance, quantum theory, 310
Residual resistance, 305
Reversible process, 39
Rollin helium film, 329
Rotational heat capacity, 55
Rotational spectra, 57, 58
Russell, Bertrand, philosophy of, 2

Saturated vapor, Bose-Einstein theory of, 200–202, 209–211
Saturated vapor, classical theory of, 92–100, 139
Saturated vapor, Fermi-Dirac theory of, 212–213
Saturated vapor of helium isotope mixtures, 214–219
Schrödinger equation, 4–8
Second sound in liquid helium, 330
Second law of thermodynamics, 34
Slater-sum, 225–232
Solid state problems, 283–311
Spin, 11–13
Spins and virial coefficients, 253
Stirling's approximation, 23, 24, 27
Sublimation, Bose-Einstein theory, 197–200
Sublimation, classical theory, 81–83
Sublimation, Fermi-Dirac theory, 199, 200, 206
Superconductivity, 305–310, 311
Superfluid helium, 177, 330, 333

Superfluid as a solid phase, 205, 206, 259
Surface specific heat, 141
Surface tension, 140
Symmetry of assembly wave functions, 9, 10
System, quantum mechanical, 2

Temperature, statistical definition, 34, 35
Temperature in grand ensemble, 248
Thermal conductivity, 303–305, 311
Thermal conductivity in helium, 311
Thermionic emission, 302
Thermodynamic equilibrium, 32
Thermodynamic equilibrium, quantum corrections for, 246
Thermodynamic laws, 38–40
Thermodynamics, irreversible, 327–329, 333
Tisza's theory of liquid helium, 330
Two-fluid model for liquid helium, 177–181, 330
Two-fluid model for superconductors, 307–309

Validity of statistical methods, 17, 30
van der Waals equation, 122

van der Waals equation as cooperative effect, 262
Vibrational heat capacity, 53
Virial coefficients, effect of spin on, 253
Virial coefficients in classical gas, 126–131
Virial coefficients in hydrogen isotopes, 241
Virial coefficients in polar gases, 140
Virial coefficients in polymer solutions, 140
Virial coefficients in quantum degenerate gases, 237–243, 251–254

Wave-particle paradox, 1, 2
White dwarf stars, 220
Whitehead, Alfred North, philosophy of, 2
Wiedemann-Franz law, 305, 306
Work function, 301

Zero-point energy of a Debye crystal, 115
Zero-point energy of electrons in metals, 299
Zero-point energy of Fermi-Dirac gas, 157
Zero-point energy of helium liquid, 184
Zero-point energy of phonon gas and photon gas, 146